FEB. 22 - 2021

D R Toi
223 Southlake Pl
Newport News, VA 23602-8323

Also by Linda Moulton Howe

An Alien Harvest
Glimpses of Other Realities, Vol. II: High Strangeness
Mysterious Lights and Crop Circles

Cover Art: *Distant Worlds* by Ron Russell © 1992

GLIMPSES OF OTHER REALITIES

VOLUME I: FACTS AND EYEWITNESSES

LINDA MOULTON HOWE

First Edition, First Printing, January 1994
Second Edition, First Printing, June 1997
Third Printing, September 1999
Fourth Printing, July 2004
Fifth Printing, September 2015

Printed in the United States of America at
Bang Printing, Brainerd, Minnesota

Library of Congress Catalog Card Number: 93-091681

ISBN 0-9620570-5-3

LMH Productions
Post Office Box 21843, Albuquerque, New Mexico 87154-1843

To my parents, Mabel and Chet Moulton.

"All this visible universe is not unique in nature and we must believe that there are, in other regions of space, other worlds, other beings, other men."

LUCRETIUS
99 - 55 B.C.

CONTENTS

VOLUME I: FACTS AND EYEWITNESSES

v	Frontispiece
ix	Acknowledgments
xi	Author's Introduction
xvii	Prologue
1	Chapter one CROP CIRCLES, BIOLOGY, AND FROZEN MUSIC
94	Chapter two ANIMAL MUTILATIONS
196	Chapter three HUMAN ABDUCTIONS AND EYEWITNESSES
248	Chapter four OTHER BEINGS
300	Epilogue
302	Appendices
321	Bibliography
325	Index

VOLUME II: HIGH STRANGENESS

Volume II, *High Strangeness* includes the testimonies of scientists, other civilian professionals and military personnel about their highly strange encounters with other realities.

Out of these experiences, a new cosmology is emerging that says there are many more dimensions than this one — that Earth exists in one particular dimension that has a particular atomic frequency. Other frequency forms from other dimensions can penetrate and even overlap our Space-Time, just as different radio and TV signals move together in a single space to be separated at a receiver by a frequency tuner. In the new cosmology, there are many other universes which can be radically different from ours in both appearance and physical make up and that intelligences other than human are *forcing* glimpses of other realities upon us.

ACKNOWLEDGMENTS

Many people have written to me about their encounters with the unknown. Some have sent sketches, photographs, and videotapes. A few in law enforcement, military, and science have talked only off the record. To all who have shared their experiences, I am deeply grateful.

I greatly appreciate the support and collaboration of pathologist and hematologist John Altshuler, M.D.; mathematician and astronomer Gerald Hawkins, Ph.D.; biophysicist W. C. Levengood, Ph.D.-eq; and psychologist Mario Pazzaglini, Ph.D.

Former NASA aerospace scientist and abduction investigator Richard F. Haines contributed drawings from his abduction files. Artist Ron Russell and author Jim Marrs contributed eyewitness reports. Tom Adams, a research colleague in the animal mutilation mystery, contributed an overview of the mysterious helicopters associated with the phenomenon. The Fyffe, Alabama Police Department provided me with updates, photographs, offense reports, and editorial feedback about the 1993 intrusion of animal mutilations, strange lights, helicopters, and round, glowing disks in northeastern Alabama. Three people there went above and beyond for me the night Carey and Teri Baker and Stephen Smith from *The Weekly Post* in Rainsville, Alabama, helped me dig up a cow to get tissue samples for Dr. Altshuler to analyze after local officials said it was only predator attack. And it wasn't.

Those colleagues and other friends who have been willing to read parts or most of the evolving manuscript have my deep thanks because it was their encouragement and comment that kept me going: Tom Adams, Jim Westby, Ann Owen, M.D., Monte Leach, Susan Markowitz, Michael Brein, Marc Barasch, Barbara and Vincent Creevy, John Burke, Chad Deetken, Shari Adamiak, Ron Russell, Robert Bigelow, Skye Ambrose, John Mack, M.D., Peter Sorensen, Marika Shields, Maryse Elias, Lisa Nichols, Dan Drasin, Fred Alan Wolf, Allan Z. Rodzinski, Denise Breton and Chris Largent. A special thanks to Michael Lindemann for his editor's eye.

Others who have helped me greatly with the physical challenge of making this book are Ann Douden, who designed its format and cover; Vincent Creevy who used computers to generate maps; and Damien Shay, a master of InDesign.

A special thanks to Lynda and Bill Beierwaltes for their friendship and support. Without them, I could not have done this book.

AUTHOR'S INTRODUCTION

"There's one theory of the universe that I rather like. Suppose our planet is a zoo for extraterrestrial beings. They planted the seeds of evolution on Earth hoping to create interesting, intelligent creatures. And they watch their experiment, interfering hardly at all. So that almost everything we do comes out according to the laws of nature. But every now and then they see something which doesn't look quite right. Like, this zoo is going to kill itself off if they let you do this or that. So they insert a finger and just change some little thing."

WILLIAM D. HAMILTON[1]
BIOLOGIST
OXFORD UNIVERSITY

[1] William D. Hamilton of Oxford University, England, is considered to be one of the most important evolutionary biologists of the 20th century. He is author of the "kin selection" theory, a landmark in evolutionary thought which proposes that altruism among families has evolved because the genes that produce the trait reside not only in the animal that fights to save its young, but also in those young who are protected. Thus, the genes perpetuate themselves.

[2] *Worlds in the Making* © 1908 by S. Arrhenius, Harper and Row.

A mysterious presence among us leaves physical traces and eyewitness testimonies in its wake like summer dew settling on a yard. Unseen forces are leaving marks on animals, the Earth and human psyches, while manipulating, traumatizing or inspiring. Yet, our human species, under the influence of rigid social, political and religious conditioning, rejects the accumulating physical evidence and human testimony which imply something very strange is interacting with the world, and most probably has been for centuries.

It is possible that all life on this planet was seeded by an advanced intelligence from this universe or another, which is still monitoring and tending its garden. The idea of extraterrestrials, or other-dimensionals, "planting" life here was first proposed by 1903 Nobel Prize laureate chemist Svante August Arrhenius. In his book *Worlds in the Making*,[2] he introduced the concept of "panspermia," the seeding of life throughout the universe by spores of living cells that could grow on planets at habitable stages.

Seventy years later in 1973, another Nobel Prize laureate evolved Arrhenius's concept to "directed panspermia." Molecular biologist Dr. Francis Crick collaborated with Drs. James Watson and Maurice Wilkens to discover the structure of DNA, a double helix molecule that contains the genetic code for creating all Earth life whether a human being, a fish, an ant, a snake or a plant. For that genetic breakthrough, the team received a Nobel prize in 1962. Crick puzzled over why there was only one genetic code for terrestrial life if a primeval soup had spawned creatures, as many biologists believed. He co-authored an article[3] with chemist Leslie Orgel in which they stated that the "uniformity of genetic code suggests that Earth life might represent a clone derived from a single extraterrestrial organism ... deliberately transmitted to Earth by intelligent beings from another planet."

Continuing struggles to understand the mysterious origin of Earth life were summarized in *Search for the Universal Ancestors* prepared at NASA's Ames Research Center in 1985:[4] "Since we define life in terms of its genetic properties, and since the only known system possessing these properties is the protein-nucleic acid system, the most easily defended position holds that the first living things were based on this system. However, the spontaneous origin of such a complex mechanism poses great conceptual difficulties."

The implications are that it is easier to comprehend the seeding of an already-developed genetic code on this planet than it is to conceptualize how our complex, replicating genetic process evolved from a primeval soup.

Fred Hoyle, the British astronomer who also speculated about extraterrestrial seeding of life on Earth, was referenced in *Newsweek* on July 19, 1993, as having compared the difficulty of combining the ingredients of life from a primeval soup into something fully alive as "about as likely as assembling a Boeing 747 by sending a whirling tornado into a junkyard."

Directed panspermia and universal ancestors seemed also to be one of the subjects in an alleged briefing paper for the President of the United States that I was shown April 9, 1983, at the Air Force Office of Special Investigations (AFOSI) inside Kirtland AFB, Albuquerque, New Mexico.[5] The paper discussed the United States government's retrieval of crashed alien disks and their non-human occupants since the 1940s. At least one alien being was supposed to have communicated about its civilization's long-term involvement with Earth, including the "manipulation of DNA in already-evolving primates to create *Homo sapiens.*" One of the most provocative statements was: "All questions and mysteries about the evolution of *Homo sapiens* on this planet have been answered." The implication was that an alien civilization referenced in the briefing paper had genetically created standing up primates and human evolution.

After I wrote *An Alien Harvest* detailing the Kirtland experience and other research, I received letters from people claiming firsthand knowledge of alien craft and other beings. *Glimpses of Other Realities* has evolved from some of those letters and hundreds of other reports from a wide range of people who are struggling to understand their experiences with what each

[3] "Directed Panspermia," *Icarus, International Journal of Solar System Studies*, Vol. 19, No. 3, July 1973 by F. H. C. Crick and L. E. Orgel, © 1973 Academic Press.

[4] NASA SP-477, *Search for the Universal Ancestors*, 1985. Editors: H. Hartman, Massachusetts Institute of Technology, Cambridge; J. G. Lawless, NASA Ames Research Center, Moffett Field, Calif.; P. Morrison, MIT, Cambridge, Mass.

[5] Chapter 7, *An Alien Harvest – Further Evidence Linking Animal Mutilations and Human Abductions to Alien Life Forms* © 1989 and 2nd Edition © 2014 by Linda Moulton Howe. Available at Earthfiles.com.

considers to be one or more non-human intelligences.

Volume I concentrates on physical evidence that can be picked up, held, and examined. I begin with the crop circle mystery. Physical imprints of geometric and non-geometric designs have been found in grasses and cereal crops worldwide. Affected plants from England, Canada, Australia, and the United States have been studied. One biophysicist has discovered biochemical and biophysical changes, which he says cannot be hoaxed.

In the crop formations, the plants continue to grow in what appears to be unaffected soil. But since the 1960s, other circles have been found in association with the worldwide animal mutilation mystery that is the subject of Chapter 2. Dry, ceramic-hard circles in which grasses are dead have been found in pastures underneath or near mutilated animals. No one knows if both phenomena are produced by one intelligence or by several intelligences with different agendas.

Motive is the most confusing part of the mysterious presence among us and our only insights so far have come from people who allege that non-human beings have taken them from cars, bedrooms or other common realities into a place beyond human understanding. This phenomenon has come to be known as the "UFO abduction syndrome."[6] In at least three cases, abductees have received information about animal mutilations, which is included in Chapter 3 along with other conscious eyewitness reports.

Abductees are also sketching, drawing, and painting non-human creatures which haunt their memories and dreams. Different types of beings are outlined in Chapter 4.

Volume II will include highly strange human experiences ranging from the testimonies of scientists and other civilian professionals to military personnel. Confidential sources say the government has been monitoring an alien presence and its technology for decades using "black" funds outside the scrutiny of Congress. Out of that clandestine process, hidden under a national security cover, have emerged nervous military people who cautiously relate their own firsthand encounters with alien beings and craft. The secrecy, they say, is necessary to prevent public panic. But the military underground is frustrated. One man told me, "Denying the alien presence, imposing a strict policy of 'ignorance is bliss,' using ridicule and misinformation to enforce that policy, does not alter the fact that this planet is being used by other life forms."

The problem is, as one military source pointed out, "if we are dealing with a Control System that can manipulate our minds and create illusions with sophisticated technology, including holograms," we humans might never be able to discern the true nature of the manipulative intelligence/s.

[6] *Unusual Personal Experiences, An Analysis of the Data from Three National Surveys,* conducted by the Roper Organization for the Bigelow Holding Corp. © 1992.

Where is all this heading? Several abductees have opinions about what might be happening in the big picture based on their experiences of high strangeness. The similarities in their stories and drawings merit consideration, even if the content seems bizarre. The puzzling physical traces combined with military/intelligence reports and eyewitness and abduction accounts seem to be building toward a revolution in consciousness akin to Galileo's[7] time. We are moving from the paradigm that we are alone in the universe to a new one in which we are not alone and something out there is interacting with us, our animals and our plant life, *forcing* glimpses of other realities upon us.

The intrusion of phenomena we don't understand disturbs people. Physicist and writer Fred Alan Wolf said to me,"Anything that forces itself upon us, that comes into crop fields, pastures or bedrooms without asking permission *and without receiving permission* — in my book, it's dark!"

But, I don't think black or white is the answer. In the beginning of my investigations in 1979 to 1980 about the environmental implications of worldwide, unexplained animal deaths, I was afraid that something terrible was at work. Many years later after exposure to other facets of the mystery, including the UFO abduction syndrome, I now wonder if the harvest of tissue and fluids from animals and humans might be used to sustain another life form at the edge of its own extinction. Or even to sustain humanity. Hints of those possible explanations have emerged from abductees.

Budd Hopkins, a pioneer in abduction research, was always suspicious about trusting alien communications. He shared Fred Alan Wolf's position that benevolent beings would not force themselves upon us. However, psychiatrist Dr. John Mack at Harvard University said that in the beginning of his abduction studies, he heard the terror of people who felt like victims of an unknown and unseen force beyond their control. As he continued his research, he learned that some people continued to grow beyond their fear and felt that the phenomenon's intent related to the evolution of the human species upward in the spiralling journey of souls. Greater consciousness about a different and more complex universe is perhaps the next step we all must take.

Whether extraterrestrial biological entities, other dimensionals, time travelers, angelic beings, or all of these simultaneously are interacting with our planet, more knowledge and less denial about what's happening could strengthen the human family. Crop formations, the human abduction syndrome, animal mutilations, Marian apparitions, military and civilian encounters with alien craft or beings — all these phenomena are worldwide.

[7] Galileo Galilei, 1564-1642, Italian scientist and philosopher who was the first person to use a telescope to study the skies. He amassed evidence that proved the Earth revolves around the sun and is not the center of the universe, as had been believed at the time. His evidence angered the Catholic Church and in 1633 he was tried by the Inquisition in Rome, ordered to recant, and forced to spend the last eight years of his life under house arrest.

They challenge us to confront other realities beyond the status quo and to reject the socially acceptable attitudes of ridicule and denial.

Throughout this first volume, I have tried to gather a large number of facts and eyewitness testimonies together for comparisons in a single text. So many local stories never reach the national and international media, and often content is compartmentalized too narrowly due to religious, political and social biases. Compartmentalization makes it more difficult to see patterns common to different facets of these strange, sometimes inspiring, sometimes disturbing, events around us. We need to stop hiding from other realities. We don't need to run or get down on our knees.

In the end, humanity might find itself learning about another intelligence that is facing environmental survival issues as we are on Earth. It's also possible that another intelligence sees our environmental pollution, realizes that humans are on a path of self-destruction, and is taking steps on its own initiative to help us, even if we don't comprehend its actions or motives.

Perhaps we humans are like bacteria on a Petri dish. We're becoming conscious that we're being studied. We have glimpses of the microscope, but no clear vision of the controlling intelligences behind it. As we become more aware of our watchers, inevitable questions about their goodness or evil emerge. My quest has been to understand the true intent of the mysterious forces around us. I offer the following Prologue as the context in which I search and the context in which I hope this book will be read.

LINDA MOULTON HOWE
HUNTINGDON VALLEY, PA.
SEPTEMBER 7, 1993

PROLOGUE

[1] "The Testament of Amram," Dead Sea Scrolls, translated by Prof. Robert Eisenman: *I saw Watchers in my vision, the dream-vision. Two men were fighting over me ... holding a great contest over me. I asked them, "Who are you, that you are thus empowered over me?" They answered, "We have been empowered and rule over all mankind." They said to me, "Which of us do you choose to rule you?" I raised my eyes and looked. One of them was terrifying in his appearance, like a serpent, his cloak, many-colored yet very dark. ... And I looked again, and in his appearance, his visage like a viper. ... I replied to him, "This Watcher, who is he?" He answered, "This Watcher ... his three names are Belial and Prince of Darkness and King of Evil." I said (to the other Watcher), "My lord, what dominion (have you?)" He answered, "You saw (the viper), and he is empowered over all Darkness, while I (am empowered over all Light.) ... My three names are Michael, Prince of Light and King of Righteousness."*

"There is a predestination doctrine known as the Two Spirit Theology, in which one's soul is said to be fated for all eternity, blessed or cursed as the result of a kind of angelic wrestling match between two of the Watcher's spirits:[1] ... a Good Angel and an Evil Angel, who struggle for possession of your soul..."

DAVID FLUSSER
ISRAELI BIBLICAL SCHOLAR
COMMENTING ON DEAD SEA SCROLLS

Qoyllur Rit'i.

The Incas in Peru use that name for a 22,000 foot glacier in the Andes. The name loosely translates as "star" and "snow." The stars are the Pleiades, a cluster of blue suns which the Incas believe have long watched over and judged them with a ruling hand.

The glacial snow, according to legend, is where heaven and Earth meet. It melts and puts water into the ground to grow plants which feed bodies and babies, an endless cycle of transformation from life to life, mineral to earth to plant to body, sex, birth, death. Inside that sacred snow, the Apu gods reside. Climbing Qoyllur Rit'i is a yearly ritual for several Inca tribes, a penance in exchange for redemption and renewal from the Apu while the overseeing Pleiades sink below the horizon in the June procession of the heavens.

I was there in 1987. First, I travelled from Cuzco by van. We drove the first day on bumpy, dusty roads through brown hills where llamas tiptoed along the steep slopes. As we got higher, the dark hills receded below huge, white Andean peaks. The camp site was above 14,000 feet and the temperature that night was below freezing. We all gathered in the cook tent to drink tea and wait for hot food.

After dinner, in spite of the bitter cold, the amateur astronomer in me was drawn outdoors. No city lights, no noise, no Big Dipper, no Orion's Belt. It was an alien sky dominated by the large Southern Cross. Off to the right was a large triangle of stars. I stared at them thinking how fresh and beautiful the strange constellations were to my North American eyes. A bright light flashed from inside the triangle. Satellite? I waited for the next flash. It came *below* the first. Another white light flashed to the right. I realized the flashes formed the corners of a triangle that fit neatly inside the larger triangle of stars. I began moving toward the cook tent. "You guys, the stars are moving out here!"

The flashes erupted in a triangular sequence again, inside the constellation triangle. I wanted to run to the tent and pull people out as witnesses, but I could not take my eyes off that astonishing sky. Perhaps something up there responded to my awe. The next action began inside the Southern Cross. It was as if a large, unseen hand drew a perfectly straight and bright, white line from the Cross to exactly the mid-point of the triangle of stars. That long, white line stayed bright between the two constellations for several seconds. Was something reading my mind? Had my thoughts about the beauty of the sky provoked someone to respond? Was the white line showing me that another intelligence knew where my eyes and mind had been focused only minutes before?

The next morning, dressed in arctic ski clothes, we mounted horses to climb the remaining 8,000 feet. Mine was a big, black-haired, gentle male. The road became a small path as the elevation increased. Children in bare feet walked next to their mothers and fathers, who wore only sandals. The women were traditionally dressed in skirts and petticoats, their legs bare. Some had walked more than two hundred miles. The mountain path became frightening. A two-foot-wide ledge and the horses' confidence were all that kept us from plunging into a deep ravine to our left. I kept my eyes on the moving feet of a woman and child in front of me. They had walked up behind our horses and patiently worked themselves around the animals to our right on the uphill side of the mountain. The woman was thin, a baby strapped on her back. Her other child was probably four. I shivered inside my parka, wondering how she and the children could stand the harsh air. Penance, prayer, redemption. Thousands walked that cold and narrow path.

My horse stumbled once on a hair-pin turn. The child in front of me never flinched. I closed my eyes in blind faith, faith that life was meant to go on, faith that the horse had good sense, faith in the power of the pilgrimage to the ice of Qoyllur Rit'i. The horse staggered against the hillside and kept going.

Several hours later we were at 22,000 feet near the summit with four hundred feet of glacier above us. Every breath, I wanted more air. A panic took over. I was going to suffocate. But we had to get the tents up before sundown and numbing cold. Survival took priority and work preoccupied our minds. But when we lay down to rest, the panic took over again: air, more air!

Drums began beating. A steady, low-pitched beat went on four days and four nights without interruption. Inca tribesmen took turns so that the rhythm like a heartbeat was never broken.

By sundown, my breathing panic subsided and I walked toward the drums. Thousands of Incas were now spread over the mountain. Only a few of us were outsiders. I was there because I was curious and wanted to experience ancient ritual. I was also there because I, too, wanted redemption, wanted to touch the face of God and know the certainty of That compassion in a universe that confused me with its harshness.

The drumbeat was coming from a circle of men dressed in Inca costumes near a large, grey stone church. The man-made structure on that wild, open mountain seemed an intrusion. But my Inca companions explained that in 1780, two boys were herding sheep near the glacier when they saw a ball of light. They followed the light to an enormous rock about fifteen feet high and wide. The children saw the light surround the rock which then cracked. The boys were convinced it was Christ himself in the light and ran to tell their parents. The elders decided the large crack was Christ's mark. To protect the miracle, the church was built and the large rock is the wall behind the altar.

That first night as I reached the church's front doorway, I could hear voices in prayer. Men, women and children were standing tightly together and moving slowly forward to pass Christ's rock. Everyone was holding at least one small, burning white candle. Some had many candles wedged between fingers in each hand. I slowly moved sideways through the crowd determined to see the rock. In front of me, I heard sobbing voices. Two women not much taller than four feet and wrinkled with age and sun were looking up toward the Christ rock. Each of their hands held four candles that were dripping hot wax on to their fingers. As they cried, they spoke out loud. I asked a man near me if he understood their pleas.

In broken English, he translated: "Oh, dear Christ, we are so sorry that you suffered for us. Please forgive us. May we suffer now, too."

As I watched the agony in their faces, I felt a sting in my eyes. The sting gave way to the pressure in my chest and I cried.

Closer to the altar, I could see that the crack in the rock had been augmented with gold paint. The artificial crown and body were superfluous to the unquestioning faith in those human hearts.

The cold air at the exit was suffocating again, but the scene before me was not. Candles and campfires turned the mountain into a starry sky. That sky continued into the black with sparkling stars above. Like a perfect mirror image on a very calm lake, stars were above, below, everywhere. There was no horizon.

I moved outside along the church wall back toward the drumbeat. The circle of men was larger, perhaps fifty feet across. In the middle, one man was dressed as an "angel" with white paint on his face. He raised a bullwhip high above his head. His target was another Inca tribesman dressed as a "devil" a few yards away. The devil also had a bullwhip. The two stalked each other slowly, cautiously. Suddenly, both lashed out and stung each other's flesh. Over and over, they whipped. Then the devil and angel embraced, backed away into the circle and a new angel and devil began another round.

I turned to my Inca friend. "Why didn't the angel win?"

He laughed at my bias and answered, "If the positive and negative get out of balance, the universe gets sick. The Incas believe that the positive and the negative must always struggle with each other and then embrace to keep the universe from falling apart."

Balance, he said, was the key to survival. Nothing was all good or all bad. The universe was neutral, not harsh. Its creator dreamed, observed and loved us all.

Keep an open mind, he urged me. Days later, he said tears were not needed for the fourteen women and babies who died from the cold during that Qoyllur Rit'i. The moment of death, he explained, was simply a walk into the next room of the dream.

Qoyllur Riti stays with me whether I am in a crop circle, examining a mutilated animal, or listening to people relate their experiences with something other than human. In these glimpses of other realities, a new cosmology is emerging, a different understanding about who we are, how the universe works, and how human consciousness might contribute to its spiralling evolution.

Spirals and labyrinths representing the cyclic renewal of life, the great round of death and rebirth, the journey of the soul, have been found carved on ancient rocks in England, Ireland, the Adriatic Sea region, Hopi Indian lands, Greece, and the island of Crete dating as far back as 4,000 years before Christ.

GLIMPSES OF OTHER REALITIES

VOLUME I: FACTS AND EYEWITNESSES

Plate 1 - *This "geometry lesson" at its longest overall measurement was approximately 330 feet and was mysteriously created between 10 p.m. July 16, and 6 a.m. July 17, 1991, near Barbury Castle north of Marlborough, England. No one has claimed to have hoaxed this formation. Photograph © 1991 by George Wingfield.*

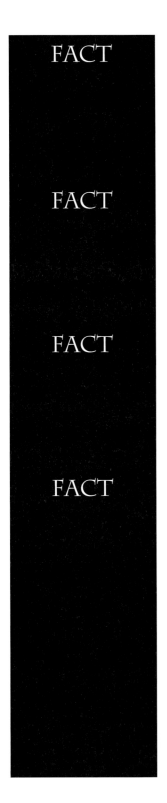

Crop formations have been found in more than a dozen countries worldwide since 1990, including Japan, Australia, Canada, United States, England, Italy, Germany, The Netherlands and other European countries.

Diatonic ratios which match the white keys on a piano have been discovered repeatedly in patterns of pure circles with satellite circles or concentric rings.

Original geometry theorems have also been discovered in the simple circles and concentric rings by adding tangents consistent with Euclidean rules. These geometries also show diatonic ratios.

Biochemical and biophysical changes have occurred in plants inside formations including:

- Lack of embryogenesis (seed development) in spring formations.
- Accelerated growth in summer formations.
- Growth nodes bent or re-oriented.
- Changes in plant cell pits that suggest varying exposures to rapid and intense energy.
- Shriveling of leaf edges, consistent with exposure to rapid and intense energy.
- Leaf and stem cracking which indicate high exposure to heat or an energy that generates heat in plant tissues.
- Significantly higher ion conductivity at the microfibril level of bract tissue in formation plants compared to controls.

CHAPTER 1

CROP CIRCLES, BIOLOGY, AND FROZEN MUSIC

"Whatever is doing these formations is affecting the fundamental biochemistry and biophysics of the plants."

W. C. LEVENGOOD, PH. D.-eq
BIOPHYSICIST

More than three thousand simple circles, Celtic crosses, and increasingly complex pictograms have been discovered in southern England's crop fields since 1978. Hundreds more have been reported in more than a dozen other countries, including Japan, Australia, Canada, United States, England, Italy, Germany, The Netherlands and other European countries. When the circle designs suddenly evolved in 1990 to complex formations that included rectangles, triangles and ovals as well as circles and rings as big as football fields, astronomer Archie Roy at Glasgow University said he was convinced humanity was encountering an advanced intelligence.

Then in 1991, other large formations emerged which resembled ladders and insects. The season culminated with a large geometric shape near Barbury Castle found at 6 a.m. on July 17. (Plates 1-2) The equilateral triangle measured approximately 177 feet each side. At each vertex of the triangle were different circular formations which averaged about 75 feet in diameter. Barbury Castle "embodies geometry of the very highest order," George Wingfield wrote.[1] The formation was *not* in the field as late as 10 p.m. the evening of July 16, when a television crew was taping nearby. The manager of Waterstone's bookshop in Bristol told Wingfield that he and two others had seen six pulsing lights and one large dark object cross the sky that night. Others talked about seeing unusual lights over Barbury Castle, north of Avebury.

Wingfield interviewed the warden who lives in a bungalow up on the Barbury Castle hill. He "heard the most colossal roar coupled with a pulsing hum at 3:30 a.m. the morning of July 17, 1991, which he described as like

[1] *Harbingers of World Change* © 1991 Gateway Books, Bath, U.K.

one hundred planes going over. This terminated abruptly after a few minutes, but he never saw fit to look outside the house at the time. This warden was familiar with low-flying aeroplanes, since Barbury Castle is close to RAF (Royal Air Force) Lyneham."

Grazing sheep near the large formation were not hurt, but the owner found the animals at the opposite end of a large pasture where they had not gone before, as if they had been frightened by something.

Plate 2 - *July 17, 1991 Barbury Castle formation near Marlborough, England. Equilateral triangle 177 feet each side with an approximately 75-foot-diameter circle formation at each corner. Photograph © 1991 by George Wingfield.*

A month later, another mathematical formation 124 feet wide was discovered in a field at Ickleton, ten miles south of Cambridge. (Plate 3)

Plate 3 - *August 12, 1991, "Mandelbrot set" formation 124 feet wide discovered in wheat near Ickleton, ten miles south of Cambridge. Photograph © 1991 by David Parker.*

The shape is called a Mandelbrot set, named after IBM research fellow Benoit Mandelbrot, who developed the field of fractal geometry used to study Chaos Theory and its application to patterns of growth in the natural world, and even fluctuating prices. Fractal geometry reveals that the way trees grow along the edge of a lake, the way ice cracks, clouds form, or cotton prices go up and down, has an eerie mathematical order.

The word *fractal* is derived from the Latin verb *frangere*, to break, and the English words *fracture* and *fraction*. James Gleick described this new science in his book *Chaos*.[2]

"Fractional dimension becomes a way of measuring qualities that otherwise have no clear definition: the degree of roughness or brokenness or irregularity in an object. A twisting coastline, for example, despite its immeasurability in terms of length, nevertheless has a certain characteristic degree of roughness. Mandelbrot specified ways of calculating the fractional dimension of real objects, given some technique of constructing a shape or given some data, and he allowed his geometry to make a claim about the irregular patterns he had studied in nature. The claim was that the degree of irregularity remains constant over different scales.

[2] *Chaos, Making A New Science* by James Gleick © 1987, Penguin Books, N.Y.

Surprisingly often, the claim turns out to be true. Over and over again, the world displays a regular irregularity. ... Above all, fractal meant self-similar. ... shapes are defined, not by solving an equation once, but by iterating it in a feedback loop," which is the essence of the Mandelbrot Set pattern.

Plate 4 - Computer generated "Mandelbrot Set" using the iteration of $z \rightarrow z^2 + c$. Take a complex number, multiply it by itself, and add the original number.

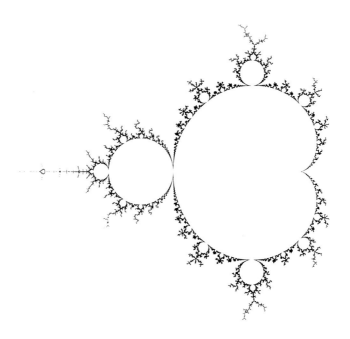

Could Something out there be trying to reinforce the idea that our universe is defined by a repeating feedback loop that is mathematical in evolution and powered by consciousness?

In March 1992, I called Isabelle Kingston in Ogbourne St. Andrew. She moved to southern England in 1984 with an inspired conviction that Wiltshire would become famous worldwide for extraordinary events yet to unfold. She felt compelled to study the history of Silbury Hill, a large, ancient construction built around 2800 B. C. (Plates 16-18) Several major crop formations have been discovered around that ancient site.

The first core samples from the hill's center were extracted in July 1969, the same month that astronaut Neil Armstrong first stepped on the moon in the U. S. Apollo program. Alternating layers of chalk and clay with sarsen sandstones at its center indicated that the sacred site was constructed with intelligence and design. Yet, its precise purpose is still unknown. Speculation focuses on the hill's relationship to magnetic lines of force that flow around the Earth. Dowsers say magnetic lines converge at Silbury Hill, but the consequences of such convergence are not understood.

"Almost five thousand years ago, these sacred sites in Wiltshire were built," Isabelle said. "Many of the religions talk about the great, tall beings who were here to instruct us and there was a change in consciousness." Neolithic skeletons found in English long barrows were related to the Sumerians of Mesopotamia in the fourth millenium B. C.[3] That culture, whose origin is unknown, lived in the land now called Iran and Iraq. The Sumerians worshipped tall "gods" associated with ziggurat towers where Sumerian royalty communicated and interacted with those gods. Statues and carvings of Sumerian divinity depict very large, dome-shaped heads covered by hats or material draped in folds over long, tapered skulls. (Chapter 4)

[3] Sir Arthur Keith, *Al-'Ubaid* and C. Leonard Woolley, *The Sumerians* © 1965, W. W. Norton & Co.

Isabelle Kingston and others studying the crop circle mystery wonder if the same intelligence associated with the tall beings might be back trying to raise our consciousness again. "Our planet needs help. Right now is a dangerous time. It's my feeling that we've been given a chance to create a new environment, or else it's all over. And the circle makers are involved somehow."

I wanted to see and feel for myself what it was like inside the formations and landed at Heathrow on July 22, 1992. That night I reached the Waggon and Horses pub in Beckhampton (Plate 5) where circle investigators and tourists gathered to eat and drink beer while they shared photographs, drawings, adventures, and philosophies.

Plate 5 - *The Waggon and Horses pub in Beckhampton, England near Avebury. Photograph* © *1992 by author.*

The pub is not far from Silbury Hill and the village of Avebury that lies within one of the largest prehistoric ceremonial sites in Europe, enclosing 28 1/2 acres. (Plate 6) Avebury is surrounded by a circular bank of chalk 1400 feet in diameter. Around the edge stands a circle and avenue of more than one hundred large silica sandstones known as sarsen, some weighing fifty tons. Silbury Hill and Avebury may have been built at the same time about 5,000 years ago.

Plate 6 - *Avebury, England, a prehistoric ceremonial site (circa 2800 B.C.), surrounded by the largest circles of sarsen sandstones in the British Isles. The village is also near the prehistoric construction of Silbury Hill. Photograph © 1991 by Barbara Lamb.*

At the pub near Avebury, I met George Wingfield. (Plate 7) George worked for IBM as an engineer before retiring in 1991 to devote full time to studying the crop circle mystery.

We drove to the Tim and Polly Carson farm in Alton Barnes to meet Colin Andrews, engineer, author and founder of Circles Phenomenon Research International, and Steven Greer, M. D., an emergency physician from North Carolina and founder of the Center for the Study of Extraterrestrial Intelligence, known as CSETI (Plate 8).

The CSETI goal is a close encounter of the 5th kind with the circle makers, meaning to go peacefully on board a spacecraft. Greer's assumption was that alien intelligences from somewhere else in the universe are visiting and interacting with Earth, including the creation of the enigmatic formations in cereal crops, and that those craft and the beings that control them can be contacted.

Plate 7 - *Crop circle investigator George Wingfield with Linda Moulton Howe at the base of Woodborough Hill in Alton Barnes, Wiltshire, England, on July 23, 1992, before a CSETI night watch. Photograph © 1992 by Ron Russell.*

Plate 8 - *L-R: Shari Adamiak, George Wingfield, Linda Moulton Howe, Colin Andrews, Steven Greer, and Michael Brein near Carson Farm at base of Woodborough Hill, July 23, 1992, prior to CSETI night watch. Photograph © 1992 by Ron Russell.*

The connection between lights in the sky and the modern age of crop circles began in the 1980s. The formations became increasingly complex and strange lights were often reported near fields where crops were later found sculpted in geometric and non-geometric patterns.

Even though there is no hard evidence to link UFOs and the formations, and no one has yet photographed or videotaped a pattern forming, two unusual events and eyewitnesses are on record. On July 12, 1990, at Adam's Grave near Milk Hill and Alton Barnes (Map Plate 11), a 400-foot-long pictogram appeared with features never previously seen. The new pattern had an appendage that looked like an old-fashioned key. Near that formation two weeks later, Steve Alexander was videotaping the pictogram when a small, white, round object suddenly appeared moving along the top of the plants, sometimes disappearing into them and then reappearing.

A year later on August 19, 1991, near Barbury Castle north of Avebury, German students Constantin and Mucki von Durckheim videotaped a similar white, disk-shaped object moving above a crop formation.[4] In 1992, Pete Glastonbury photographed a moving light in a dumbbell formation at Berry Pomeroy (Page 61, Plate 56). All the mysterious lights are still unidentified.

Colin Andrews interviewed one eyewitness in June 1989, who watched an unusual orange light. Andrews had flown in a helicopter with a CBC Canadian television crew to film eleven crop circles adjacent to Silbury Hill. At 12:45 a.m. the next morning, a local resident walked into his backyard and saw a bright orange light he estimated to be about thirty feet in diameter moving vertically down toward the field in front of Silbury Hill. The man could see a tree on the boundary line of the wheat field silhouetted between him and the orange light, so he knew the object touched down in the field of eleven circles. The next morning, a twelfth circle had been added.

Andrews said, "I think this is as close and direct an association as we ever had with a UFO and the crop circles. I'm totally satisfied with this man's firsthand, genuine eyewitness account of an unusual light in the sky and a mysterious crop marking."

[4] *Cropcircle Communique,* (documentary film) © 1991 Circlevision, Shropshire, England.

Plate 9 - *Pictogram in barley two miles southwest of Stonehenge near Longbarrow crossroads, June 29, 1992. Photographed by George Wingfield shortly before the farmer harvested the field early to avoid publicity.*

In the Wiltshire countryside, more than one hundred pictograms were reported between May and August 18, 1992. Several were near Alton Barnes and Silbury Hill. (Map, Plate 11)

On June 26, three large circles were joined together in wheat at Boreham Wood northeast of Alton Barnes. (Plate 13) A large pictogram appeared near Stonehenge on June 29. (Plate 9).

The next major formation was a 414-foot-long "snail" discovered July 9, in a wheat field not far from Woodborough Hill in Alton Barnes. (Plates 12 and 14) A week later on July 16, a few miles west of the "snail," a formation was found at Milk Hill that meandered nearly 400 feet long in circles, corridors and ninety degree angles under the Lockeridge White Horse. (Plate 15) The next day, a 324-foot-long "pointer" appeared in Avebury near Silbury Hill. (Plates 16-17) A similar double pictogram had been found in the same field two years earlier on July 27, 1990, pointing directly at Silbury Hill. (Plate 18)

Around July 24, a 258-foot-long formation was discovered at East Meon (Plate 24), a half-hour south of Alton Barnes by plane, and later confirmed to be a hoax. Also on July 24, a triangle with three sides averaging 172 feet appeared in wheat below Oliver's Castle seven miles west of Alton Barnes. (Plates 21; 38-40; 54)

The pictograms continued in August with at least five major formations in Froxfield and Ogbourne Maizey (Plate 19) east of Marlborough; West Stowell near Alton Barnes in Wiltshire; south toward East Meon again where two formations appeared on the same day at Exton; back to Froxfield for a 327-foot-long sprawl of circles, lines and "celery stalk" appendages which some insist was a hoax; and ended near Silbury Hill with a circle containing seven symbols and a man-made water trough attached like charms on a bracelet that measured 226 feet from top to bottom and 158 feet diameter in the main ring. (Plate 22)

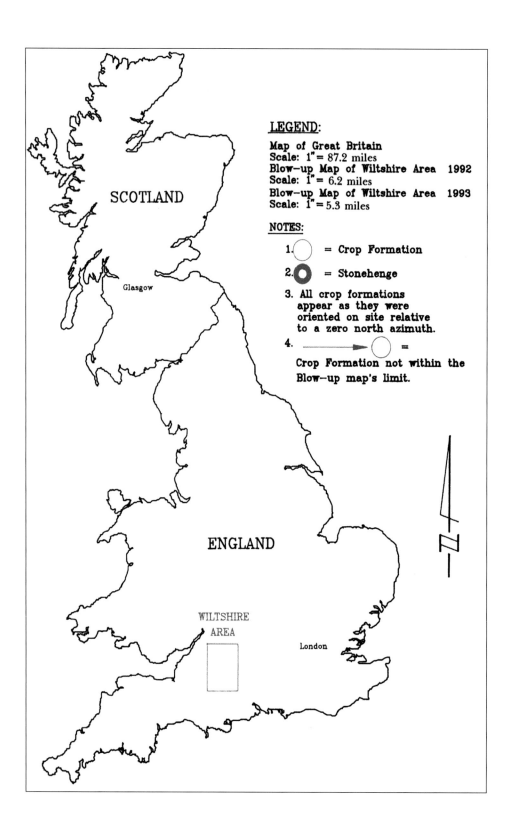

Plate 10 -
*Map of Great
Britain,
Wiltshire
highlighted.*

LEGEND:
Map of Great Britain
Scale: 1" = 87.2 miles
Blow-up Map of Wiltshire Area   1992
Scale: 1" = 6.2 miles
Blow-up Map of Wiltshire Area   1993
Scale: 1" = 5.3 miles

NOTES:

1. ◯ = Crop Formation

2. ◉ = Stonehenge

3. All crop formations appear as they were oriented on site relative to a zero north azimuth.

4. ⟶ ◯ = Crop Formation not within the Blow-up map's limit.

SCOTLAND

Glasgow

ENGLAND

WILTSHIRE AREA

London

Plate 11 -

Orientation map for 1992 Wiltshire, England, formations by Vincent Creevy, P.L.S. © 1993 LMH Prods. Approximate measurements based on surveys by John Martineau.

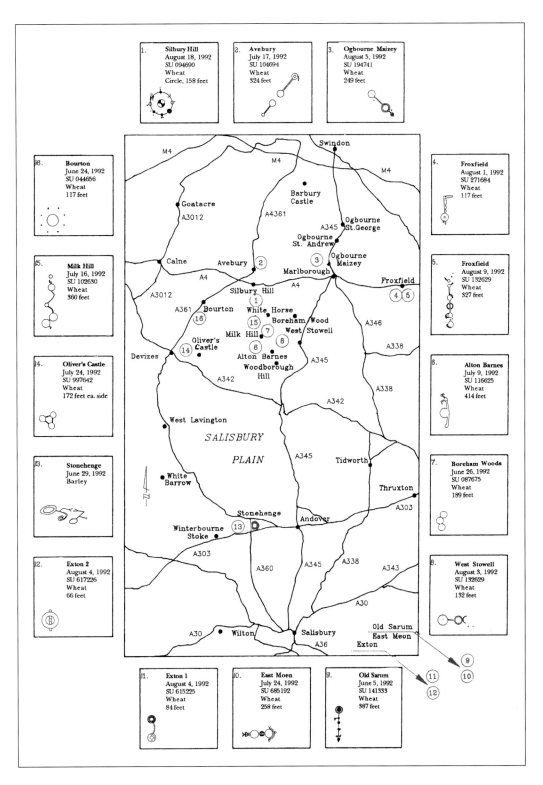

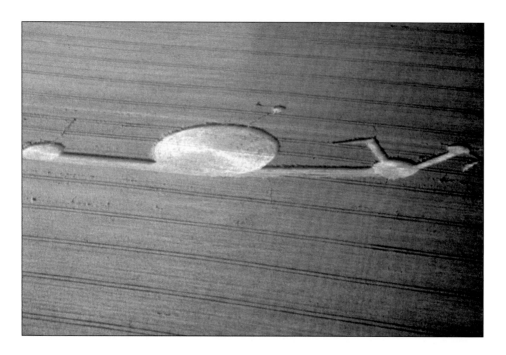

Plate 12 - *"Snail" July 28, 1992. Aerial photograph © 1992 by Edwin B. Nelson.*

Plate 13 - *Boreham Wood circles discovered June 26, 1992, a few miles northeast of Alton Barnes. Aerial photograph © 1992 by Linda Moulton Howe.*

Plate 14 - *July 9, 1992, a 414-foot-long "snail" formation discovered in an Alton Barnes wheat field not far from Woodborough Hill topped by trees in background. Foreground are Shari Adamiak and Linda Moulton Howe. Photograph © 1992 by Ron Russell.*

Plate 15 - *July 16,1992, a nearly 400-foot-long wheat formation found below Milk Hill and the Lockeridge White Horse, a 19th Century copy of a Neolithic creation originally found near Uffington. This site was a few miles west of the Alton Barnes "snail." Aerial photograph © 1992 by Linda Moulton Howe.*

Plate 16 - *July 17, 1992, a 324-foot-long "pointer" appeared in an Avebury wheat field near Silbury Hill. Aerial photograph © 1992 by Jurgen Kronig.*

Plate 17 - *Silbury Hill, a sacred site artificially constructed circa 2800 B. C. with alternating layers of chalk and clay. Aerial photograph © 1992 by Linda Moulton Howe.*

Plate 18 - *Two years
earlier on July 27, 1990,
a double pictogram
similar in style to Plate 16
was found in the same
Avebury field pointing
directly at Silbury Hill.
Aerial photograph © 1990
by George Wingfield.*

Plate 19 -
*Ogbourne
Maizey,
249-foot-
long
pictogram
discovered
August 5,
1992,
northeast of
Marlborough
and Alton
Barnes.
Aerial photo-
graph
© 1992
by Jurgen
Kronig.*

Plate 20 -
*Ogbourne Maizey,
nearly identical
formation the year
before on July 20,
1991. Aerial
photograph © 1991
by Barbara Lamb.*

Plate 21 - *Oliver's Castle triangle formation averaging 172 feet each side found July 24, 1992, in a wheat field seven miles west of Alton Barnes. Aerial photograph © 1992 by Jurgen Kronig.*

Plate 22 - *"Charm Bracelet" or "Celtic Wheel" at Silbury Hill, 158-foot-diameter circle with appendages discovered August 18, 1992. Aerial photograph © by Busty Taylor.*

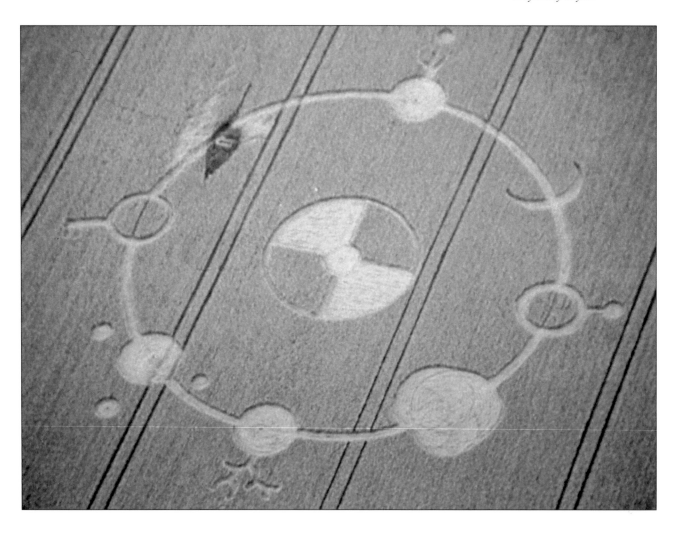

NIGHT WATCHES

Colin Andrews helped Steven Greer coordinate 1992 night watches between July 22-29, 1992. Andrews picked the top of Woodborough Hill near the Tim and Polly Carson farm in Alton Barnes where circle formations had been concentrated in the past.

The CSETI philosophy is that if communication and contact with another intelligence can be provoked, night watches are worth the effort. Greer described his goal "to precipitate or facilitate a landing, with mental concentration and then a conscious meeting with these visitors. There are those who smile and think it's a bit advanced at this point in time, but our position is that this should have been going on for the last forty years."

Colin Andrews is also convinced that investigators can influence the phenomenon. In 1988, he says he "laid in bed one night and visualized a Celtic cross. I literally asked in my mind for it to arrive in a field as close to my home in Andover as possible" to make detailed study easier. The next morning Andrews received a phone call from a farmer not far away who said, "You won't believe what is in the field here."

Andrews flew over the crops and saw "a huge and extraordinarily pretty Celtic cross. Looking down on that very religious symbol was a time that changed my life. It was such a religious, graphic and obviously intelligently constructed circle that it just had to be important. And it was a formation identical to what I had concentrated on in my thoughts the very night it did in fact arrive." In past years, others have noticed that their thoughts or visualized images sometimes showed up in the formations, as if something in the unseen absorbed human thought and reflected it back in an odd form of dialogue.

On July 22, around 9 p.m., about twenty of us climbed Woodborough Hill, including Colin Andrews, George Wingfield, Steven Greer, Ron Russell and Shari Adamiak from Denver, local resident and psychic Maria Ward, and a psychologist from Ohio who prefers privacy. I will call her Mary Smith.

That night was an important baseline. People were watching in every direction, and we verified each other's sightings of moving lights. Most were airplanes or helicopters. We could see orange flares from military night training maneuvers south of us on the Salisbury Plain. We saw the flashing strobes of airliners and pinpoint lights that were satellites moving overhead.

The only unusual object we saw in the sky was a cantaloupe-orange point of light that was not a military flare. What it was, no one knows. It would appear, catch our attention, fade, brighten, disappear. Greer used powerful halogen spotlights to sweep the sky as a welcoming signal for contact. Some of us expected to stay out until morning. But we were miserable and shivering, dressed for summer when we needed winter coats in the cold, humid English night.

The next evening, July 23, 1992, we were more prepared with blankets and coats. Steven Greer asked some of us to sit in a circle for meditation. Maria Ward told us that the day before she had received a mental impression of circles in the form of a triangle in which the number nine was important. She suggested that we concentrate on visualizing such an image to reach out telepathically to any intelligence that might be receiving. Later, she sent Colin a drawing of the pattern she imagined. (Plate 23) On her drawing she wrote: "It would look like a molecule in a chemistry lab, but the number nine is important. In this design, it means something. The whole shape rotated anti-clockwise and fell to the ground. Something to do with Cromwell."

July 22, 1992. Wednesday.

Shape seen in 3-D, during visualisation.

tilted and moved around.

Solid bars

Spheres

like a molecule figure in a chemistry lab.

I do not know — but the number 9 is important in this design. _It means_ something. The whole shape rotated anti-clockwise and then 'fell' to the ground. Something to do with 'CROMWELL'?

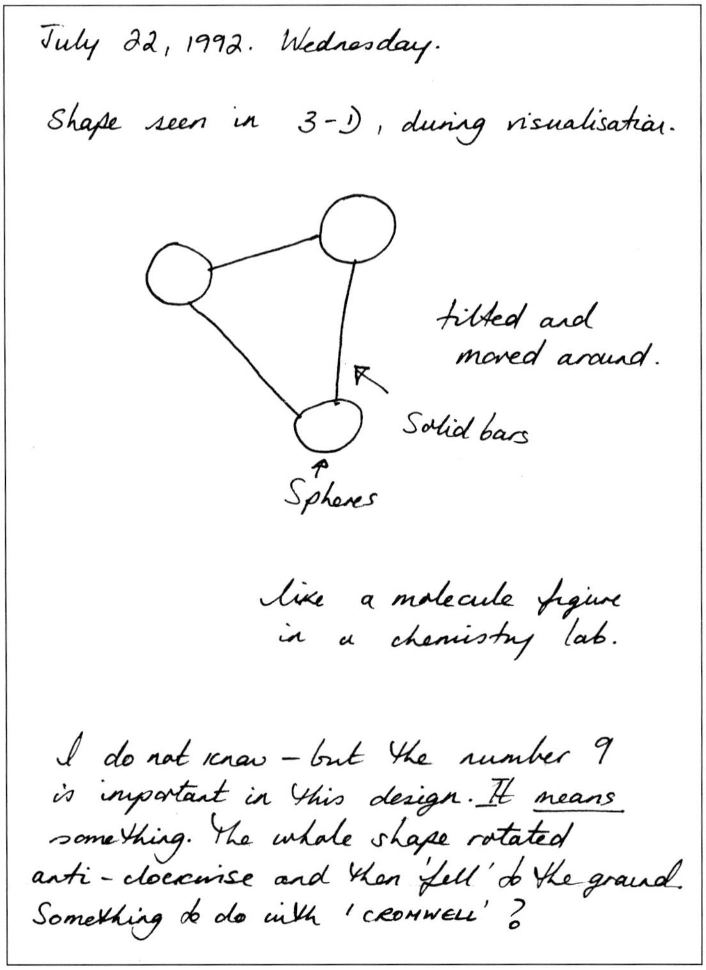

Plate 23 - *Maria Ward received this mental impression on July 22, prior to the first CSETI night watch at Woodborough Hill. She later drew this for Colin Andrews. Reprinted here with her permission.*

A formation was found the next day on July 24th, twelve miles west of Alton Barnes in a wheat field below Oliver's Castle hill. (Plate 21) Oliver Cromwell fought there in 1643 against King Charles I in a vicious battle during England's civil war. Hundreds of men fell to the ground and died.

However, the night watch group did not hear about that formation until July 27. Instead, on the morning of July 24, Colin Andrews received a phone call about a large 258-foot-long formation discovered at East Meon, about a half-hour south by plane from Woodborough Hill. Andrews drove there first and entered the formation with the farmer's exclusive permission, he thought. But he was only one of many the farmer allowed in his field because the formation had been hoaxed with his cooperation. The farmer had even been paid for the damaged wheat.

A year later in August 1993 at the Waggon and Horses Pub, documentary filmmakers John MacNish and Jayne Wilde of Circlevision, told me how they paid the farmer and asked the infamous hoaxing duo, Doug and Dave,[5] to create the formation at night for their starscope camera. "Our documentary will show Doug and Dave making East Meon," MacNish told me. "I designed the formation myself and Doug and Dave took an hour and a half to make it in the wheat field."

Even though that farmer had gone along with Circlevision's videotaped hoax, many other farmers in the summer of 1992 were angry about the intrusions of tourists and circle makers, both the truly mysterious and the hoaxers. There were many people trampling crops. In July, an official hoax contest had been sponsored by *P. M. Magazine* of Munich and the Arthur Koestler Foundation of London. The Koestler Foundation offered a five thousand pound reward to anyone who could prove who the circle makers are and how they create the formations. No one collected. There were also rumors that intelligence agents from both the U. S. and U. K. were involved with creating hoaxes and spreading hoax rumors about all formations in a counter-intelligence strategy to confuse everyone in order to divert public interest from the genuinely mysterious phenomenon. But why, many people asked, would governments want to disrupt public interest in the crop formations?

Some farmers even harvested crops early to avoid publicity. One loss was a barley field pictogram near Stonehenge that was harvested soon after it was discovered. Fortunately, George Wingfield was able to fly over and photograph the formation before it was gone. (Page 12, Plate 9)

Not knowing anything about Circlevision's involvement with the East Meon formation, Colin Andrews thought it was worth seeing from the air. He, Ron Russell and Steven Greer were flown there in a four-seater to take

[5] Doug Bower and Dave Chorley made headlines in September 1991 with their claims that they had hoaxed the crop circle phenomenon. Worldwide television networks and other media reported that those two men from southern England were the answer to the worldwide mystery without question or further investigation. However, the phenomenon had been reported in more than a dozen countries and scientific research indicated hoaxing could not create the fundamental biochemical and biophysical changes found in some formation plants.

aerial photographs the afternoon of July 24, 1992. (Plate 24) That night a group of us were at dinner in Marlborough discussing East Meon and other formations when a man from East Sussex named Chris Mansell introduced himself from a nearby table. He said he had been studying the crop circles over four years and was comparing their patterns to ancient symbols and cave art.

He'd already driven down to East Meon, too, and told us with great enthusiasm that on close-up inspection, "the braiding in the main circle was absolutely incredible. I've never seen anything like it," meaning that stems were woven together like a plait of hair.

Mansell told us he had been in the Almeria caves in southern Spain which are famous for their prehistoric paintings and engravings dating from approximately 30,000 B. C. to 10,000 B. C. There he learned about a symbol called an "indalo" that resembled one end of the East Meon formation. He was told that the half moon with antenna represented the new moon, or a boat in which the soul travels, and wondered if the formation had something to do with a time period and spiritual communication. John MacNish told me he knew and liked the Spanish indalo symbol and had specifically incorporated it into the East Meon design in honor of his first child's birth the same week Doug and Dave made the formation.

Plate 24 -
East Meon 258-foot-long formation found July 24, 1992, a half-hour south of Alton Barnes by plane.
Created for a Circlevision documentary. Photograph by Ron Russell
© 1992.

The East Meon controversy pointed up an issue which was to emerge again in the 1993 crop season: the formations were provoking people to discuss ideas not often mentioned before the phenomenon began. Crop circle hoaxer Robert Irving asked me, "What difference does it make whether I make a formation or Something Else makes it as long as people wake up?" Wake up, he meant, to other forces around us, human and other, which are manipulating and sometimes inspiring. Even Irving, Doug Bower and David Chorley did not make any claims on the creation of the Barbury Castle "geometry lesson" or the Ickleton Mandelbrot set or hundreds of other circles, rings and other shapes found in other countries around the world.

With no knowledge about the East Meon hoax, several of us from the United States went with Chris Mansell the next day, July 25, into another large and complex wheat formation below Milk Hill and the Lockeridge White Horse, a 19th Century copy of a Neolithic creation originally found in Uffington. (Plate 25) Later we were to learn that plants from the 360-foot-long Milk Hill formation revealed biophysical and biochemical changes which biophysicist W. C. Levengood said could not be hoaxed. (Pages 43-51) There were five large circles, all swirled clockwise, connected by meandering loops and punctuated with 90-degree angled corridors spread over the length of a football field. (Plate 26) Beneath all the complicated turns and angles was another layer, like a foundation. (Plates 27-29) Everything was smooth, flat and unbroken, as if water had rushed through it.

While we were inside the Milk Hill formation, a dark-colored helicopter flew very low over us. Chris Mansell said he had seen many low-flying helicopters above the crop formations, several circling as if photographing or monitoring. According to George Wingfield and Colin Andrews, theEnglish Army deliberately created a hoax circle in 1990. This was during Operation Blackbird when England's BBC-TV and Japan's Nippon TV tried unsuccessfully to record a circle forming. For several days, cameras and sophisticated monitoring gear operated around the clock. "At the peak of the operation," Andrews told me, "I counted as many as thirty-two TV and radio networks on site and many of them were satellite broadcasting back into the United States on Good Morning America, CBC to Canada, ARD into Germany, Channel 9 into Australia, BBC and ITN into the UK, and so on. There was an extremely nervous British government on whose ground we were located. I certainly don't have any doubts that the hoax was perpetrated by the British Army, and also that other maneuverings that I'm aware of at Blackbird were also played by the Army's hand."

The unanswered question is: Do governments know, or think they know, information about the phenomenon that requires misinformation and repression of the truth? If so, what are the national security concerns?

Plate 25 - *Milk Hill formation below the Lockeridge White Horse, July 24, 1992. Photograph by author.*

Plate 26 - *Ninety degree angled corridors and narrow loops connected five clockwise circles in Milk Hill formation. July 24, 1992. Photograph by author.*

Plates 27-29 - *A*
"foundation rib"
flowing underneath one
of the large circles in the
Milk Hill formation.
Plants examined by
biophysicist W. C.
Levengood revealed
biochemical changes
"that cannot be
hoaxed."
Photographs by author.

After exploring the complicated looping corridors, 90-degree angles, and circles at Milk Hill, we went back to our cars via a tramline. Tramlines are formed by tractor wheels as farmers drive up and down fields at the beginning of the growing season. This practice did not begin in England until 1980. Before then, circles had been found in the middle of large cereal crop fields that had no visible points of entry.

Plate 30 - *Wind damage in a wheat field about one mile from the Milk Hill formation. Photograph by author.*

About one-half mile away, I photographed actual wind damage (Plate 30) in a wheat field that shows the contrast between a circle formation and natural flattening by wind.

In the United States, wind damage was said by some to be the cause of unusual formations found near Linfield, Pennsylvania, and a couple of miles away in Limerick, on May 24, 1992. (Plates 31-33) A psychologist from Ursinus College named Bruce Rideout, who has a degree in biology, photographed the locations and took plant samples for study. He found in both sites, and especially at Linfield, sections of wheat were parted like hair with each side going in opposite directions. (Plate 32) He also found odd bending or re-orientation of growth nodes that biophysicist W. C. Levengood in Michigan had discovered earlier in samples from English formations. (See pages 50-51; 61)

If the Pennsylvania wheat was affected by the same mysterious energy force involved in other regions of the world, perhaps the purpose behind the crop formations is more complicated than symbols. Last summer, one investigator even speculated that the formations might be "markers in living tissue" used by an advanced intelligence to monitor experiments in the past, present and future of this planet. In that context, changes around formations or "wind damage" would be the consequence of tinkering with time lines. If nothing else, such speculation shows how far people have reached for explanations.

Plate 31 - *Wheat field found scalloped and flattened for 600 feet in Linfield, Pennsylvania, on May 24, 1992. Photograph by Bruce Rideout.*

Plate 32 - *One of several "hairline parts" found in the Linfield, Pennsylvania, wheat field that was flattened and scalloped. Photograph by Bruce Rideout.*

Plate 33 - *Aerial view of Limerick, Pennsylvania wheat field showing odd pattern of flattened wheat discovered May 24, 1992, about two miles from Linfield site. Plants from both locations showed cell changes and growth node re-orientation. Photograph by Julia Robertson © 1992.*

Back in England by Sunday, July 26, 1992, I had traveled on to Glastonbury Tor and Stonehenge to explore those sacred sites and returned to Marlborough on Tuesday, July 28. I learned that four people in a CSETI watch had seen what they called a "structured craft" at 12:30 a.m., early Monday morning, July 27th.

The following report about the hours preceding that event was provided by Ron Russell, a Denver, Colorado, artist who was with the CSETI group.

Report on Events of July 26, 1992, In Ring
Formation Near Woodborough Hill In Alton Barnes
by
Ron Russell © 1992

"The night was filled with the largest amount of anomalous phenomena that I witnessed in my short stay in England. It began in the late evening when we all noticed that somehow it wasn't getting dark. We puzzled over this for quite awhile. There was a thin, low cloud cover which obscured most stars. There was no moonlight and yet it was surprisingly light until around 11 p.m. where we were in Alton Barnes. We could all see quite well. I noted that my Nikon camera failed to function for unknown reasons, so I put it away.

We were in the big ring formation in the field near Woodborough Hill and Tawsmeade copse (thicket of trees). We saw some peculiar amber spheres of light that floated and bobbed up and down. They went behind trees about one-half mile away and then reappeared. I saw at one time five of these lights, although most of the time there seemed to be four. Occasionally there were only three, two or one. The lights seemed to be intelligent. They moved in a way that occasionally would respond to willful thought coming from me. My thought, for example, would will "move upward." The light would respond almost instantaneously by moving slightly upward. I found this to be amazing, but I could not link with it all the time. Our job was to watch all sectors of the sky, not just where this particular phenomenon was happening. So, my attention was split and I only consciously interacted with the lights on a couple of occasions. It did not feel in any way threatening, whatever it was.

Concurrently with this, there appeared behind Woodborough Hill an interesting phenomenon that filled thirty degrees of sky with a square-shaped box of bluish-white light. When we talked about this, we thought there must be somebody there with their headlights on behind the hill, or a barn light on, or something like that. But, none of us were satisfied with the prosaic explanations. It did not look like ordinary light – more like an aurora. It had not been seen any of the previous nights. This light phenomenon silhouetting Woodborough Hill went on for an hour and a half or so until I left.

Earlier that evening, too, sometime around 11:30 p.m., there appeared a strange light above the clouds over the East Field that resembled a wheel with spokes slowly turning in a clockwise direction. I could see the rim of the wheel with spokes rotating, moving around. It was as if it were done by a big light projector from up above the clouds, perhaps beaming this image back on top of the clouds toward earth, so we would see the projection like a giant symbol in the sky.

When Chris Mansell came to visit us about midnight, he said there were no lights on the other side of the hill, there were no cars parked with their lights on, there were no barn lights, there was no light source that he could tell us about from the other side of the hill where he had just been. As far as Chris knew, that light was some amazing phenomenon that was only being seen by us.

Around midnight, it began to drizzle in a peculiar way. It was as if a rain cloud formed around us and began to materialize water droplets which fell to Earth from all around us. It was not as if it rained just on our heads and shoulders. It was as if the rain was materializing even around our waist and falling from there even to the ground. A most peculiar kind of rain. It caused us to leave the circle with all the equipment and dash for cars to get shelter. Later, I compared notes with Busty Taylor, who was, I believe, on Milk Hill just a quarter of a mile away. He reported that it was not raining anywhere but in the Woodborough Hill area. It seemed to be a tiny little localized sort of rain that had us packed in, but Busty was dry. My speculation is that this peculiar light and the odd density and moisture of the cloud which turned itself into rain like very heavy dew around us was some kind of cloaking effect from the craft that later appeared to Steve Greer, Chris Mansell, Dr. Smith and Annick Nevejan.

At 12:15 a.m., I left to go back to the room and pack, for I had a plane to catch in a few hours. At about 2:30 a.m. or so, Steven Greer and Dr. Smith burst into the room at the Merlin Hotel in Marlborough and reported in vivid detail the sighting of the object that they saw right after I left."

Steven Greer, Chris Mansell, his Belgian friend, Annick Nevejan, and Dr. Smith decided to wait in their cars to see if the rain would stop.

Mansell said he was smoking a cigarette in the driver's seat and looked out his open window. "I was actually watching the dark space in the drizzle when — whatever it was — seemed to either appear from out of the ground or to appear suddenly from out of nowhere."

He drew a sketch of what he had seen through binoculars (Plate 34), the psychologist drew what she had seen (Plate 35) and Annick Nevejan sketched the group's positions in relationship to the object as it moved and appeared to change shape. (Plate 36)

Mansell described several lights in a straight line that were blinking from red at the left side through white to a blue-green color at the right, which gave him the impression of something round and revolving. He got out of the car and hurried over to alert Steven Greer and the psychologist.

"Steve said, 'Oh, my God, what's that?' which was all of our reactions because it was not like any other light formation that we've witnessed," said Mansell.

All four watched approximately fifteen minutes while the object moved slowly, stayed very low, and passed behind some trees about one-quarter of a mile away.

"We thought it moved south, but we never knew for sure," Greer explained, "because we couldn't get the compass to work. It just kept going round and round, giving different readings." (Plate 37) Chris Mansell, looking through binoculars, estimated the object was about eighty feet in diameter based on its relationship to the trees.

The moving lights came to a clearing and stopped. Three orange lights formed a triangle above a dimmer line of lights that continued to change color from red to white to blue-green. Greer said it reminded him of a Christmas tree. Dr. Smith said she thought the triangle of lights appeared above the object. Mansell had the impression "that the object was disk-shaped and somehow flipped upwards and we were looking at the bottom of it. But it's possible that when it became stationary, it could have somehow changed its form and projected something from its center upwards. The center amber light was definitely higher than what I experienced as the width of the original sighting."

Everyone saw a red light detach itself and move across the horizon. Mansell said it looked like a single red light to his naked eye, but through the binoculars he saw a small cluster of red lights.

"Then the red light re-oriented with the whole structure. It was at this point that we were all going crazy on the road. I'd never seen anything like that before in my life."

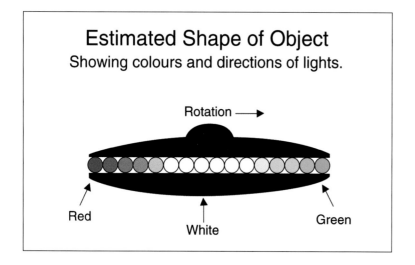

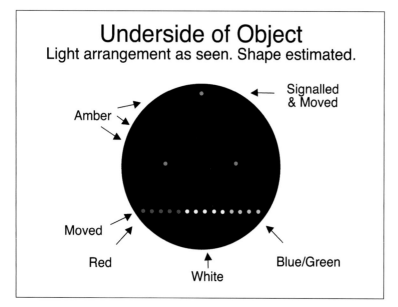

Plate 34 - *Drawings by Chris Mansell of East Sussex, England, based on his observations with binoculars of a moving sky object at 12:30 a.m. early Monday morning, July 27, 1992. The object seemed to change shape. Location was near Woodborough Hill in Alton Barnes.*

Plate 35 - *Drawings by psychologist Mary Smith based on her eyewitness observations of unusual object that changed shape at 12:30 a.m., July 27, 1992, near Woodborough Hill.*

To: Linda Moulton Howe

Date: 9-9-92

U F O Sighting early Monday, July 27, 1992
Alton Barnes Farm, Alton Barnes, England

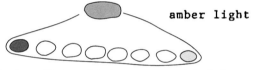

amber light

Red   White lights   Bluish green

I do not know how many lights there were because they were strobing in a counter-clockwise direction

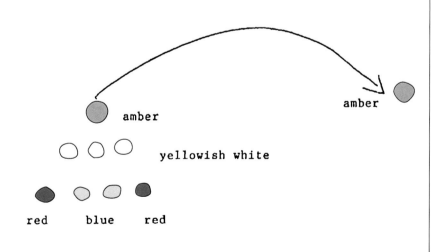

amber

amber

yellowish white

red   blue   red

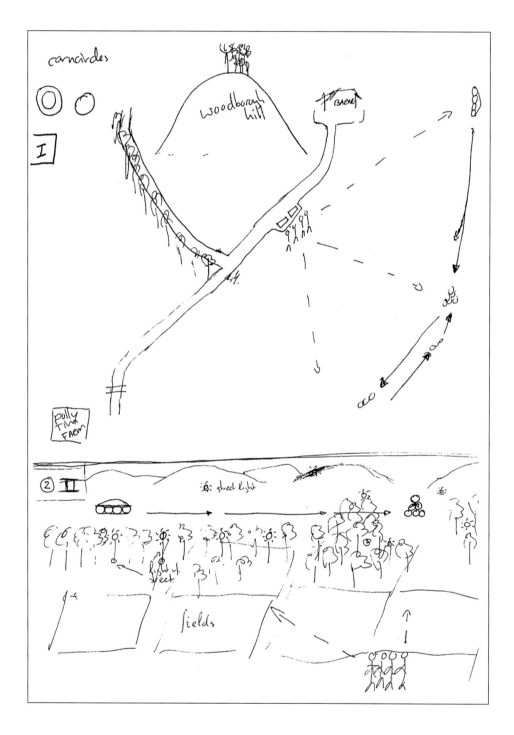

Plate 36 - *Drawing by Annick Nevejan of Belgium based on her eyewitness observations standing next to Chris Mansell, Steven Greer, and psychologist Mary Smith at 12:30 a.m., July 27, 1992. Annick also saw the object change shape.*

Plate 37 - *Chris
Mansell watched
unidentified flying
object while Steven
Greer watched compass
rotate at 12:30 a.m.,
July 27, 1992, near
Woodborough Hill,
Alton Barnes,
England.
Photograph by
Annick Nevejan.*

Greer pointed one of his portable, battery-powered halogen lamps at the object and flashed twice. The top amber light on the craft flashed back twice in the same rhythm. Flashing signals were repeated six or seven times and the object responded each time. Then the top amber light flew away and eventually the object disappeared.

"We were all completely surprised," said Mansell, "gob smacked! to use a great English word."

The next afternoon, Mansell and Nevejan returned to the scene to check the trees where they had seen the object.

"There weren't any roads. Anything moving would have to go through hedges, so you'd have to have something in the air," Mansell concluded.

By then, the CSETI group learned that a triangle formation averaging 172 feet each side had been found about seven miles west of Woodborough Hill in a wheat field below Oliver's Castle. There was confusion about the date of its discovery and everyone at first wondered if the unidentified aerial object was somehow connected to the crop formation. The shape was approximately the same as Maria Ward's drawing of her July 22 visualization which had been used as a symbol for meditation by the CSETI group on July 23 and subsequent nights.

Later it was confirmed that the Oliver's Castle formation was first seen on July 24, 1992, three days *before* the July 27 aerial object sighting and the morning after the July 23 night watch. No one has undisputed proof that the mysterious lights and sky objects are the makers of crop formations. One speculation has been that the UFO intelligence might be monitoring the mysterious force responsible for the worldwide crop formations.

There was also discussion about whether the circle making phenomenon had inspired Maria Ward's mind with the triangular image and then made the pattern? Or could the phenomenon have responded to Maria's thoughts about a triangular image, as in Colin Andrew's experience with the Celtic cross formation near his home?

Mansell articulated one of the confusions in many peoples' minds: "If the formations are symbols of communication, why aren't they more comprehensible in human terms? It seems very strange to me that if there is a motive for UFOs to make crop circles, if they are trying to communicate with us, they're just as bad at communicating as we are at understanding. If I had to talk to somebody, to communicate in another language like German, I'd either learn to speak German or find a translator who can speak both languages. I wouldn't give him a set of hieroglyphics and say, 'Figure this out!' after perhaps travelling one hundred million light years to get here!"

On July 29, I joined Colin Andrews, Steven Greer, psychotherapist and author Chet Snow, and others to visit the Oliver's Castle formation. (Plates 38-39) All the wheat in the circles and connecting corridors flowed in a clockwise direction. (Plate 40)

Chet Snow mentioned that the formation reminded him of an ancient symbol for the Sirius star system. I learned that the Egyptians used a triangle hieroglyph to represent the star Sirius (Chapter 4), which they tracked to monitor seasons and the flooding of the Nile. A similar symbol named "Yod" or "Yodh" is found in an ancient magical Hebrew alphabet and translates as "hand" "I," or "I am." The same triangle with circles at each vertex was also an alchemical sigil for the element silver and for the moon.[6]

I took wheat samples from inside one of the big circles. When I carefully pulled a flattened stalk with roots from the soil, there was no crease, bend or other physical blemish on the stem. (Plate 41) I also collected control plants from about a block away. I had helped organize scientific efforts with W. C. Levengood, biophysicist and owner of the Pinelandia Biophysical Lab in Michigan. (Plate 44) So, I sent my samples to him.

[6] *The Secret Teachings of All Ages* by Manly P. Hall, 19th Ed., 1973, Philosophical Research Society, Los Angeles, Calif.

Plate 38 - *Aerial of Oliver's Castle formation. Photograph by author.*

Plate 39 - *L-R: Chet Snow, psychotherapist and author; crop circle investigator Colin Andrews, and CSETI founder Steven Greer, inside one of the three circles found in wheat below Oliver's Castle seven miles west of Woodborough Hill on July 29, 1992. Photograph by author.*

Plate 40 - *Inside one of the three large circles below Oliver's Castle hill in background. Photograph by author.*

Plate 41 - *Unbroken wheat stalk that author pulled from Oliver's Castle formation and sent with other plant samples to biophysicist W. C. Levengood for examination. Photograph by author.*

SCIENTIFIC ANALYSIS

[7] B. S. Physics & Mathematics, Univ. of Toledo, Ohio, 1957; M. A. Bioscience, Ball State Univ., Muncie, Indiana, 1961; M. S. Biophysics, Univ. of Michigan, Ann Arbor, 1970; Ph.D.-eq, Univ. of Michigan, 1970; Assoc. Research Physicist, Univ. of Michigan, 1961-1968; Dir., Biophysical Research Sensors, Inc., Ann Arbor, 1970-1976; holds seven patents, including seed analyzer; Owner, Agro Sciences, Inc., Ann Arbor, 1976-1983; Owner, Pinelandia Biophysics Laboratory, 1987-2014.

Biophysicist W. C. Levengood[7] is convinced that whatever causes the crop circle phenomenon uses a rapid and intense energy which produces cell changes in affected plants. He studied plant samples in 1991 to 1993 from the United States, Canada, England and Australia. Many samples were collected in 1992 by a research team called Argus. It was organized by Michael Chorost, a student in English at Duke University, and Marshall Dudley, an engineer working at the time with a nuclear laboratory in Tennessee. (Plate 42)

In 1991, soil from one formation had been tested at an Oak Ridge, Tennessee, nuclear facility and results suggested unusual isotope changes. Researchers agreed that more soil sampling was necessary. Marshall collected and studied several 1992 soil samples, but did not find isotope changes. However, plants from inside formations in England, Canada, the United States and Australia have shown consistent changes in cell structure, seed and growth development.

Plate 42 - *Michael Chorost and Marshall Dudley taking plant and soil samples from a ringed circle in Alton Priors on July 29, 1992, an Argus team investigation in cooperation with biophysicist W. C. Levengood, Michigan. Photograph by author.*

Chorost sent biophysicist Levengood several samples from the hoax contest. Everyone was hoping for one instant test that would distinguish the truly anomalous crop formations from the human-made designs. At first, it appeared that expansion of cell wall pits (Plate 43) might be the answer.

1) Cell Pit Changes:

Plant cell pits, as shown in Plate 43, are microscopic cavities variously arranged throughout cells which allow metabolite and gasses to flow through living plants. Levengood (Plate 46) discovered a wide range of cell pit changes in anomalous formation plants, more than in hoaxed formations, which had more randomly distributed cell pit changes. He attributed the random cell pit enlargements in the hoaxed formations to the pressure of feet or machines trampling on the plants and forcing the stem's liquid to gush through the cell wall pits. Plate 45 shows what typical circular cell pits look like at 450x magnification in wheat bract tissue. The arrow in Plate 46

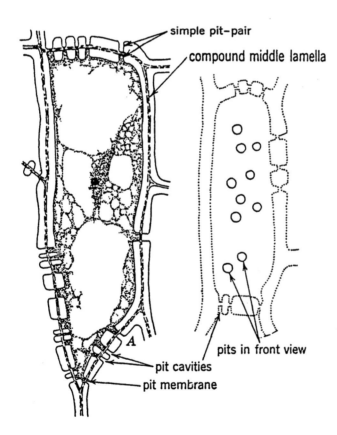

simple pit–pair
compound middle lamella
pits in front view
pit cavities
pit membrane
A

Plate 43 - *Cell pits are microscopic cavities in primary and secondary plant cell walls which allow exchange and flow of metabolite and gasses through the plant. The pits are variously arranged in different cells and are not spaced uniformly, even in a single cell. Drawing from* Plant Anatomy *by Katherine Esau © 1967.*

Plate 44 -
*Biophysicist
W. C. Levengood in his
Grass Lake, Michigan,
laboratory, 1993.*

points to elongated pits that were randomly enlarged from foot-stomping at West Wycombe, England, on July 11, 1992.

Levengood examined my samples and others from Oliver's Castle. Based on thirty cell pit samples, he found a 21% average increase in all measured pit diameters in that formation compared to normal controls.

He also discovered that cell pit size increased in a consistent gradient from the edge of the plant leaf to the center and from the outer edges of formations to their centers. So far, the only way he has been able to reproduce such cell pit changes in control plants was to place them in a microwave oven that produced heat at 1.19 J/cm^2/sec. That energy would be equivalent to the heat one would feel briefly touching a 500 watt light bulb.

Even though Levengood has found consistent patterns of cell pit enlargements in some formations, he said that simply measuring pit sizes cannot be used to verify a genuine formation. "It is *a combination of several factors together,*" he stressed, "which separate the genuinely mysterious formations from the hoaxed ones."

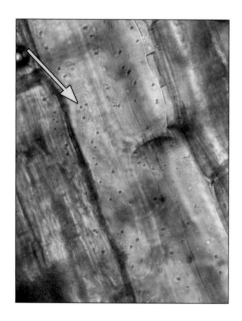

Plate 45 - *Photomicrograph at 450x magnification of typical-size circular cell pits in region indicated by arrow. Photomicrograph by W. C. Levengood*

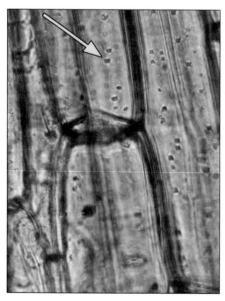

Plate 46 - *Arrow points to laterally elongated cell pits from July 11, 1992, manmade formation in West Wycombe, England. Photomicrograph by biophysicist W. C. Levengood.*

2) Rapid Heating:

After thirty seconds of microwave oven exposure, the cell pits were enlarged 14% by the heated, expanded water in the plant cells. If exposed longer than thirty seconds to the microwave radiation, the plant cells shriveled from dehydration. Since most formation plant samples Dr. Levengood examined were not dehydrated, he concluded that *"the heating must occur at a rapid rate."* This is a very important fact to keep in mind since human hoaxers need two or three hours to create manmade patterns. The scientific data suggested that many formations have been exposed to an intense energy for not more than thirty to forty-five seconds. Any longer exposure, the plants would have been cooked. Instead, formation plants have continued to grow.

In Troy, Illinois, circles in sweet flag grass occurred in the same two spots in June 1991-1992. (Plate 47)

Levengood found that the cell pits in these circles were 50% larger than normal. He also found that the leaves were oddly ruffled on one side like stretched crepe paper. (Plate 48) He said a rapid burst of heat in a microwave oven on only one side of the leaves could produce the effect. "There is no way a hoaxer can do this by simply tromping on the plants."

Sherry Yarkosky, a chemist trained in plant physiology, who works for

Plate 47 - *Circle in sweet flag grass in Troy, Illinois, June 1992. Similar circle found in same spot, June 1991. Photograph by Pete Bostrom.*

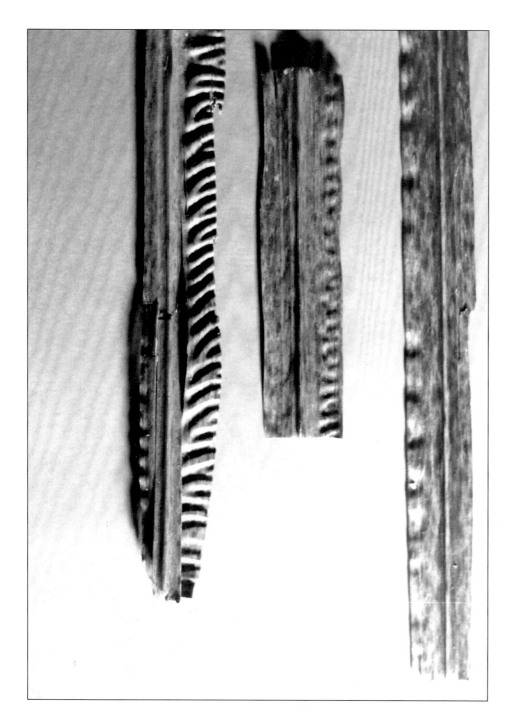

Plate 48 - *Rippled leaf edges from the sweet flag grass circle in Troy, Illinois, June 1992, suggesting one-sided exposure to energy source that produced rapid heating. Photograph by W. C. Levengood.*

Alvey Labs in Belleville, Illinois, found that the sweet flag grass from Troy showed sodium levels twice as high as those in unaffected plants. She also noted a 5% decrease in nitrogen content. The exact cause of the rippling and chemical changes was not known.

3) Changes In Seed Growth:

Dr. Levengood found a complete lack of seed development, "no embryogenesis at all," in plants from early spring formations. (Plate 49)

But in later, more mature plants affected from July on, he found normal appearing seeds (Plate 50), which in some formations germinated faster than control seeds and had a statistically significant increase in growth rate. "Some grew 45% faster than control plants," Dr. Levengood reported. (Plate 51) Agriculture seed experts say if they can produce a 5% increase in growth rate, they are doing well. "45% faster is astonishing!" says Levengood.

Biophysicist Levengood also found that the outward appearance of

Plate 49 – *These undeveloped anthers were removed from wheat plants sampled from an early spring circle formation in England. Dr. Levengood has found that seed development is halted for unknown reasons in formations occurring before summer growth. Photograph by W. C. Levengood.*

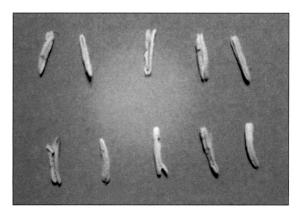

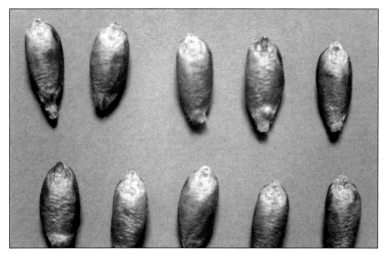

Plate 50 - *Normal seed growth. Photograph by W. C. Levengood.*

Plate 51 - *When seeds from mid-summer formations were planted, Dr. Levengood measured 45% faster growth rates than in control plants. Photograph of 1991 English wheat growth comparison from inside and outside circle by W. C. Levengood.*

seed heads from formations compared to controls was the same, "but there were striking embryo size differences. The embryos in the circle samples were less than one-half the size of those in the controls."

4) Bent and Cracked Growth Nodes:

Professor Bruce Rideout of Ursinus College in Collegeville, Pennsylvania, studied plants from the Linfield and Limerick, Pennsylvania, formations northwest of Philadelphia in May 1992. (Plates 31-33) Dr. Rideout discovered that growth nodes were split or cracked in affected plants and many nodes were mysteriously bent. Dr. Levengood confirmed Rideout's findings and said he had found similar changes in reproductive and germination tissue from English crops. (Plate 52)

Dr. Levengood said that in the Pennsylvania formations, "There was a pronounced elongation and lateral twist of the growth nodes anywhere from 30 to 90 degrees from the vertical. In the dehydrated stems, the growth nodes disclosed very apparent brown streaks which ran laterally across the outside of the bent node. This lateral splitting was observed in all four sets of circle samples and was not seen in the four sets of control samples. The formation of this type of fissure would require complex stresses in order to rupture the semi-rigid longitudinal fibers in the epidermal tissue. For

Plate 52 - *Peculiar angled re-orientation of growth nodes in circle formation plants found in Alton Barnes, England, 1991. This same anomaly was also observed in the Limerick and Linfield, Pennsylvania formations by Professor Bruce Rideout. Photograph by W. C. Levengood.*

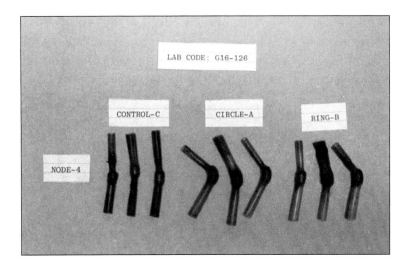

example, it would require the node to be weakened and expanded from an internal force such as might be caused by transient heat energy. This would be followed by a longitudinal extension or tension stress. That combination of forces is unlikely to be generated by a wind storm." Further, all four Pennsylvania samples showed an increase in the cell wall pit diameters that ranged from 22% to 34%.

5) Ion Transport In Bract Tissue:

Since cell pit enlargement has been seen consistently in some formations that have other biochemical changes, Dr. Levengood thinks it is logical "to consider the possibility that these crop circle energies are also producing perturbations within the complex microfibril construction of the cell wall itself." Dr. Levengood has tested ion-membrane transport across the thin bract tissue of wheat heads in both control plants and formations.

"In bracts from several crop formations, the oscillation amplitudes have been significantly higher than those in control tissue. These data suggest that this method is a useful approach for studying, and possibly confirming, genuine formations."

Summary:

After three years of finding a combination of several consistent changes in formation plants, Dr. Levengood concluded: "Whatever is doing these formations, is affecting the fundamental biophysics and biochemistry of the plants."

Another scientist has also been impressed by the enigmatic crop formations. Scottish astronomer Archie Roy[8] has said: "Since 1980, scientific hypotheses have been framed and then scrapped. Other, stranger guesses have multiplied as fast as the circles themselves. Several books have been written about them; an international conference has been held (at Oxford Polytech College), and its proceedings published. Scores of television programs have covered them. Hundreds of hours of flying time and foot-slogging have been spent in visiting them. Thousands of photographs have been taken. Reports and articles published in the local and national press have now passed well beyond counting. Yet the mystery, far from being solved, continues to grow."

[8] Professor Archie E. Roy, served as President of the Centre for Crop Circle Studies; Honorary Research Fellow in the Dept. of Physics and Astronomy at Glasgow University; a Fellow of the Royal Astronomical Society of Edinburgh and British Interplanetary Society; 1993 President of the Society for Physical Research; a member of the Int'l. Astronomical Union and the Scottish Society for Physical Research.

THE "FROZEN MUSIC" OF GEOMETRY

[9] Gerald S. Hawkins, Ph.D., astronomer and mathematician, was Chairman, Astronomy Dept. at Boston University; Research Associate at the Harvard College Observatory; Dean of Dickinson College; Science Adviser to the Director of the U.S. Information Agency; and co-author of *Stonehenge Decoded* with John B. White © 1965, Souvenir Press.

Mathematical analysis by astronomer and mathematician Gerald S. Hawkins[9] has deepened the mystery. (Plate 53) "Geometry has on occasion been called 'frozen music' since the time of Pythagoras," he says, "because, like pure harmony, perfect mathematical accuracy is the nature and beauty of a theorem." To his surprise, he discovered the diatonic ratios of music and new geometric theorems in the crop formations.

Plate 53 - *Gerald S. Hawkins at his farm in Rappahannock, Virginia, December 13, 1992. Hawkins has studied the geometries of the crop circle mystery. He has found repeating diatonic ratios that are equivalent to the white keys on the piano. Photograph by author.*

He co-authored *Stonehenge Decoded* in 1965, which hypothesized that the ancient circle of huge tertiary sandstones in England could have functioned as a computer to track the moon as it moved along the horizon with an 18.6 year period in 2,000 B. C.

After working twenty-two years in universities, including Harvard College, Professor Hawkins retired in 1989 and lived with his wife at the Watergate apartment complex in Washington, D. C., and a farm in Rappahannock, Virginia. He was playing and running with a kite when he collapsed on May 26, 2003, at age 75.

During a visit to England in 1990, he bought *Circular Evidence*[10] by Colin Andrews and Pat Delgado and returned to the farm to read. His mathematical curiosity led him to analyze the photographs in terms of geometry. Using two simple rules, he discovered a surprising relationship. When the circles are concentric with a ring around a circle, he compared the area of the larger to the smaller. When the circles are not concentric, such as a quincunx of four small satellite circles around a central larger circle, he compared the diameters.

"I discovered that the first formation in the book was a ratio of 1:1, the next was a ratio of 3:2, the next 5:3 and 4:3. I said to my wife, Julia, "It looks like I'm tuning a harp. I'm getting a series of diatonic ratios here. I'd better analyze the whole book.""

Later Colin Andrews supplied the survey measurements for the Celtic cross on the cover of *Circular Evidence*. The ratio of those circle diameters was also diatonic and equivalent to the note A in the second octave.

Diatonic ratios are fundamental to music because with each successive octave above middle C, the same ratios are used, but doubled. For example, middle C pitch is 264 hertz (vibrations per second), and for C', the octave above, the pitch is 528, giving an exact ratio of 2:1. Hawkins discovered that out of eighteen crop circle photographs provided to him by Colin Andrews, eleven had diatonic ratios.

"A ratio in the diatonic scale," explained Hawkins, "is the step up in pitch from one note to another. It can be measured exactly. From C to G is an increase of 1.5 times, or the ratio of 3 over 2. The whole set makes an octave of eight white notes on the piano."

White keys are named with letters of the alphabet. Starting with middle C, an octave runs up the keyboard D, E, F, G, A, B and starts over again at another C' octave, then another C" octave, and so on. In the crop formations, Hawkins originally discovered these seven diatonic ratios:

C	D	E	F	G	A	B
1	9/8	5/4	4/3	3/2	5/3	15/8

[10] *Circular Evidence* © 1989 by Colin Andrews and Pat Delgado, Bloomsbury Press: A summary of crop circle formations measured and photographed by Colin Andrews and Pat Delgado between 1981 and 1988.

[11] *Cosmos, A Journal of Emerging Issues,* Vol. 2, No. 1, April 1992.

Some argue that the diatonic repetition could still be a consequence of an unidentified natural process. Gerald Hawkins himself outlined explanations for the crop circle phenomenon in a five-page article for the *Cosmos Journal of Emerging Issues* in April 1992.[11]

"There are two main theories as to the cause — either crop circles are a natural phenomenon, or they are made by hoaxers. Beyond these two extremes, people have invoked Earth gods, extraterrestrials, or human personalities that have survived death. Until pictograms appeared later on, sprouting complicated and fantastic shapes — antennae, claws and arcs — natural theories held sway. The plasma vortex theory, for example, explained how the flattening of the crops was due to a natural, electrically charged whirlwind."

In his article, Gerald Hawkins described the consistent pattern of diatonic ratios he had discovered that matched the white keys on a piano. Hawkins said he felt the consistency of the ratios tended to eliminate random natural processes such as whirlwinds. "The probability that this was random chance was 1:25,000," Hawkins calculated.

Assuming something else must be at work beyond a natural process, Hawkins wondered about the intellectual profile behind the phenomenon, which demonstrated understanding of mathematical and spatial relationships important to western culture.

Hawkins told me: "As a careful scientist, I'm not saying the patterns are musical, only that the sizes follow the same mathematical law as the intervals of western music. The creators seemed to know of these fractions, taking care to encode them in the shapes so that they could be retrieved by someone studying aerial photographs. The accuracy required in a typical 20-meter circle is about fifteen centimeters, or six inches. Without the precisely-made edges, my analysis would not have been possible."

In the Oliver's Castle formation, for example, Hawkins began examining the geometry by constructing tangent lines from circle to circle. (Plate 54)

Plate 54 - *Oliver's Castle formation, July 1992, lines superimposed by Gerald Hawkins. Photograph by author.*

When he discovered that all three tangents crossed precisely in the middle of the equilateral triangle drawn by the circle makers, "it was like a bell going off. It meant something geometric."

So, using one circle as a center and placing his compass pencil on the bottom line of the triangle, he drew another larger circle consistent with Euclidean rules of construction.

Now he had two concentric rings D and A and using the rule of comparing areas, he discovered the ratio 9/1, or D.

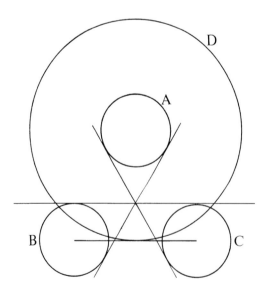

Next, there were the two lone satellite circles, B and C, satellites to A. Hawkins compared those diameters and they equaled 1/1, or Middle C. That gave him two diatonics, C and D''' in the Oliver's Castle formation.

In his *Cosmos* article, Hawkins raised the provocative question: Could the circle makers be using an alphanumeric code in the formations? The implication was that the letter combinations might be initials, perhaps of famous people living or dead? If the seven discovered ratios equivalent to the diatonic notes CDEFGAB are laid on a piano keyboard beginning at Middle C and are continued up the keys with the rest of the alphabet, as a cryptographer might think to do, this is the result:

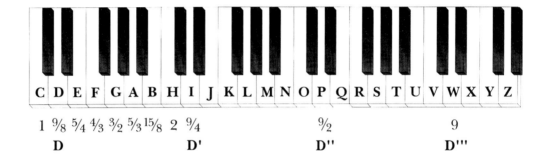

This example shows how the diatonic ratio for the note D is doubled each octave with frequencies of 9/8, 9/4, 9/2, and 9/1 (9). On the keyboard, those ratios correspond to the letters D, I, P and W. In the Oliver's Castle geometric crop formation, the 1/1 and 9/1 Hawkins found correspond to C and W on the keyboard.

Hawkins summarized, "These are the facts, and the sequence of events is intriguing. Maria Ward gets a channeled picture on July 22 connected with the number 9 and Cromwell; a group on July 23 projects the pattern; the pattern appears in a wheat field near Cromwell's battlefield on July 24; a scientist in the U. S. studies a photograph of the pattern, not knowing the background to it, and derives the diatonic value 9 which fits the keyboard code letter W. And the other diatonic value was 1, or C. So, we have C. W. or W. C."

Hawkins also found that he could fit one of the formation circles exactly within the sides of the Oliver's Castle triangle which is his Theorem 2 (Appendix) and generates the diatonic ratios for the notes C" and G'. On the keyboard, those ratios are equivalent to the letters O and L.

Hawkins said that at the end of the 1992 crop season, he had found two diatonic ratios corresponding to two letters of the alphabet in each geometric crop formation. The pair of ratios and letters varied from formation to formation in 1992 and the previous years of photographs he analyzed back to 1978. But those do not represent the whole phenomenon. There have been many other pictogram formations since 1990, which are not geometric.

New Geometry Theorems

Hawkins also discovered new geometry theorems in the crop circle patterns. In June 1988 at Corhampton in Hampshire, three equal circles were pressed into barley with centers at the corners of an equilateral triangle. Hawkins put a straight edge down on the photograph and saw that he could draw a straight line tangent that would touch each of the circles. Hawkins deduced a geometry theorem from this formation. A theorem is a fact, or proposition, that can be proved by the logic of mathematics. Euclid wrote thirteen books full of theorems circa 300 B. C.

Hawkins found five new geometric relationships and wrote out four theorems, leaving the fifth as a challenge for mathematical minds to solve. (Appendix) None of the theorems he discovered are in Euclid's books.

The February 1, 1992, issue of *Science News* featured crop circle analyses by Gerald Hawkins in its cover story. In it, he detailed the four theorems and alluded to the fifth, which the magazine's 267,000 readers were challenged to discover. In April 1992, Hawkins placed the fifth theorem in a sealed envelope at Boston University to reveal at some future date if that specific geometry emerges in the crop fields or from someone who figures it out. By the fall of 1993, no one had submitted the correct answer and no crop formation had matched.

Hawkins said the 1991 Barbury Castle formation (Plates 1 & 2) is based on his Theorem II and several new theorems he has discovered involving circumferences and summations. "Whoever made the patterns has the knowledge to conceive original theorems that haven't been stated before," Hawkins told me, "and the pattern at Barbury Castle has to be admired for the complexity of design and for the precision in its making. The totality of shapes could not be recognized by a person standing in the wheat — only aerial photographs and ground surveys showed its complex shape."

"My scientific colleagues have checked out the mathematics and they confirm what I have discovered," says Hawkins, "but usually their interest stops there. Unless I can tell them how the circle makers have entered the fields undetected, managing to bend living plants without cracking the stalks, they regard the events as a problem of no scientific interest. I sup pose in our modern academic climate, it would be difficult for them to get a grant for crop circle research. For me, I do not need a grant, and I look beyond the circle makers' new communication technology to the intricate information conveyed."

The 1992 season concluded on August 18, in a wheat field near Silbury Hill with a strange formation consisting of a circle and several symbols attached to it, "a charm bracelet," as it was dubbed locally, or "Celtic Wheel." (Plate 22) Even though American hoaxer Jim Schnabel has tried to convince people that this formation was his creation, Dr. Levengood received plant samples and found significant increases in cell wall pit size, significantly higher growth rates, and bract tissue oscillations that fit the profile of unusual biochemical and biophysical changes which cannot be hoaxed. Perhaps a formation was already there and Schnabel decided to alter and claim it as his own in order to confuse the crop circle investigators and public.

Hawkins is investigating the hoax theory, too, and says "each year the crop circles give us new surprises. I am keeping an open mind."

He also discovered two diatonic ratios in the 1993 Etchilhampton formation (Plate 82). "It's a geometry, a six-sided figure which is my Theorem 4 and equals F on the keyboard," Hawkins explained. "Also, the ratio of inner and outer circles equals 1/1, or C. So the Etchilhampton formation in 1993 produced two letters, C and F, possibly initials for something or somebody."

After our interview, Hawkins wrote to me: "Scientists have often ignored or rejected evidence of new phenomena that haven't conformed to acceptable paradigms. In 1610, Galileo discovered the moons of Jupiter. He was ridiculed by skeptics who refused to look through the telescope to see for themselves. In the 18th century, when meteorites were reported to be hitting the earth, the skeptic Voltaire said, 'I could more easily believe that astronomers would lie than that stones could fall from heaven.'"

One man named Pete Glastonbury was inspired by Dr. Hawkins's work in 1992 and decided to try an experiment. He wanted to play the diatonic notes in a crop field near his home to see what might happen. He gathered stringed instruments tuned to a seven note diatonic scale including a harp and a hammer dulcimer. He also tried a handheld Psion computer that can produce a range of sounds.

"We started our first session at midnight on July 17, 1992, sitting in a single circle, the second formation to appear at Berry Pomeroy near Totnes. The first was a dumbbell found June 11 (Plate 55), and that same day I had seen and photographed an unidentified light moving near that formation. (Plate 56) I also photographed barley stems at the Berry Pomeroy formation that were angled from the growth nodes (Plate 57), which I understand match what Dr. Levengood has seen in other formations.

"So, in July, we played in a free style to see if music could elicit more response from the circle makers. After fifteen minutes, we heard a sound just outside the circle. It sounded very like the crackling you hear around your head when taking off a heavy woolen jumper. We stopped playing. The sound stopped with the music, dying away to the north.

"The next day we discovered a small formation exactly where we had heard the sound the night before. And the following Friday, July 23, a large dumbbell like the earlier June formation appeared in oats across the road from the circle we had played in. I went there with my five-year-old daughter, Katie. We both saw a small ball of light hovering in the crop beyond the edge of the formation. Katie said, 'It looks like a bat flying into itself.' Through binoculars, I saw that it did indeed look like something spinning into itself. I could see several small balls orbiting into a central point. It looked exactly like the small ball captured on video at Milk Hill in 1990 and Barbury Castle in 1991. It had an undulating motion and was dipping in and out of the crop."

Plate 55 - *June 11, 1992, dumbbell formation discovered in barley at Berry Pomeroy on the southwest end of the British Isles near Totnes. Photograph by Pete Glastonbury.*

Plate 56 – *June 11,
1992, moving, unidentified
light in barley (left) near Berry
Pomeroy dumbbell formation.
Photographs
by Pete Glastonbury.*

Plate 57 – *On right,
two unexplained angled nodes
in Berry Pomeroy dumbbell
formation.*

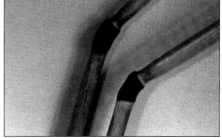

1992 FORMATIONS
AFTER ENGLISH HARVEST

United States:

<u>Potato Circle in Clark, South Dakota</u>

After I returned from England to the United States in August 1992, I learned from biophysicist Levengood that a farmer in Clark, South Dakota, on September 8, discovered a dark circle in his potato field that was 600 feet in diameter. All the plants were dead. Lyman Wookey's family has run the Wookey Potato Company since 1937. "In all that time, I have never seen anything like this circle in the potatoes," he told me when I called him. "Everything outside the circle was normal green. Everything inside the circle was completely dead," said Mr. Wookey.

At first he wondered if it was chemical damage. But the closer he looked at the plants, the more he became convinced that was not the answer. "Chemical damage doesn't make a perfect circle," he explained. Unfortunately, neither Mr. Wookey nor anyone else took a photograph of the huge, dead circle of potato plants.

Mr. Wookey saw a small article in a local agriculture journal about Dr. Levengood volunteering to analyze plants from unusual formations. He called and arranged to ship both plants and potatoes to the Michigan lab.

Dr. Levengood found cell pit enlargement ranging from 19% to 28% in the sample plants and a striking difference between potatoes from inside the circle and potatoes from outside. The normal control spuds were smooth and red with no blemishes. Samples from inside the circle had yellow streaks along their surfaces and cracks in their outer epidermis. He found no difference in the internal tissues of control and sample potatoes.

<u>Corn Rectangle in Austinburg, Ohio</u>

A week earlier, on August 30, 1992, in Austinburg, Ohio, a large rectangle was found in a young, sweet corn garden planted by Donald A. Wheeler. The rectangle measured 8-by-25-feet and Mr. Wheeler told me: "In all my gardening years, I have never seen anything like it before."

Carl Feather, reporting for the Ashtabula, Ohio, *Star Beacon*, wrote: "It just appeared as if something came down out of the sky, pushed the stalks flat on the ground and left without leaving any other trace in the soft ground." (Plates 58- 59)

Plate 58 - *September 2, 1992*, Star Beacon, *Ashtabula, Ohio.*

Star-Beacon, Wednesday, September 2, 1992 **B1**

50 Years Ago

■ The Rev. Wilbur H. Lyon was named pastor of Pierpont Presbyterian Church.
■ The greatest volume of iron ore for a single month in the 50-year history of the Conneaut Harbor was recorded — 1,747,946 tons were unloaded during the month of August.

ay
e education news
and nation: Edu-

Outdoors
Currents

Who's been sleeping in my cornfield?

Austinburg man would like explanation to mysterious rectangle in his garden

By CARL E. FEATHER
Lifestyles Editor

AUSTINBURG — Donald Wheeler is baffled by what he discovered in his cornfield Sunday morning.

Returning home from a several-day trip, Wheeler discovered that something, someone or some phenomenon had produced a rectangular impression in the field behind his Route 45 home. An interior section of the field, measuring approximately 25-by-8-feet, had been leveled. All of the corn stalks were bent down in one direction.

"None of the stalks were broken," Wheeler said.
Suspecting deer, Wheeler made a thorough check of the perimeter of the cornfield looking for tracks. But there were none — deer, raccoon or man, for that matter. Further, the ears were untouched by the intruder.

Next, Wheeler examined the field and area around his home for possible wind damage. But he said the stalks were not twisted and nothing else in the yard showed any ill effects from wind. It just appeared as if something came down out of the sky, pushed the stalks flat on the ground and left without leaving any other trace in the soft ground.

Although some might lean toward a visit from a spacecraft as an explanation, Wheeler isn't speculating.
"There's no evidence of that kind of stuff," he said.
Rather, he's chalking up as a unsolved mystery.

"It's just one of those things that happen and you have no explanation for it," Wheeler said. "One of the problems with man is he can't stand to have something go unexplained."
One thing is for certain, a portion of Wheeler's handsome sweet corn crop won't make it to the dinner table.
"It was the best part of my corn, too," Wheeler lamented.

CARL FEATHER - The Star Beacon

Donald Wheeler of 9151 Route 45 examines the rectangular impression left in his cornfield. Wheeler said there are no tracks or other sign of entry into the field, but something leveled a 25-by-8-foot patch of the corn.

Plate 59 - *On September 1, 1992, Donald Wheeler of Austinberg, Ohio, examined an 8-by-25-foot rectangle of flattened corn. There were neither tracks nor signs of entry into the wet soil. Photograph by Carl Feather,* Star-Beacon.

When I telephoned him, he said local farmers thought the soil was simply too wet and the corn fell down. But Feather, who took photographs, said all the corn stalks were lying generally in one direction, not randomly as might be expected if moisture were responsible. "None of the stalks were broken and none of the ears were taken," Donald Wheeler said. At first, he suspected deer, but when he checked his field for tracks, he could not find any. Then he thought that maybe a freak storm had hit. But the corn stalks were not twisted, and nothing else showed any signs of storm damage.

The crop was young because it was located near Lake Erie where the water can moderate temperatures, allowing a longer growing season for second plantings. Connie Sistek, an investigator in Ashtabula, talked with Levengood about the odd corn formation. He asked her to gather plant and ear samples on September 2 and October 5, both from inside the 8-by-25-foot rectangle and outside for controls, so he could have different growth stages.

The corn tassels on control plants outside the rectangle were tightly closed. But inside the rectangle, the tassels were opened up. (Plate 60) "These differences in tassel growth," said Dr. Levengood, "suggest that the formation plants developed at a more rapid rate than the controls. Generally, tassel opening is very closely timed in a field of corn. Under normal conditions, one does not see the differences in tassel formation that were observed in this Ohio case."

Plate 60 - *Corn tassel on right has accelerated development, taken from rectangle formation found August 30, 1992, Austinburg, Ohio. On left is normal control corn tassel from outside rectangle which is still closed. Photograph by W. C. Levengood.*

Biophysicist Levengood found other differences. "All the ears from the formation plants appeared a darker brown color and the pericarp on the tiny kernels had a roughened appearance and were smaller in size compared with the controls. The seed weight within the formation ears was only 1/6th the seed weight in the controls. This seed weight difference was surprising in view of the fact that the ear sizes were the same as those in the controls." Another important difference was that none of the formation corn seeds would germinate. "Several aspects of the findings from this sample set indicate that at the time of the crop formation — a suppression of the embryo growth occurred — a developmental perturbation that did not appear to be carried over into the somatic tissue."

There was also abnormal ear development between a September 2 sample and an ear picked October 5, 1992. (Plate 61) Both ears were the same size and stage of development on September 2. The bulbous growth at the upper end of the ear picked four weeks later on October 5, contained much larger, more completely formed kernels indicative of normal development after the earlier retarded growth associated with whatever energy affected the plants at the end of August 1992.

Plate 61 - *Corn growth at the apex of an ear became more normal four weeks after apparent suppression of embryo growth by unknown energy source that flattened rectangle of corn in Austinburg, Ohio, on August 30, 1992. Photograph by W. C. Levengood.*

Sometimes such unusual ear growth can occur as a result of insect damage within the ear. However, there was no indication of insect damage or unusual silk formation in this or any of the other samples analyzed.

Dr. Levengood wrote in his report: "The abnormal ear is again indicative of embryo development suppression at the time of the formation. The somatic tissue continued to develop and due to a hormonal situation known as apical dominance, a new ear with normally developing seeds was formed at the apex. This sample group is quite in line with what has been observed in other samples obtained during the 1992 crop season. In every case where embryo growth has been suppressed, the formation occurred very early in the plant development cycle."

Canada: Milestone, Saskatchewan
<u>Flattened Porcupine in Wheat Circle, 1992</u>

On August 29, 1992, near Milestone, Saskatchewan, Canada, a porcupine was found in the middle of a wheat circle pressed flat like a cartoon character with front and back legs sticking straight out in an X-shape. "A mature porcupine weighs 20 to 25 pounds and stands twelve inches tall," Canadian circle investigator Chad Deetken told me. "It was as if the little animal had been standing and something pressed it down to two or three inches thick."

He contacted farmer Joe Rennick in Milestone after Saskatchewan Mutual UFO Network (MUFON) investigators Danny Clairmont and Ruth Walde, in association with Canadian Director Michael Strainic, had taken plant samples. The farmer found the flattened porcupine in the wheat circle after he got back from a week-long trip. Mr. Rennick figured it had been lying there for at least five to seven days, but there was no odor or decay. Wheat inside the circle was dried out and brittle in contrast to the green, growing plants outside the circle. The ground was dried out, too. Rennick said that when he walked into his field to investigate (Plate 62), his shoes caked with very wet clay soil until he got to the hard, dry circle.

Plate 62 - *Wheat farmer Joe Rennick of Milestone, Saskatchewan, Canada, walking in circle where he found flattened porcupine on August 29, 1992. The soil under the flattened wheat "was hard as cement, like someone put it inside an oven and baked it," in contrast to wet clay outside the circle. Photograph by Mary McArthur.*

"That ground," he said, "was hard as cement, like someone put it inside an oven and baked it." If Dr. Levengood is correct in his hypothesis that rapid, intense heat energy, such as microwaves, is involved in the creation of crop formations, that same energy might have dried out the soil and baked the porcupine, slowing autolysis in its body. Seeds were also shrunken and wrinkled. (Plate 63)

Unfortunately, Rennick threw the porcupine away without photographing the bizarre, flattened body. Investigators did find broken quills at the outside edge of the circle and a trail of them leading to the center where the body had been.

Deetken said there was "a skid mark in the soil embedded with broken quills." He wondered if the porcupine had been caught at the edge of the formation by whatever force made the circle and dragged into the center. "Its quills lay in the same direction as the swirl of the wheat. Porcupines don't run when frightened. They roll up into a ball with their quills sticking out for protection. That's probably what it did," Deetken guessed, "and was sucked or drawn like a rolling, prickly ball into the middle of whatever force flattened the wheat, too."

Plate 63 - *Scanning electron microscope image of normal, smooth, control seeds (C) from the Milestone, Canada, wheat; shrunken and wrinkled seeds (#2 and 4) from inside the circle where porcupine was found. Photograph by W. C. Levengood.*

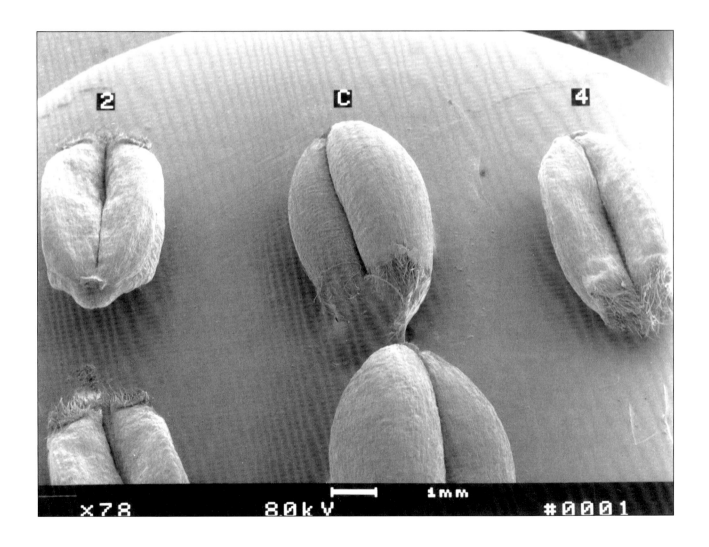

Albertville, Saskatchewan Oat and Wheat Circles

On September 24th, Deetken visited farmer Ed Beauchesne in Albertville, Saskatchewan, who had found a 36-foot-ring surrounding a lopsided circle that measured variously sixteen and eighteen feet in diameter in his oat field. The same morning of the 24th, Beauchesne found a second circle in wheat that was fourteen feet in diameter with a $22\frac{1}{2}$ - foot ring around it. All the rings and circles swirled counterclockwise. (Plate 64) The center of the $22\frac{1}{2}$ - foot circle in Albertville, Saskatchewan, was complicated and reminiscent of some formations in England. (Plate 65)

Plate 64 - *Counterclockwise swirl of $22\frac{1}{2}$ - foot diameter ringed circle in wheat near Albertville, Saskatchewan, Canada, one of two circles found September 24, 1992, by farmer Ed Beauchesne. Photograph by Chad Deetken.*

Plate 65 -

*Center of the
22 $\frac{1}{2}$ - foot
diameter wheat
circle near
Albertville,
Saskatchewan,
Canada,
September 24,
1992. Photo-
graph by Chad
Deetken.*

Chad Deetken was curious about how the seeds would germinate and grow from the Albertville formation, given Levengood's increased growth rate results from England and U. S. formations. On February 14, 1993, Chad planted the seeds of both control and formation plants and kept them alive in his house until mid-March when it was warmer. At that time, he planted both sets of seedlings in the shade, curious to see if reduced light levels would have an effect.

Deetken wrote to me: "For awhile, the plants did nothing. Then in late April, I began to notice the circle samples doing much better than the controls. You can see the difference on May 28th in the photograph. (Plate 66) The controls did about as well as I expected under the stressful conditions, but the circle samples were amazing. They were almost as tall as my Milestone samples on the deck (which were planted in full sun). The implications are that under stressed conditions, the circle samples have energy to spare."

Plate 66 - *Tall plants on left were grown from seeds taken from inside the Albertville, Saskatchewan formation, found September 24, 1992. Plants on the right are controls. Both groups were grown in shade. In that stressful low light, the formation plants grew at a 40% increased rate which is consistent with the 45% increase that Dr. Levengood has found in plants grown from other\ formation seeds. Photograph by Chad Deetken.*

Deetken shared the results of his experiment with biophysicist Levengood who said: "Chad Deetken spent considerable time on his hands and knees searching for signs of human entry or foot prints and none were found. Seed heads were sent to (my) laboratory and some were retained by Chad. Germination tests were conducted independently. In Deetken's germination and seedling experiment, the plant height difference is in the order of a 40% increase in the formation group." That is consistent with other findings of a 45% growth rate increase in plants germinated from seeds taken from English formations. (Page 50)

Nipawin, Saskatchewan Wheat Circles

On October 2, 1992, Bruce Grandfield of Nipawin, Saskatchewan, found three circles, each eight feet in diameter and swirled counterclockwise in wheat on the banks of his Saskatchewan River farm. The circles were in a remote part of the field and Deetken found no traces of human entry. (Plates 67-68)

Plates 67-68 - *On October 2, 1992, farmer Bruce Grandfield investigated three circles on his farm, each eight feet in diameter and swirled counterclockwise in his wheat near the banks of the Saskatchewan River in Nipawin, Saskatchewan. Photographs by Bruce Grandfield.*

Estevan, Saskatchewan Wheat Circle and Dead Porcupine, 1989

Chad Deetken called other farmers in the area and learned that another dead porcupine was found in a wheat circle in late July 1989 one hundred miles southeast of Milestone in Estevan, Saskatchewan. "There were two twelve-foot circles that touched each other like a figure 8," Deetken told me. "From one side where the circles touched, a short, narrow path came off at right angles and ended in a small circle only a few feet in diameter. In this small circle lay a dead porcupine that disintegrated rapidly into a black, sooty substance." (Plates 69-70)

Plate 69 -
In July 1989, a farmer in Estevan, Saskatchewan, found a dead porcupine in the middle of a wheat circle. Photographs provided by Chad Deetken.

The owners contacted the Royal Canadian Mounted Police (RCMP) and asked for analysis to see if the animal had been cooked or burned. But strangely, the RCMP report stated there was no indication of burn. That raised more unanswered questions about what happened to produce the dark residue that looked like carbon residue after heat exposure.

A black, oily substance was found on July 15, 1993, covering three rings, each about twelve feet in diameter, that formed a triangle around the home

Plate 70 -
Black, sooty
substance
remained in
center of wheat
circle after
RCMP
investigator
took porcupine
to lab for
analysis.
Strangely, the
RCMP report
stated no evi-
dence of burn.

of Clinton McKinney in Brazil, Indiana. The Putnam County Sheriff's Department in Greencastle, Indiana investigated. In Case Report 93-07-2317, the investigating officer wrote in his complaint form, "Poss. UFO landing zone!" This was one of three such reports that law enforcement investigated in Indiana in which grass rings were covered with a black, oily substance.

Carbon also has a black color and slippery feel. Dr. Levengood had found black carbon on a few English plants he studied in 1992. He concluded that something heated the waxy coating of the leaves rapidly enough to reduce the wax to its carbon constituent without cooking the plants.

On July 27, 1993, Roger and Kathy Schlueter of Butler, Kentucky, discovered a twelve-foot diameter ring in the stubble of their freshly cut hayfield. All the hay in the ring was completely brown and dead. A neighbor three-quarters of a mile away told the Schlueters that the night before the circle was found, her farm animals woke her up with cries of alarm. She got up and saw an oval-shaped lightwhich hovered over the field for at least ten minutes.

OVER-
VIEW
1993

Cynicism about hoaxers permeated England in 1993. Whether manmade or created by a mysterious energy source, this overview simply summarizes some 1993 formation reports. Between May 2 and May 31, 1993, seven crop formations were discovered in the southern English counties of Buckinghamshire, Hampshire, Wiltshire, and Berkshire and were reported to the Center for Crop Circle Studies (CCCS). Back in the United States on May 29 in Kennewick, Washington, a "pictogram" 193 feet long was found in wheat. (Plates 93-98)

By the end of June, thirty more in England had been reported to the CCCS, and the geographic area had spread to include the counties of Avon, Gloucester, South Yorkshire, Kent, West Sussex and other sites. At the beginning of June, several formations appeared within one field near Devizes. A few days later in another Devizes wheat field, a circle with an "F" appeared similar to the Kennewick, Washington formation. Several triangles were reported near Cherhill/Beckhampton, along the M25 highway that circles London, and between London and Wiltshire. Between June 23 and June 28, four formations were discovered at Sompting and Lancing in West Sussex, three in wheat and one in barley. On the 27th, a 135-foot-long formation of circles and corridors was found near the long avenue of ancient sarsen stones in Avebury.

July did not have the increased formation activity that circle watchers have come to expect in that month. Perhaps the most unusual was a six-spoked configuration 175 feet in diameter found in Etchilhampton on July 19 in wheat. (Plate 82) In the United States on July 26, a 237-foot-long formation of circles and corridors was found in a rye field about ten miles south of Utica, New York, in Herkimer County, Columbia Center. (Plates 90-92) That month, several rings that varied from seven to fifteen feet in diameter were discovered in both grass and cut hay in Indiana and Kentucky.

A dozen more formations occurred in England in August, including one at Windmill Hill on August 4. It bore some resemblance to the 1992 East Meon hoaxed formation, but no one in 1993 was claiming to have made Windmill Hill. (Plates 84-85) That same day, a 225-foot-long kite-shaped formation and a 336-foot-configuration of circles and avenues were found at Cheesefoot Head. (Plates 86-87) At the Hog's Back in Guildford on August 5, there were two new formations: a crescent in a circle, and another reminiscent of the 1991 Barbury Castle's circle-within-a-triangle-within-a-circle. (Plate 88) On August 8, a 445-foot-long pictogram was found in a wheat field below the White Horse at Cherhill. (Plates 72-80) On August 15, a formation in wheat across the road from Silbury Hill was said to look like a "handicapped" symbol. Before anyone could survey, the farmer "erased" it with his harvester. Two days later, the same design appeared in another wheat field between East Kennett and West Overton. (Plate 89)

Plate 71 -

Orientation map for 1993 southern England formations by Vincent Creevy, P.L.S. © 1993 LMH Productions. Survey measurements and estimates by Colette Dowell, Chad Deetken, Paul and Mavis Vigay, and CCCS.

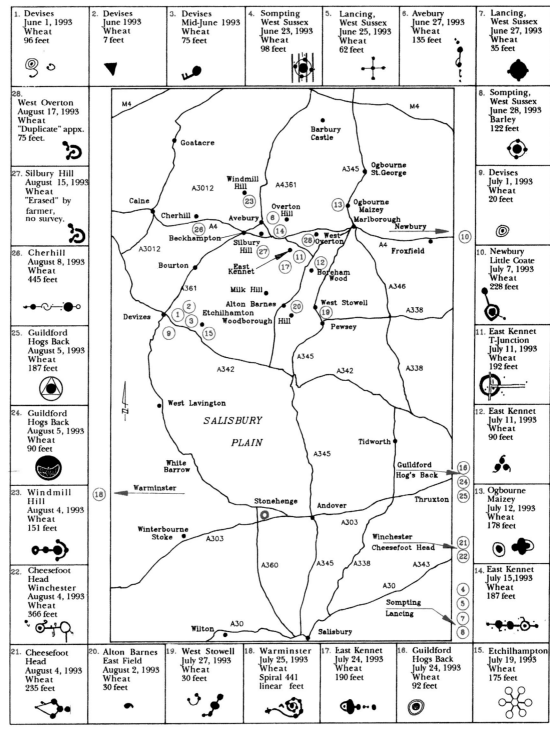

1. Devises
June 1, 1993
Wheat
96 feet

2. Devises
June 1993
Wheat
7 feet

3. Devises
Mid-June 1993
Wheat
75 feet

4. Sompting
West Sussex
June 23, 1993
Wheat
98 feet

5. Lancing,
West Sussex
June 25, 1993
Wheat
62 feet

6. Avebury
June 27, 1993
Wheat
135 feet

7. Lancing,
West Sussex
June 27, 1993
Wheat
35 feet

8. Sompting,
West Sussex
June 28, 1993
Barley
122 feet

9. Devises
July 1, 1993
Wheat
20 feet

10. Newbury
Little Coate
July 7, 1993
Wheat
228 feet

11. East Kennet
T-Junction
July 11, 1993
Wheat
192 feet

12. East Kennet
July 11, 1993
Wheat
90 feet

13. Ogbourne
Maizey
July 12, 1993
Wheat
178 feet

14. East Kennet
July 15, 1993
Wheat
187 feet

15. Etchilhampton
July 19, 1993
Wheat
175 feet

16. Guildford
Hogs Back
July 24, 1993
Wheat
92 feet

17. East Kennet
July 24, 1993
Wheat
190 feet

18. Warminster
July 25, 1993
Wheat
Spiral 441
linear feet

19. West Stowell
July 27, 1993
Wheat
30 feet

20. Alton Barnes
East Field
August 2, 1993
Wheat
30 feet

21. Cheesefoot
Head
August 4, 1993
Wheat
235 feet

22. Cheesefoot
Head
Winchester
August 4, 1993
Wheat
366 feet

23. Windmill
Hill
August 4, 1993
Wheat
151 feet

24. Guildford
Hogs Back
August 5, 1993
Wheat
90 feet

25. Guildford
Hogs Back
August 5, 1993
Wheat
187 feet

26. Cherhill
August 8, 1993
Wheat
445 feet

27. Silbury Hill
August 15, 1993
Wheat
"Erased" by
farmer,
no survey.

28. West Overton
August 17, 1993
Wheat
"Duplicate" appx.
75 feet.

England - 1993

In August 1993, I returned to England to speak at a conference. The first night I arrived in Alton Barnes, on Saturday, August 8, a 445-foot-long pictogram was created in a wheat field on a hill at Cherhill Down and Oldbury Castle a few miles west of Avebury. (Plate 72)

By noon Sunday, I joined Chad Deetken from Canada, Colette Dowell from North Carolina, and Simon Lackford from Cornwall inside the Cherhill formation to survey and photograph with the farmer's permission. We moved downhill on a tramline to avoid trampling the wheat and through the huge formation into the nautilus-shape at the bottom.

Dowell had been in England for two months and Deetken for a month, so their combined experience included most of the 1993 summer formations. Deetken had also investigated Canadian formations since 1989. Both researchers were impressed by the Cherhill pictogram and Deetken thought it was one of the best he had seen that summer.

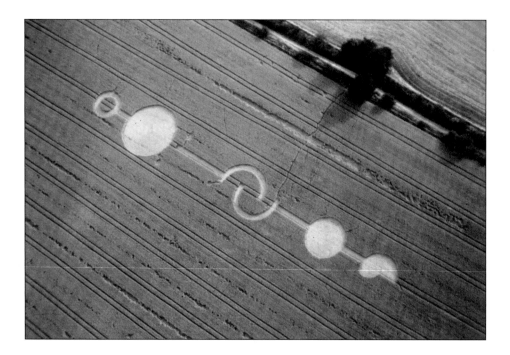

Plate 72 - *445-foot-long formation found August 8, 1993, in a wheat field below the White Horse at Cherhill Down and Oldbury Castle a few miles west of Silbury Hill. Aerial photograph by Colin Andrews © 1993, after people had trampled paths (center and left) to pictogram and small "grapeshot" circles near upper left largest circle.*

In the smaller circle below the two overlapping arcs, there were three "whirlpools" or "vortices" laid out in a straight line. (Plate 73) In the bottom nautilus-shape, the meticulously feathered wheat swept around and over another "vortex" that was nearly hidden under the surface swirl. (Plate 74) Thin "dividers" of standing wheat intersected the main corridor in two places. (Plate 75) Three "grapeshot" swirls of small wheat circles were embedded a few feet beyond the main formation. (Plates 76-79) The one I have labelled "B" in Plate 76 was almost invisible from our ground perspective. The wheat around that grapeshot was thick and unbroken. We had to push sideways through the ripe crop to reach that small circle. (Plate 78) The hoax theorists would say the circle maker might have hung from a hovering helicopter, or constructed a ladder bridge.

A couple staying in a bed and breakfast across the road from the formation said there was no design in the wheat field on Saturday night when they went to bed. It was a hot night for England and they slept with their windows open. The woman asked, pondering the manmade controversy, "How could people have been out there making this huge thing and us not hear any noise?"

Plate 73 - *One of three "vortices" layed in a straight line across smaller circle below overlapping arcs. Background is Cherhill Down and Oldbury Castle with White Horse and obelisk boundary marker. Photograph by author.*

Plate 74 - *Swirl of wheat in "nautilus" over coiled "vortex" in foreground. Photographs by author.*

Plate 75 - *One of two dividers created by thin wall of wheat that intersected long corridor.*

Plate 76 -
*Three "grapeshot"
A, B and C in
drawing by Peter
Sorensen.*

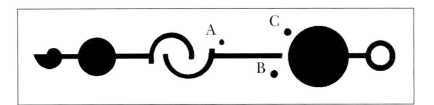

Plate 77 -
*Grapeshot A,
four feet, eight
inches diameter.*

Plate 78 -
*Grapeshot B,
five feet
diameter.*

Plate 79 -
*Grapeshot C,
five and a half
feet diameter.*

Cherhill had many standing stalks, some in a neat line, either bent a few inches above the ground at ninety degree angles or twisted 180 degrees where the stem was reduced to a thin ribbon of fiber. (Plate 80)

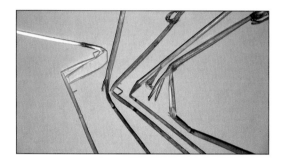

Plate 80 - *Stems sampled from the Cherhill circle that had three "vortices." Photograph by Chad Deetken.*

The central overlapping arcs at the center of the Cherhill formation are similar to an Old European script sign for "lu." (Plate 81) Old European script was in common use between 5300-4300 B. C. and was, according to archaeologist Marija Gimbutas,[12] "a form of sacred writing that is found inscribed on religious objects. Its purpose was the communication between individuals and deities. This script developed during the Neolithic period from the extensive use of a variety of symbolic signs, some of which were continuous from very ancient times and could have had a phonetic sound."

[12] The Civilization of the Goddess, The World of Old Europe © *1991 by Marija Gimbutas, HarperCollins Publishers.*

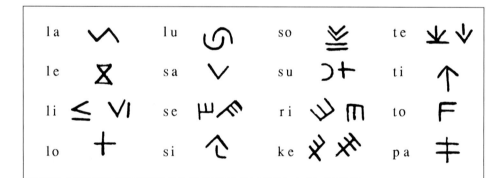

Plate 81 - *Examples of Old European script signs, including "lu" symbol, commonly used between 5300-4300 B. C. as sacred writing to inscribe on religious objects and as communication between man and the gods.*

That night, August 8, 1993, at the Alton Barnes pub called The Barge, Chad Deetken and I had a chance to meet and talk with one notorious English hoaxer. Robert Irving is a friend of American hoaxer Jim Schnabel. Their team came in second place in the official 1992 hoax contest. Both hoaxers were accused of working for intelligence agencies in their respective countries, specifically the CIA for Schnabel in the United States. George Wingfield began referring to them as The Snake and The Spider.

When I asked Irving if he had heard about Cherhill, he said, "What?"

"The new Cherhill formation," I repeated.

"I don't know what you are talking about," he countered.

Chad and I explained. Irving denied any knowledge of it. He insisted he had created "maybe ten, maybe fifteen, but not more than twenty formations" in his life. "I enjoy the sound of the wheat as it goes down," Irving said, "And there is an excitement about doing it at night. Maybe something out there inspires me. Who knows?"

Around us in the pub were many angry people who resented him and anyone else who hoaxed formations because hoaxing mocked the phenomenon which had evolved over more than a decade and had affected people in their hearts and minds, had touched them with thoughts about the unseen and other powers and intelligences beyond human daily life. If the sacred were dying amid the electronic noise of gadgets, televisions, cellular phones and the pollution of air, water and land, at least the mystery of the crop formations on a worldwide scale was provoking people to think and ask about higher powers again.

"What difference does it make," Irving argued, "whether I make a formation or Something Else does, as long as the art of it, the mystery of it, makes people stop in their tracks and think thoughts they weren't thinking a minute before. Something has to wake people up to their narrow thinking and their gullibility, whether to hoaxed formations or to manipulation by forces around them."

A month later, biophysicist Levengood had compared bract tissue from wheat heads collected inside the Cherhill formation with control heads collected outside in the same field. The amplitude of the oscillations in the ion membrane conductivity test were greater than controls. "The consistent pattern of conductivity measurements in some formations compared to controls," Dr. Levengood told me, "indicates that the basic microfibril structures of the plants have been altered. Such cellular changes cannot be hoaxed."

A sampling of other 1993 formations included a six-spoked geometric formation at Etchilhampton (Plate 82) in which Gerald Hawkins found two diatonic ratios (Page 59); a dumbbell with circles near Devises (Plate 83); another dumbbell formation at Windmill Hill, similar to the 1992 East Meon formation, with a close-up of its central "fountain" of wheat stalks (Plates 84-85); two large formations at Cheesefoot Head (Plates 86-87); a circle/triangle configuration at the Guildford Hog's Back (Plate 88); and a "handicapped" symbol first found in wheat across the street from Silbury Hill on August 15, was erased within hours by the famer and his harvester and reappeared two days later in another wheat field between East Kennett and West Overton. (Plate 89)

Plate 82 -
Etchilhampton,
July 19, 1993, a
175-foot-diameter
geometric formation
in wheat. Photograph
by Colin Andrews
© 1993.

Plate 83 -
Devises,
August 1993, size
estimate 250 feet long in
wheat. Photograph by
Ron Russell © 1993.

Plate 84 -
Windmill Hill,
August 4, 1993,
151 feet long in
wheat. Photograph by
Ron Russell © 1993.

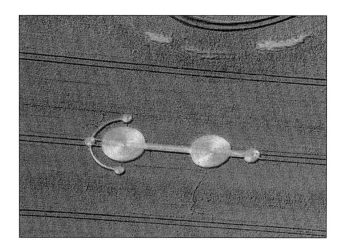

Plate 85 -
Tuft of wheat
at center of
Windmill Hill
formation. Photo-
graph by Ron Russell
© 1993.

Plate 86 -
Cheesefoot Head,
August 4, 1993,
235 feet long in
wheat. Photograph
by Colin Andrews
© 1993.

Plate 87 -
Cheesefoot Head,
August 4, 1993,
366 feet long in
wheat. Photograph
by Ron Russell
© 1993.

Plate 88 -
Guildford Hog's Back,
August 5, 1993,
210 feet in diameter
found in wheat which
matches Gerald
Hawkins's Theorem II.
(See Appendix)
Photograph by Colin
Andrews © 1993.

Plate 89 -
Between East Kennett
and West Overton,
August 17, 1993,
approximately 75 feet
long in wheat, a repeat
of "handicapped" symbol
found wo days before across
the street from Silbury Hill
on August 15, and cut out
within hours by the famer.
Photograph by
Ron Russell © 1993.

United States - 1993

While doing a live *Coast to Coast AM* radio broadcast at 4 a.m. on Monday, August 9, 1993, from a red telephone booth near The Barge, I learned that back in the United States a large formation of circles and connecting corridors had been found July 26, in a rye field ten miles southeast of Utica, New York, in Columbia Center, Herkimer County. (Plates 90-92)

The formation made headlines in local newspapers as well as radio and television news. Ron Taylor of the Central New York Questers joined Jim Cormia of MUFON and others to investigate, measure, and ship plant samples and controls to biophysicist Levengood in Michigan. Dr. Levengood found biochemical and biophysical changes in the New York formation that were similar to Cherhill, England, and other formation plants sent to him from Australia, Canada, the U. S. and other parts of the world.

Plate 90 - *Fields surrounding rye formation found July 26, 1993, in Herkimer County, New York, ten miles southeast of Utica. Photograph by Ron Taylor © 1993.*

Plate 91 - *Front page, August 2, 1993,*
Syracuse Herald-Journal,
Syracuse, New York.

SYRACUSE
HERALD-JOURNAL

AUGUST 2, 1993   VOL. 117, NO. 211,218   METRO EDITION   © 1993 The Herald Company ■   35 Cents

The work of aliens, or just a prank?

▶ Hundreds line road for a peek at circles in a field.

By Stephen W. Dill
Contributing Writer

COLUMBIA CENTER — They came from Syracuse, Watertown, Albany and many places in between.

They came by car, truck and some by motorcycle.

Hundreds of people — many from Central New York — flocked Sunday to an oat field in rural Herkimer County to see a strange pattern of crushed stalks. The circles cover about a football field.

"Chop it and they will come," said Tony Squiteri, arms raised to the sky.

Some said pranksters did it. Others suggested aliens from space. A weather man said it could be thundershowers.

No one agrees on the source, but they still come.

Cars lined both sides of Route 28 for a quarter of a mile about 10 miles southeast of Utica. People sat on hilltops with cameras and video recorders. Others stood on cars. Nearly all were curious about the strange pattern that appeared in the field last week.

The design reminded many of the spectators of unexplainable patterns sometimes found in farmers' fields around the world. The phenomenon has been featured in many television shows dealing with mysterious happenings. Some claim the designs are reportedly linked to sightings of strange lights near the farms.

"I saw a similar one on TV. It was near London," said Squiteri, a firefighter from Fulton.

■ TO MANY, Page A7

CIRCLES OF flattened oat stalks appeared last week on a farm in Herkimer County.

The Associated Press

Plate 92 -

Formation in rye crop near Columbia Center, Herkimer County, New York near Utica, July 6, 1993. Longest measurement was 237 feet. Photograph by Ron Taylor © 1993.

At 9:30 a.m. on May 29, 1993, teenager Michael Wakefield was traveling on Interstate 82 south of Kennewick, Washington, when he saw a large, circular ring in his family's wheat field. He went back to the farm to get his dad, Cash Wakefield. Mr. Wakefield's first reaction was, "I don't know what it is, but it's not natural."

The formation had an inner circle that was sixty feet in diameter flattened clockwise, surrounded by standing wheat in a counter-clockwise ring about seventeen feet wide. (Plates 93-94) Around the standing wheat was another ring of wheat flattened counterclockwise. From the circle and rings, a straight corridor extended for seventy-two feet, intersected by two perpendicular crossing corridors each about fifty feet long. An appendage that looked like the letter "F" emerged from the ring, similar to "F" or "key" shapes found in English crop formations.

Plate 93 - *Aerial photograph of 193-foot-long Kennewick, Washington, formation discovered May 29, 1993, in wheat field. Photograph by ilyes.*

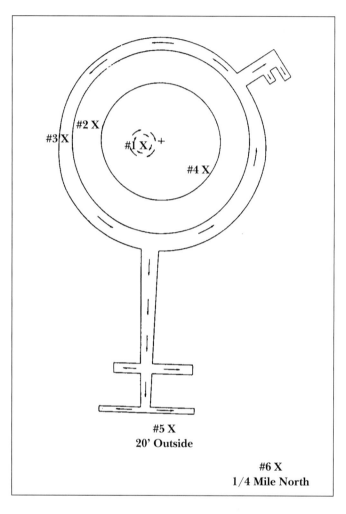

#2 X

#3 X

#1 X

#4 X

#5 X
20' Outside

#6 X
1/4 Mile North

Plate 94 - *Kennewick, Washington, wheat plant samples taken from six locations marked with X's. Formation was 193 feet long and 110 feet in diameter at the rings. Drawing and survey measurements by Jerry Phelps.*

Plate 95 - *Kennewick formation wheat plants curved flat to ground without breaks or cracks. Photograph by ilyes.*

Jerry Phelps, a mechanical engineer and member of the Kennewick Mutual UFO Network (MUFON), visited the site with Ms. ilyes, U. S. Coordinator of the Centre for Crop Circle Studies/U. S. Network, who lived in Port Angeles, Washington. ilyes prefers not to capitalize her one name. Phelps measured and drew a survey map and helped ilyes collect six plant samples, four from inside the formation and two controls from outside. (Plate 94) She took a photograph of one plant that showed a smooth bend in the wheat stalk without crease or cracking. (Plate 95) They shipped formation plants and controls to Levengood in Michigan. Dr. Levengood found node swelling, stem node bending, lateral splitting, (Plates 96-98) and oscillations in the

Plate 96 -
Node split from sample taken in location #3.

Plate 97 -
View of inner bend split from sample location # 1, center of ring.

Plate 98 -
Normal control from location #6.

ion membrane conductivity test that were consistent with other anomalous formations. He said the anatomical and physiological transformations, including severe node splitting, in the Kennewick formation plants are typical of those found in plants from many other formations."

Dr. Levengood concluded:

"If from all these studies, there is one clear positive statement that can safely be made, it is this: <u>The energies involved in crop circle formations are extremely complex, randomly interactive and, in detail, essentially unpredictable.</u>

For those who have said the formations are hoaxed, the hoaxer would have to explain in detail how all the biophysical and biochemical changes are brought about in the plants, including:

1) The type of energy and method of application needed to produce node swelling, node bending and severe lateral node splitting that is uniformly expressed within plants covering a sharply defined circular area at least 110 feet in diameter, as in the Kennewick case.

2) Reduction in embryo growth and development (reduced seed weight), in a uniform manner and over a large area, without affecting the developing somatic (non-reproductive) tissue or outward appearance of the plant.

3) Increased growth rate and development from those seeds that have reduced weights and characteristics of low viability.

4) More rapid seedling development, even under stressful light and nutrient conditions, from formation seeds."

The unexplained biochemical and biophysical changes described in this chapter have been found most often in growing, healthy plants. Biophysiciset Levengood has hypothesized that an intense energy has created the genuinely mysterious formations, an energy which has rapidly heated plant cells and caused fundamental changes in the microfibril cellular structure of plant bract tissue. The source of the energy is unknown.

The next chapter is also about mysterious physical traces found worldwide, including England. But the phenomenon is one that most people do not want to hear about or see: animal mutilations. The crop formations are beautiful and suggest a refined intelligence behind them. The animal mutilations are repulsive and suggest something dangerous. Both phenomena involve evidence of intense energy, and circles have been found near dead animals in pastures since the early 1970s.

The force or forces responsible and the motives would seem quite different. If the same force is involved, its mixed signals are confusing. For whatever reasons, something out there is interacting with us, our animals and our plant life, *forcing* glimpses of other realities upon us.

In my Introduction and Prologue, I tried to give a broader context in which to consider these phenomena and would like to repeat portions for emphasis here, beginning with Fred Alan Wolf's statement: "Anything that forces itself upon us, that comes into crop fields, pastures or bedrooms without asking permission *and receiving permission* – in my book, it's dark!"

I don't think black or white is the answer. In the beginning of my investigations in 1979 to 1980 about the environmental implications of worldwide, unexplained animal deaths, I was afraid that something terrible was at work. Fourteen years later after exposure to other facets of the mystery, including the UFO abduction syndrome, I now wonder if the harvest of tissue and fluids from animals and humans might be used to sustain another life form at the edge of its own extinction. Or even to sustain humanity. Hints of those possible explanations have emerged from abduction experiences.

Whether extraterrestrial biological entities, other dimensionals, angelic beings, or all of these simultaneously are interacting with our planet, more knowledge and less denial about what's happening could strengthen the human family. Mysterious lights and crop formations, animal mutilations, the human abduction syndrome, Marian apparitions, military and civilian encounters with alien craft and/or beings — all these phenomena are worldwide. They challenge us to confront other realities beyond the status quo and to reject the socially acceptable attitudes of ridicule and denial.

Throughout these chapters, I have tried to gather a large number of facts and eyewitness testimonies together for comparisons in a single text. So many local stories never reach the national and international media, and often news is compartmentalized too narrowly due to religious, political and social biases. Compartmentalization makes it more difficult to see patterns common to different facets of these strange, sometimes inspiring, sometimes disturbing, events around us. We need to stop hiding from other realities. We don't need to run or get down on our knees.

In the end, humanity might find itself learning about another intelligence that is facing environmental survival issues as we are on our own planet. It's also possible that another intelligence sees our environmental pollution, realizes that humans are on a path of self-destruction, and is taking steps on its own initiative to help us, even if we don't comprehend its actions or motives.

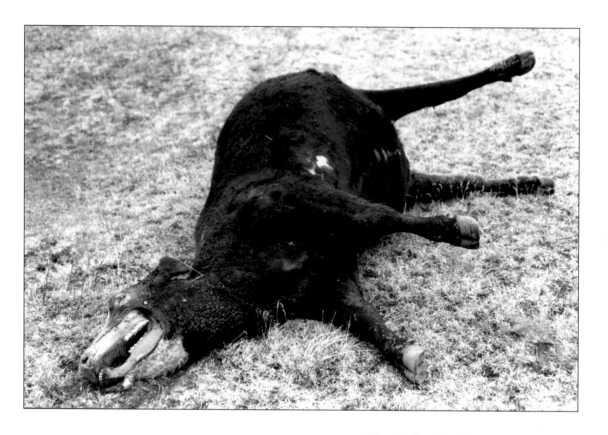

Plate 1 - *Steer found January 31, 1992, in Caldwell, Kansas. Jaw flesh, bone and teeth had been excised in bloodless, oval cuts. A pathologist examined the tissue and reported the excisions had been cut with high heat, hot enough to cook the hemoglobin. Photograph by Chuck Pine.*

FACT
    The worldwide phenomenon of animal mutilations without blood, tracks, or signs of struggle have been reported since the 1960s in Canada, the United States, Mexico, Central America, South America, Australia, the Canary Islands off the coast of Africa, parts of Europe and Japan.

FACT
    The first animal mutilation reported by international media was an Appaloosa mare named Lady found dead and stripped of flesh from the neck up on September 9, 1967, in the San Luis Valley of southern Colorado. A pathologist confirmed that all chest organs had been removed and the excisions had been made with high heat.

FACT
    Pathology studies of the 1967 horse and several other mutilated animals since 1989 have confirmed the tissues have been cut with high heat, hot enough to cook the hemoglobin.

FACT
    Law enforcement has been frustrated since the 1960s by the lack of tracks or other evidence around dead and mutilated animals. Often, unidentified helicopters; large, round, orange lights; or beams of light have been reported to law enforcement in or near pastures where mutilated animals have been found.

FACT
    Cattlemen's associations have offered reward money since the 1970s for information about the mutilators, but no one has provided hard evidence to collect.

FACT
    Daytime eyewitness accounts by a Milam County, Texas, rancher and a couple in Springfield, Missouri, have described non-human beings with animals that were later found dead and mutilated, or had disappeared.

CHAPTER TWO

ANIMAL MUTILATIONS

"That documentary you did about the cattle mutilations upset some people in Washington. They don't want animal mutilations and UFOs connected together in the public's mind."

RICHARD C. DOTY, SPECIAL AGENT
AIR FORCE OFFICE OF SPECIAL INVESTIGATIONS
KIRTLAND AIR FORCE BASE
ALBUQUERQUE, NEW MEXICO
APRIL 9, 1983

Unusual circles on the ground have provoked curiosity long before the crop circle mystery. In December 1974, a pilot and photographer flew over a Meeker County, Minnesota, pasture in which a young cow had been found dead. The heifer was lying inside a perfect circle of bare ground on a snow-covered field. The eyes, left ear, tongue and part of the lip had been removed with a surgeon's precision. Around the body, there were neither footprints nor animal tracks and the cuts were bloodless. From the airplane, the men were surprised to see dozens of circles in odd, random patterns spread over several acres. (Plate 2) The St. Paul, Minnesota *Dispatch* featured one of their photographs in an article headlined: "UFOs zapping cows?"

Earlier that fall on October 13, 1974, a buck deer was found in a stubble field south of Stratford, South Dakota. Brown County Sheriff Elroy Johnson reported that its "sex organs were cut out" without any bleeding. He looked for tracks around the deer, but couldn't find any. Dr. Calvin Glenn, a veterinarian from Aberdeen, South Dakota, examined the animal and said the deer was "definitely molested and this was not by predators at all." Dr. Glenn said the sex organs and stomach had been removed by a knife. These mutilations were only a few of the thousands reported worldwide since the 1960s. (Plate 3)

The mystery began in September 1967 when an Appaloosa mare named Lady was found dead and stripped to dry bone from the neck up

Plate 2 - *Mysterious circles in a Meeker County, Minnesota pasture, December 1974. A mutilated heifer was found dead inside a circle. Photograph by Al Madsen, permission by Terrance Mitchell.*

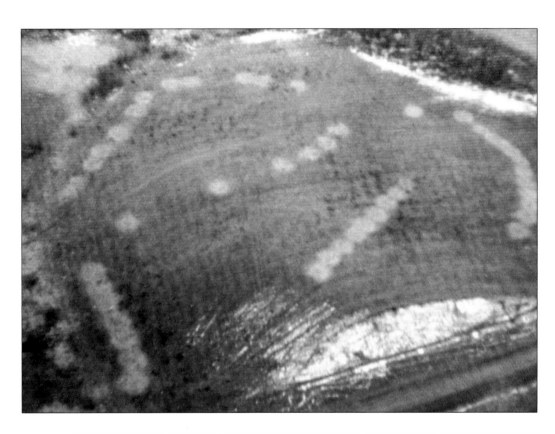

Plate 3 - *Steer found January 31, 1992, in Caldwell, Kansas, with jaw flesh, bone and teeth excised in bloodless oval cuts. Pathology studies confirmed the tissue was cut with high heat. Photograph by Chuck Pine.*

in the San Luis Valley of southern Colorado. (Plate 4) The skeletal head and neck on the mare's body was eerie. Unidentified flying objects and moving lights had been seen in the area. Newspapers worldwide reported there might have been a connection between the horse's death and the presence of UFOs. One reporter erroneously mixed the mare's name up with another male horse called "Snippy" and that name stuck in media reports.

Plate 4 - *Lady, about three weeks after bizarre death in September 1967, in the San Luis Valley of Colorado. Photograph by Don Anderson.*

All the internal organs in Lady's chest had also been removed "surgically with heat,"[1] said Dr. John Altshuler from Denver. He was starting his practice as a pathologist and hematologist in 1967 and out of private curiosity and in no official capacity, he drove to the San Luis Valley to look for strange lights that were reported so often that summer near the Sangre de Christo Mountains. He did not know about animal mutilations.

When a park ranger asked him to examine the dead Appaloosa, he was shocked at what he found. There was no blood and the cuts were surgically precise. When he took tissue samples from the excisions back to his hospital lab microscope, he discovered the hemoglobin had been cooked, indicating that high heat had been used to cut the tissue. When I interviewed Dr. Altshuler for my 1989 book *An Alien Harvest - Further Evidence Linking Animal Mutilations and Human Abductions to Alien Life Forms*, he told me he was puzzled about how the excisions had been made.

[1] Lasers were not used for surgery in animals or humans until the 1970s. In 1974, Dr. Joseph Bellina, Prof. of Obstetrics and Gynecology at Louisiana State University, was first to try a laser in gynecological surgery.

There was a circle near the horse, too – a three-foot circle of six or eight holes in the ground about four inches across and three to four inches deep. When Berle Lewis, the mare's owner, searched the ground, he discovered that Lady's tracks stopped about one hundred feet southeast of her body. "It looked like she jumped around in a circle," Berle said. "There was nothing else, no tracks of any kind between there and where we found her." But forty feet south of her body were a broken and burned bush and the circle of holes.

Sixteen years later on April 9, 1983, I was in Albuquerque, New Mexico, developing a script for an HBO documentary about evidence that alien life forms are intruding on our planet. A meeting had been arranged for me to talk with an Air Force Office of Special Investigations Agent named Richard C. Doty. He took me into an office at the AFOSI Headquarters in Kirtland AFB and said as we sat down, "That documentary you did about the cattle mutilations upset some people in Washington. They don't want animal mutilations and UFOs connected together in the public's mind."

He was referring to my film *A Strange Harvest* [2] in which I investigated the worldwide animal mutilation mystery (Plate 5). He implied that the alien life form connection to the phenomenon was known by his superiors.

[2] *A Strange Harvest,* a1980 Emmy award-winning TV film documentary by Linda Moulton Howe for KMGH-TV (CBS), Denver, Colorado, and later updated by Howe © 1988.

Plate 5 - *Linda Moulton Howe, Director of Special Projects, KMGH-TV, Denver, Colorado, narrating introduction for documentary* A Strange Harvest *in March 1980, with Richard Lerner, camera, and Mark O'Kane, audio.*

In addition to Lady in 1967, thousands of cows, horses, other domestic and wild animals have been found with oval or circular-shaped, bloodless excisions. Often, abdominal cuts are only the depth of the hide and do not penetrate muscle tissue. Veterinarians have been surprised by the surgical removal of internal organs, including heart and bladder, without external body excisions.

Typically missing from the animals are an ear, eyeball and surrounding eye tissue, lower jaw flesh, sometimes jaw bone and teeth. The tongue is often removed from deep within the throat in a vertical, smooth cut. (Plates 6 & 8) The rectum is usually cored out in a hole that is approximately four inches in diameter and six to fourteen inches deep. (Plate 9) Sometimes the tail is removed in a smooth cut through the tail bone. (Plates 10-11; 117) In males, the entire penis and scrotum are often removed in an oval, hide-deep excision (Plate 12); sometimes only a testicle is removed, leaving the scrotum sac intact without a hole or cut. Female udders are often removed with a hide-deep excision (Plates 13-15), or only the teats are removed leaving neat, bloodless holes in the udder. (Plate 16)

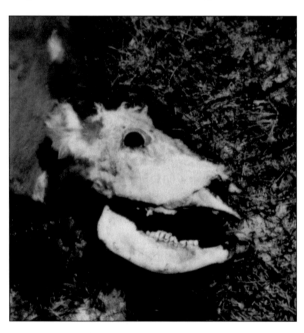

Plate 6 - *1976 Sterling, Colorado cow was typical of so many: circular excision of tissue around eye, eyeball removed from socket, tongue excised from deep within throat, jaw stripped of all flesh, smooth excision of upper jaw bone and teeth. Dead only hours, animals like this were warm to touch when sheriffs reached the scene. Photograph by Logan County, Colorado Sheriff Tex Graves.*

A cow has one set of front teeth on the lower jaw only. Further back, both upper and lower teeth line up evenly together. (Plate 7) The Sterling, Colorado cow in Plate 6 had teeth and some bone missing in the upper jaw.

After *A Strange Harvest* was broadcast, I received a call from a Royal Canadian Mounted Police investigator in Calgary, British Columbia. He told me he was disturbed by the clean removal of teeth and jaw bone and asked me if cases in the United States involved teeth removal. I told him many did.

He said the RCMP was not publicizing the teeth removal in order to keep one clue to themselves in case there were human copycats confusing the situation. His office was trying to prove that a satanic cult was involved with animal mutilations in his province. Since that 1980 conversation, many more mutilations have occurred in which teeth and jaw bone have been removed. No arrests with arraignment have been made in either Canada or the United States.

Plate 7 - *Anatomy of a bovine skull with teeth from* Atlas of Topographical Anatomy of the Domestic Animals *by Prof. Peter Popesko, D.M.V., Vol. 1, 4th Edition, W. B. Saunders Co., © 1985 Priroda Bratislava.*

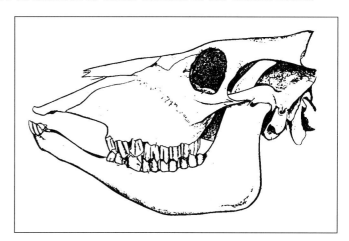

Plate 8 - *One of two cows found dead and mutilated in Grove Oak, Alabama, in January 1993. Jaw stripped and tongue removed like the 1976 Colorado cow in Plate 6. Photograph by Fyffe, Alabama Police. Officer Ted Oliphant.*

Since Lady's 1967 death, animal mutilations have been reported every year somewhere in the world. On January 31, 1993, at a Grove Oak, Alabama farm, two cows were found dead and mutilated. One (Plate 8) had its jaw stripped like the 1976 Colorado cow. Its rectum and vagina were also cored out in two separate incisions. The other cow's udder had been removed.

In a 1976 case near Sterling, Colorado, a veterinarian did a necropsy examination of a mutilated cow in the pasture at the request of Logan County Sheriff Tex Graves. He found that the heart had been removed from its pericardium, but *the pericardium sac was uncut.*

"How could the heart be removed without tearing or cutting the encasing sac?" Tex Graves asked me when I was filming *A Strange Harvest* in 1980. I took the question to Dr. Arlen Meyers, a laser surgeon at Rose Medical Center in Denver. Dr. Meyers told me that in his own laser research, he was trying to find a way to create tissue-specific lasers that could excise a diseased gall bladder, for example, without cutting skin, nerves, blood vessels, bone, muscle or other organs. He said in the 21st century such research might produce instruments that could cut into internal organs without cutting the surrounding bones and tissues. But it definitely was not 1980's technology.

Texas reporter and writer Jim Marrs[3] heard similar questions about cow hearts when he was working for the *Fort Worth Star-Telegram* in 1979. Marrs remembered one veteran rancher who asked in April 1979, "How can a predator pull out an animal's heart through a perfectly circular hole in its neck?" That's when Marrs attended the first major conference on the mystery of cattle mutilations in Albuquerque, New Mexico the fall of 1979. It was a one-day conference requested by former astronaut and then-U.S. Senator Harrison Schmitt of New Mexico. Marrs provided the following account for inclusion in this chapter:

[3] *Crossfire: The Plot That Killed Kennedy* © 1989 by Jim Marrs, published by Carroll & Graf.

> "It quickly became obvious to me that the 1979 conference was pitting authorities (primarily federal) against ranchers, citizens, researchers, and lawmen, who were very concerned over the numerous incidents of cattle mutilations around the country. New Mexico U.S. Attorney R. E. Thompson said he felt the FBI could enter the case because of the reported use of unmarked helicopters and the fact that several mutilations had taken place on Indian, hence federal, land. He went on to urge those law enforcement people present "not to bring out any evidential material which might be used at a later trial." This edict effectively muzzled the lawmen present, and public presentations of their cases were withdrawn. But privately, in the hallways, they were outspoken in their anger and frustration.
>
> It was in these circumstances that I met Lt. Don Rystrom, a deputy with the Benton County Sheriff's Office in Bentonville, Arkansas, and Sgt. Doug Fogley with the Arkansas State Police. They were particularly upset by the restrictions imposed at this

conference because of what they said was photographic evidence of a strange nature.

Rystrom had officially investigated a cattle mutilation near Bentonville and had taken a series of color slide photographs as evidence. He said upon returning to his office and developing the slides, he discovered a <u>strange blue shaft of light rising above the dead cow</u>. This shaft of light was visible in all of the photos he took of the cow regardless of the angle, and was in the same position which tended to eliminate the possibility that the light was some artifact of mishandling in the darkroom. Rystrom said he obtained brand-new film which was checked for deficiencies, then returned to the scene where he re-photographed the cow. As before, no one at the scene saw the blue shaft of light.

However, after developing the second batch of slides, the strange blue shaft of light was again present. Rystrom was convinced that no camera or processing malfunction could have accounted for this light and had brought the slides with him to the New Mexico conference. I held those slides in my hand and studied them at length. The cow was lying on its side and the shaft of light was rising from its middle section perpendicular to the ground. As I recall, the blue was not an intense navy blue, but instead, a pale, sky blue color. It was in the shape of a cylinder, perhaps three or so inches in diameter, and it rose about two feet from the stomach area of the cow.

I asked if I could borrow at least one of the slides for publication in my newspaper and the officers agreed. Then Rystrom said they were his only prints and he would send me copies after he returned to Arkansas.

After returning home, I tried on many occasions to reach Rystrom by telephone, but was unsuccessful. He was out, then he was on leave, then he was no longer working there. It all seemed odd to me. After several weeks, I tired of trying to reach him and turned my attention back to other stories. But I never forgot those slides I saw that clearly showed a strange, blue shaft of light rising from the stomach of a mutilated cow in Arkansas."

In the summer of 1993, I talked with Don Rystrom, who confirmed he had photographed one mutilated cow twice, on two different days, and that negatives and prints both times showed a blue beam extending from the cow's mid-section upward.

▲

He also confirmed that the Benton County Sheriff's photo lab had no explanation. I asked if the photographs were available. He said he had none and that all prints and related files had been removed from the sheriff's office, but he did not know to where or why.

I also talked with one of the veterinarians in Benton County who examined three unusual mutilations in the late 1970s in which he found that a specific internal organ, such as a bladder, had been surgically removed without trauma to any surrounding organs or tissues.

He knew that predators had not performed the sophisticated surgery,

Plate 9 - *Hereford cow found in Oakley, Idaho, with its rectum cored out, September 1, 1989. Photograph by Bear Lake County Sheriff's Deputy.*

Plate 10 - *October 8, 1989, six-month-old Hereford steer calf found in Oakley, Idaho, with rectum cored out and tail removed in smooth excision from tailbone. Photograph by Bear Lake County Sheriff's Deputy. See Plate 118 for similar calf mutilation in Shaftesbury, England, July 1993.*

Plate 11 - *Young calf found April 20, 1976, near Sterling, Colorado with its tail cut off and rectum cored out. Photograph by Logan County Sheriff Tex Graves.*

Plate 12 - *Steer calf found February 10, 1993, in same Grove Oak, Alabama pasture as cow in Plate 15. Genitals excised in neat, bloodless oval. Photograph by Fyffe Police Officer Ted Oliphant.*

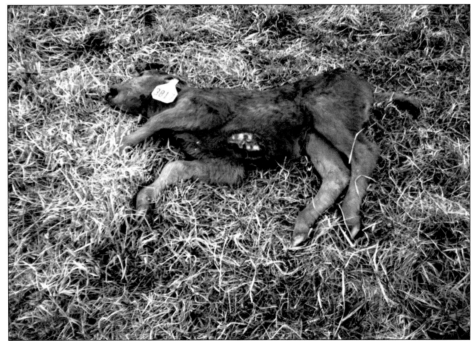

Plate 13 - *Vaginal and rectal tissue removed in deep, bloodless hole from cow found October 14, 1975, near Sterling, Colorado. Udder also removed with a hide-deep scalloped pattern similar to Plate 14. Photograph by Logan County Sheriff Tex Graves.*

Plate 14 - *Cow found July 2, 1976, near Sterling, Colorado, with its udder removed in a hide-deep scalloped excision similar to the cow in Plate 13. Photograph by Logan County Sheriff Tex Graves.*

Plate 15 - *Pregnant cow found February 10, 1993, with bloodless excision of udder in Grove Oak, Alabama. See also Plates 12, 66-67. The cow was lying on four-strand barbed wire outside the pasture fence that she apparently pulled down while running from something. Even steel fence posts were bent. Photograph by Fyffe Police Officer Ted Oliphant.*

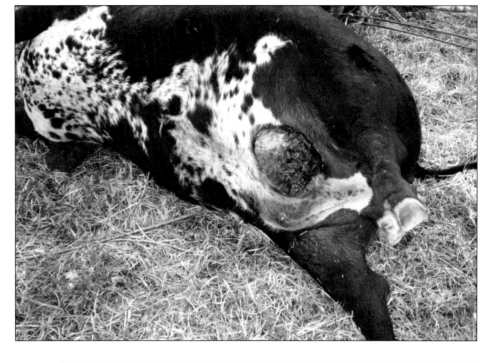

Plate 16 - *October 9, 1989, four teats bloodlessly excised from udder of young female cow in Nounan, Idaho. Photo by Bear Lake County Sheriff Deputy.*

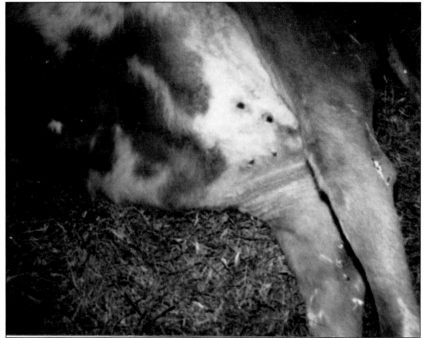

but none of his professional opinions reached the public. He was afraid of professional ridicule if he reported the truth from his necropsy investigations. I have repeatedly encountered that fear among veterinarians, and none would comment on the record for my documentary *A Strange Harvest,* broadcast May 25, 1980, on KMGH-TV (CBS) in Denver.

The issue of lasers comes up in the animal mutilation cases because often the clean, bloodless excisions appear darkened on the edge and feel

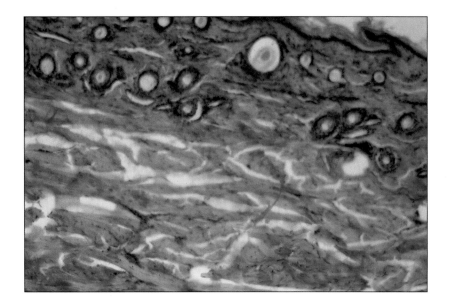

Plate 17 -
Normal cow collagen.

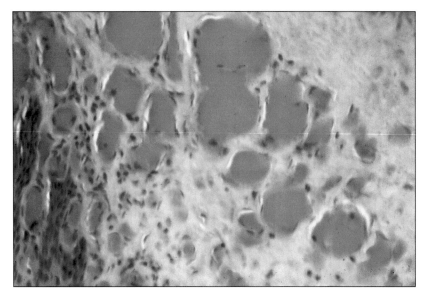

Plate 18 -
Cooked hemoglobin.

harder than normal tissue. In fact, pathologist John Altshuler, M. D., has confirmed in more than thirty cases since 1989 that the tissue had been cut with high heat. Plate 17 shows normal cow collagen, the fibrous constituent of connective tissue. Plate 18 shows cooked hemoglobin along the cut in the belly of a cow found dead and mutilated in Hope, Arkansas in 1989.

In addition to high heat at the excision lines, occasionally the internal organs are dry and bloodless when veterinarians do necropsies. In a 1991 Idaho case,[4] a veterinarian necropsied a dead and mutilated horse and found that all the internal organs, including the heart and lungs, had been completely desiccated and were dry to touch. Even the lower heart chambers were dry. Other ranchers and farmers have reported finding livers in mutilated animals that looked and felt like dry rubber.

Another characteristic of animal mutilations since the 1960s is the absence of tracks. One cow in Elbert County, Colorado, was found on wet sand without any tracks around the body, not even her own. Others have been found on trackless snow and wet dirt. For decades, law enforcement officials have been puzzled by the lack of tracks and evidence at mutilation sites and concluded that some kind of aircraft was involved which could lift heavy animals from pastures and return them without signs of struggle.

No one knows for certain how many animals have been mutilated over the years and around the world. In two Colorado counties in a two year period from 1975 to 1977, there were nearly two hundred reports. The maps in Plates 19 and 20 show areas where mutilations have been reported since 1967.

[4] August 29, 1991, 15-year-old palomino mare owned by Eva Patterson and Tom Blessinger and examined by Bob Stoll, D.V.M., McCall, Idaho.

Plate 19 - *Mutilations
in Canada and United States
from 1967 to 2015, color-coded
by periods of years. Map by author.*

1967-1968

1970-1974

1975-1976

1977-1979

1980-2015

Plate 20 - *Worldwide animal mutilation reports since 1967, white areas.*

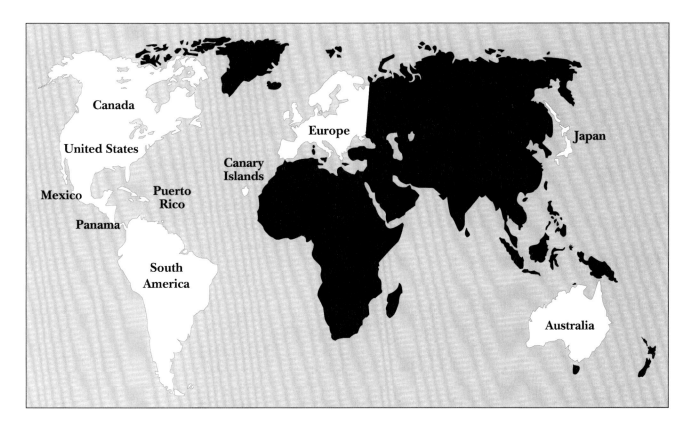

Beyond Canada and the United States, mutilated animals have been reported in Mexico, Panama, Puerto Rico, Brazil, England, France, Germany, Sweden, Australia, Japan, and the Canary Islands off the African coast.

1993 - ALABAMA

In early January 1993, I received several phone calls from Fyffe, Alabama police officer Ted Oliphant (Plate 21) about animal mutilations occurring in northeastern Alabama. (Plate 22) There were also many reports of strange, moving lights in night skies. One farmer saw a red-orange pulsing object the size of the full moon at 2 a.m. over a pasture where they found a mutilated cow later that day. Other lights were compared to the blue-white of the planet Venus and said to be three or four times brighter than that planet. A family of five watched one light above their home and said it was so intense, "it lit the ground brighter than moonlight."

There were also reports of unidentified and unmarked helicopters, day and night, seen in or above private pastures where no helicopter should have been. One farmer copied letters and numbers off a chopper in his pasture, which the Albertville Police Department checked through the Federal Aviation Administration. The helicopter was *not* registered with the FAA, so Detective Tommy Cole (Plate 23) concluded that it either belonged to military or government intelligence.

Plate 21 - *Ted Oliphant, Police Officer, Fyffe, Alabama Police Department, February 1993.*

Plate 22 - *Map of*
northeastern Alabama,
highlighted areas denote
mutilations, odd lights
or helicopter reports.

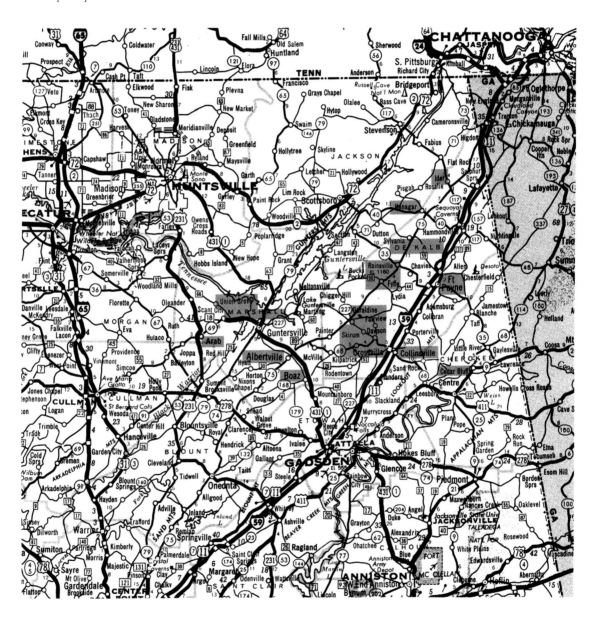

Oliphant, Cole, and other law enforcement officials were frustrated by reports of unmarked helicopters landing in pastures, some at night without running lights. Farmers said they could hear the loud, roaring sound of a chopper landing. But in a few instances, when the loud helicopter sound was heard, nothing was visible in the sky. Similarly, in Colorado and other states in the 1970s, people also reported hearing helicopters they could not see, day or night.

Plate 23 - *Tommy Cole, Chief of Detectives, Albertville Police Department, Albertville, Alabama, February 1993.*

Residents in Geraldine, Ft. Payne, Sylvania and Cedar Bluff, Alabama, videotaped unidentified moving lights on their camcorders and time-lapse cameras in January and February. (Plate 22)

Fyffe, Alabama has long had a history of strange, moving lights in the sky. In 1989, people from all over the world visited hoping for a glimpse of UFOs and other phenomena. Rainsville's *Weekly Post* Editor, Carey Baker, told me, "Back in 1989, we had a flood of sightings. An enormous number of people were seeing lights in the sky they couldn't identify, seeing objects ranging from the circular saucer-shaped object to one that had three lights in the shape of a triangle underneath. One man described those lights as each being the size of a small house and said the craft itself was larger than a football field. That's 300 feet long and 150 feet wide. So we had some enormous objects reported in 1989."

"How many were multiple witnesses?"

"A lot of them were. The football field-sized craft was also seen by another fellow who described the craft as being huge with the same three lights underneath.

"How many of these eyewitness reports were going directly to police or law enforcement?"

"The Fyffe Police Chief and his assistant were one of the first to report an object that flew over their patrol car. They estimated it moved about 1500 feet high above them — no noise, a silent, huge craft, triangular-shaped, with red and green and blue lights. So the police officers have been involved in this as much as anybody else."

"When did unusual sightings begin in Fyffe?"

"1989 wasn't the first sightings we've had here. They go back as far as people can remember."

Unusual "far back" stories include the myths of the Cherokee Indians who were well-established in northeastern Alabama, Tennessee, Georgia, the Carolinas, and Virginia by 1540 when Spanish explorers intruded into their lives. The Cherokees were afraid of a light that moved at night which they called *Atsil-dihye gi*, "The Fire-carrier." The Indians thought it was dangerous, but they did not know much about it. "They do not even know exactly what it looks like, because they are afraid to stop when they see it. It may be a witch instead of a spirit," [5] author James Mooney discovered in his research about Cherokee legends. The Indians had many stories about Yunwi Tsunsdi, or "Little People" who live in rock caves on the mountain side. "They are little fellows, hardly reaching up to a man's knees." It was believed that if a person had a crystal, it could be used to call one of the Little People at any time to do that person's bidding. There was also a party of giants who had come once to visit the Cherokees. "They were nearly twice as tall as common men and had their eyes set slanting in their heads, so that the Cherokee called them *Tsunil kalu*, 'The Slant-eyed people.' The Indians said that these giants lived very far away in the direction in which the sun goes down."

[5] *Myths of the Cherokee and Sacred Formulas of the Cherokees* © 1982 by James Mooney, Charles and Randy Elder-Booksellers, Nashville, Tennessee.

I went to Alabama with a video crew the last week of February to explore the light and animal mutilation mysteries for a new documentary, *Strange Harvests 1993*. One of the earliest and most dramatic encounters occurred in the middle of January at 2 a.m. in Geraldine, Alabama. Baptist minister Roger Watkins, his wife Betty, and teenage son Chris told me they were jolted out of sound sleep "by the sound of a tornado coming through the walls and the house shaking so bad I thought it was going to come apart," Reverend Watkins said.

He got out of bed and ran to the window that looks out over an open field next to his house. (Plate 24) Chris went to the window in his bedroom on the second floor. Both told me they were looking at an enormous object no more than six feet off the ground at their fence line about fifty feet away.

Plate 24 - *The Rev. Roger Watkins home and pasture where a 150-foot round, glowing object hovered about six feet off the ground at the metal fence line outside the bedroom windows in Geraldine, Alabama, mid-January 1993. Photograph by Fyffe Police Officer Ted Oliphant.*

"It was shaped like a plate," explained Rev. Watkins, "with pulsing lights of many colors all around what looked like silver metal." (Plate 25) Based on the distance between the fence posts, Rev. Watkins estimated the diameter of the glowing object to be one hundred fifty feet. The house kept shaking badly and Chris Watkins told me he was certain that "Christ himself had come to take my Mom and Dad in the Rapture to heaven."

Instead, after about ten minutes the object began to lift upward, spinning as it did so, and then vanished.

"My wife was so frightened, she never even got out of bed," Rev. Watkins said. "And as soon as it left, I got back in bed, too, without even going upstairs to see Chris. We just yelled at each other about it going."

Rev. Watkins said he couldn't go back to sleep and simply lay there waiting for the sun to come up so he would not feel so scared. When he got up and walked through the living room to the kitchen, he found evidence that the night terror had been real. On the coffee table were three goblet-shaped fish bowls. Each had contained three gold fish. The water and all the fish except one had spilled out onto the table. Those fish were dead.

"I don't know what we saw," said Rev. Watkins, "but I know it was real, it shook those fish out of the bowls, and it didn't look like anything I'd ever seen on this earth before."

Plate 25 - *Drawing by Rev. Roger Watkins of round, unidentified, aerial object with many colored lights pulsating around its edge that he and his teenage son watched in Geraldine, Alabama , the middle of January 1993.*

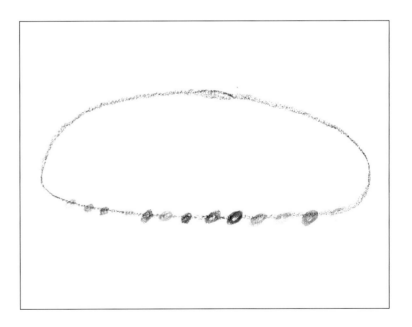

Two weeks later on January 28 in Ft. Payne, Sue Johnson was getting ready to go to work. It was 5 o'clock in the morning when she heard a sound she had never heard before. When she tried to imitate the noise for me, it was something like bees buzzing, but with a rhythmic oscillation. She ran to the backdoor of her house trailer to look out. Coming straight at her from the field next to her home was a row of pulsating red and green lights. When the lights reached her metal fence line about fifty feet from the open back door where she stood, the object turned and displayed a much longer profile of the same pulsing red and green lights. (Plate 26)

"It looked about the size of a big car then and it seemed round or oval-shaped," she said, "because I could see reflections of something like metal between the lights." When it began to move along her fence, she could hear the strange buzzing sound until it reached the end. Then all sound stopped. The sudden silence frightened her. Then, the mysterious object disappeared.

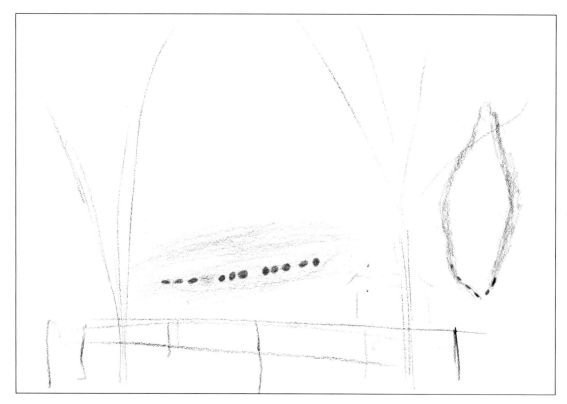

Plate 26 - *Sue Johnson's drawing of the lighted object that first appeared narrow and then rounder as it turned about fifty feet from her trailer home door at 5 a.m. on January 28, 1993, Ft. Payne, Alabama.*

Two nights later, again in Ft. Payne, the Hubert Twilley family of five watched a light over their home which they said was four or five times brighter than the planet Venus. The object seemed stationary in the air for some time before it began to move slowly, "like a cloud," they said. It cast a bright light over the pasture, "somewhere between bright moonlight and sunlight," was the family's description. (Plate 27) While that light remained low near their home, another series of lights appeared higher in the sky. Overhead the Twilleys watched a triangle formation of red and white lights move slowly. They thought there were three separate pairs of objects in formation, but said it could have been one gigantic object with red and white lights at three tips. The Twilleys estimated the distance between the triangle of paired lights to be about 1,000 to 2,000 feet wide, depending upon the altitude. (Plate 28)

Plate 27 - *Bright light across road from Hubert Twilley's house, Ft. Payne, Alabama, January 30, 1993. Drawings by Steven Stiefel.*

Plate 28 - *Drawing of the triangle-shaped formation of red and white lights estimated by the Twilleys to be about 1,000 to 2,000 feet from end to end.*

Plate 29 - *Front page of the* Gadsden Times *illustrating Sue Johnson's January 28th encounter and the Twilleys' January 30, 1993 sightings.*

AUBURN: McCartney confirmation in trouble **B1**

FOOTBALL SIGNEES: Top prospects make it official **D1**

INSIDE
good Times
• What's Happening
• Liz Smith
• Is Tom Arnold In control?

Gadsden Times

126th Year — 217th Issue   Gadsden, Alabama, Thursday, February 4, 1993   ★25¢ Newsstand

Deja vu! UFOs return to skies over DeKalb?

By Darrell Norman
Times Staff Writer

FORT PAYNE — A week of reports of strange lights over DeKalb County has police officials building a file on the county's latest encounter with unidentified flying objects.

Sue Johnson was drying her hair about 5 a.m. Jan. 28 when a noise she cannot describe brought her to the kitchen window of her home in Dogtown.

What she saw practically in her backyard was some sort of airborne object, covered with glimmering red, green and white lights, and moving slowly below the treetops.

It was just after 8 p.m. Saturday when Karen Twilley got a call from her mother-in-law across the road in Lickskillet, telling her to go outside and look at the strange lights.

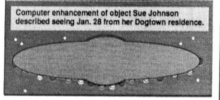

Computer enhancement of object Sue Johnson described seeing Jan. 28 from her Dogtown residence.

When she, her husband and son got outside, they were shocked by a different kind of light show. In one direction they saw three triangle-shaped objects covered in red and white blinking lights, in the other a single large globe-shaped white light.

Then Tuesday about 9 p.m. Susanne Austin and Ernest G.

"Gene" Mooney, both of Geraldine, saw a strange light in the sky from different places but in the same direction.

"It's been going on a week now," Sgt. Ron Ogletree, commander of the Gadsden trooper post, said Wednesday. "We are investigating each reported sighting and trying to put together a com-

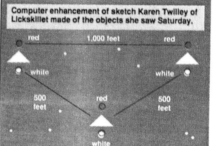

Computer enhancement of sketch Karen Twilley of Lickskillet made of the objects she saw Saturday.

plete file.

"We are treating all of them seriously because these are serious people. They are not publicity seekers who made all this up to get their name in the papers."

It was in 1988 that huge crowds of people flocked to Fyffe after numerous reports of UFO sightings. Streets of the Sand Mountain town took on a carnival atmosphere.

Ms. Johnson, 29, said she first thought the object out her window was a helicopter, but she could no longer hear the sound that attracted her. Opening her door, she said, she saw an array of lights about 50 feet straight ahead and could make out its shape.

"It was bigger than an automobile, and it was thicker in the middle than it was on the ends," Ms. Johnson said. "I tried to make a drawing of it for the troopers, but I couldn't get on paper what I saw with my eyes."

She said the object moved laterally so slowly that it appeared almost stationary. The lights that covered it did not actually blink on and off, but glimmered or shim-
Please see Lights, A5

On February 8, 1993, several people in different parts of DeKalb County saw bright, moving lights in the sky. One man in Skirum named Gary Coker took black and white time lapse photographs of one object. (Plates 30-31)

Then ten days later on February 18, Coker saw the object again near his house and made more time lapse images. (Plates 32-33)

Plates 30 - 31:
February 8, 1993, thirty to sixty second time exposures of a moving light estimated to be "three or four times brighter than Venus," according to photographer Gary Coker of Skirum, Alabama. He used 400 ASA Tri-X B&W film in a 35mm Minolta camera with a 70mm-205mm zoom lens set at various F-stops.

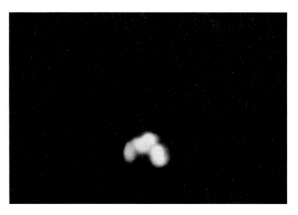

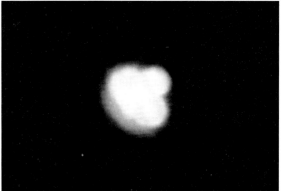

Plates 32 - 33:
February 18, 1993, thirty to sixty second time exposures of moving light again near his Skirum, Alabama home. Photographs by Gary Coker using same camera, lens, variable exposures and Tri-X film as February 8 photographs.

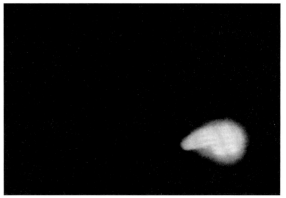

February 18, 1993, the same night that Gary Coker was getting his second series of time lapse photos, a mother and daughter stood in their Ft. Payne front yard and watched a bright, white light move above the trees. Susan Eads got her camcorder and videotaped the object for several minutes with her mother as a second witness.

A photograph taken of one of her video frames looked like the "Batman" emblem and was featured on the front page of the *Gadsden Times.* (Plate 34) When Eads zoomed her camera toward the moving light, she did not rack the focus correctly and the Batman shape was the result. That camcorder focus problem has confused many people, including Belgians in 1989-90 who photographed lights and unidentified triangle-shaped objects. One of those Batman sequences ended up on national television in Europe and the U. S. But even though there have been misunderstood focus problems, people have recorded something that moves low, erratically, and stops mid-air. One of the strangest incidents occurred in February 1993.

Plate 34 - *February 20, 1993* Gadsden Times, *Gadsden, Alabama.*

Mountain Lakes Edition

Gadsden Times

GIRLS	
Cherokee Co. 58	Gadsden 61
Hokes Bluff 24	Etowah 38
Litchfield 68	Fyffe 57
Glencoe 63	N. Sand Mtn. 56
Boaz 73	Sand Rock 75
Guntersville 60	White Plains 49

BOYS
Litchfield 64, Glencoe 45
see sports beginning on B3

126th Year — 233rd Issue | Gadsden, Alabama, Saturday, February 20, 1993 | 25¢ Newsstand

More strange lights seen in DeKalb skies

By Donna Maltbie
Times Staff Writer

FORT PAYNE — Susan Eads was skeptical when she started hearing stories about strange lights in the sky above DeKalb County.

Eads

But seeing is believing after she and her mother were interrupted from a trip to the grocery store Thursday night when they noticed a bright white light in the sky.

Mrs. Eads' mother first saw the light, which was above Mrs. Eads' home in the Pine Hills community in south Fort Payne.

"My mother said, 'Is that a star?' but we could see the stars, and this was much bigger," Mrs. Eads, 32, said. Her mother asked if she had binoculars, but she did not. Instead, she went inside to get her videocamera, which has a zoom lens.

She went outside with videocamera in one hand and cordless phone in the other, calling a neighbor to come look also.

As Mrs. Eads' videotape shows, the object is a fuzzy white light, until the camera zooms in. The object then looks like a circle, with two notches at the top and one notch at the bottom. The edges are well-defined. Mrs. Eads was hesitant to say what she thought of as soon as she zoomed in on the light.

"It looks like the Batman emblem," she said. Mrs. Eads' pictures of the light she saw are different from previously described lights over DeKalb County. In the past weeks several people have reported strange lights in several parts of the county.

Mrs. Eads caught the object on tape for several minutes.

After family members took the tape inside to watch it, she went back outside with her videocamera and made another tape of the object.

She also called Fort Payne police, and the officer who came to her mother's house agreed with them on one point: It was the weirdest thing any of them had ever

Please see Lights, A3

GADSDEN TIMES
This is what Susan Eads captured on videotape using her videocamera on Thursday night. Mrs. Eads and her mother noticed the bright light in the sky near their home in the Pine Hills Community in Fort Payne.

Mississippi man recalls seeing similar object in December '91

By Darrell Norman
Times Staff Writer

It's been more than a year since Rocky Dearman decided to keep quiet about his sighting of a strange object in the sky near his home in Whynot, Miss.

But, after reading a news report this week of a similar sighting in Northeast Alabama, he has decided to speak out.

"It was in December of 1991, and I've never said much about it because people think you're crazy when you say you've seen things like that. ... I was amazed when I read the description of what that woman saw in Alabama," Dearman said by telephone Friday.

Dearman, a 36-year-old optician, said he had been hunting at Whynot, near Meridian, and was walking out of the woods between 5:45 p.m. and 6:15 p.m. when a faint sound caused him to look over his shoulder.

"It was some kind of gigantic airship or airplane, and it came right over me real slow," Dearman said. "It wasn't down to tree level, but it was low. If the pilot was trying to stay below radar, he was probably doing a good job."

Dearman described the craft as a triangle of roughly equal sides, with one of the points leading. There were lights on each of the points, and in between the body was black and solid.

"There was a bright moon and a lot of stars that night," Dearman said. "You couldn't see the stars through it, and it cast a shadow over me when it passed."

He said the only sound he heard was something like that of a vacuum cleaner, "or maybe the cooling machines you can hear in the background when you go into a building like a hospital."

He said three things made the craft he saw hard to believe: its

Please see Sighting, A3

Sunday, February 21, 1993, thunder and lightning raged throughout northeastern Alabama, Georgia, and Tennessee. Tornadoes caused severe damage. The video crew and I were in Ted Oliphant's police car listening to radio reports about strange lights between Fyffe and Albertville. There were also calls about unidentified helicopters, which puzzled law enforcement because the weather was too violent for choppers to be flying. When the police checked airports for identifications, no one knew of anyone on flight plans.

While we were chasing light reports, Mrs. Pat Beard and her son, James, were videotaping first one big light and then several others moving above their house between 7:30 to 8:30 p.m. Central Standard Time. The Beards live in a remote area near a large lake about thirty miles southeast of Fyffe in Cedar Bluff, Alabama. The only road there does not have street lights. "At night," Pat Beard said, "in the three years we've lived there, we've never seen anything like this before. Very strange." James said the large moving light "was a whole lot bigger than the stars and through binoculars, we could see red, blue and green lights circling around it."

The mother and son taped off and on for nearly forty-five minutes. Then the bright, white object that had rotating colored lights suddenly disappeared and in its place were several bright flashes "going on and off at different times" across a large section of the sky. The Beards wondered if it was one object jumping in space, or perhaps lights flashing on and off attached to an enormous dark object which could not be seen. The mother and son did not know what they were looking at except that the big white light "popped off and on" while the smaller, bright lights flickered over a wide area.

Suddenly at the end of nearly an hour, the larger light (Plate 35) reappeared with two smaller lights nearby as if in formation. (Plate 36) Those two smaller lights pulsed off and on. (Plates 37-38) Then a fourth light moved toward the big light and passed below the larger light. (Plates 39-40) The camera was moved right and picked up two more lights which appeared to move closer together, then further apart, and finally the lower one moved past and both lights dimmed. (Plates 41-46). The entire action-reaction sequence — that involved several unknown objects that brightened, faded, disappeared and reappeared — lasted about fifty seconds.

Pat Beard and her son labelled their camcorder tape "Space Ships" and said they thought of the movie *Star Wars* because the light intensities changed and pulsed as if the objects were reacting to each other.

Plate 35

Plate 36

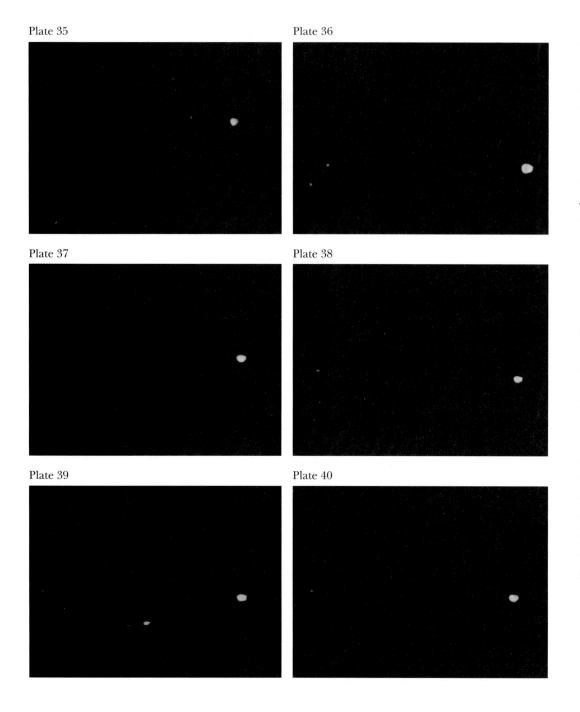

Plate 37

Plate 38

Plate 39

Plate 40

Plates
35 - 46:
*Frames from
February 21,
1993,
videotape in
Cedar Bluff,
Alabama, by
James and Pat
Beard.
Unidentified
lights pulsed,
dimmed,
brightened
and moved
past each other
throughout a
50-second time
period after a
single, large,
moving light
that had red,
blue and green
rotating colors
around it had
been observed
and video-
taped for the
previous hour.*

Plate 41

Plate 42

Plate 43

Plate 44

Plate 45

Plate 46

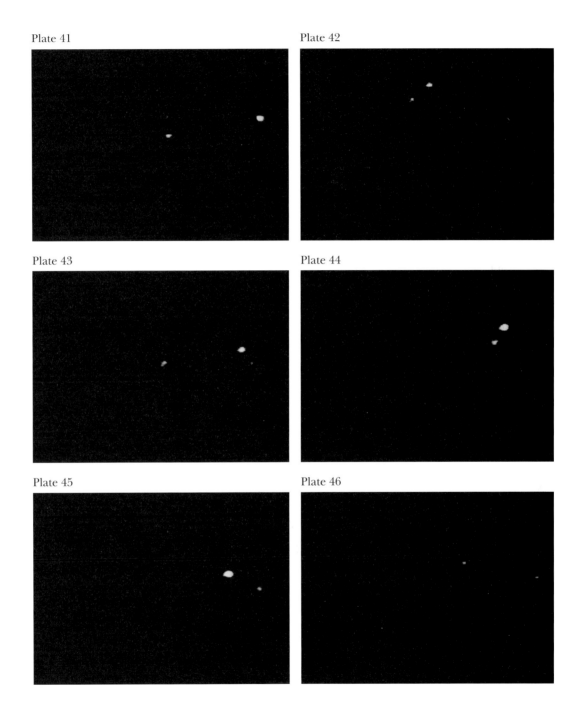

Alabama Mutilations - 1993

A circumstantial association between unusual lights in the sky, helicopters, and animal mutilations has been reported since the 1960s. A confidential source at the NASA facility in Huntsville said he grew up in rural northeastern Alabama and remembers when he was a kid in the early 1960s that he found dead squirrels, mules, and cows with strange, bloodless excisions in woods near his home. He also saw a silver disk hover in the sky above the same trees in 1963.

The first mutilation in the current cycle of animal deaths in Alabama was reported on October 20, 1992, in Albertville. It was a pregnant, black Angus/Holstein cow. (Plate 47) The udder was cleanly removed in a hide-deep, bloodless oval.

Plate 47 - *October 20, 1992. Pregnant cow owned by John Strawn in Albertville, Alabama, discovered with its udder removed in a large, oval excision only hide deep. Photograph by John Strawn.*

On November 7, 1992, another Albertville farmer, Jared Jarvis, found one of his male goats dead and mutilated. (Plate 48) The testicles and penis had been removed. This was one of eight goats found dead between November 1992 and February 1993 in Marshall County. Then fourteen more were found dead and mutilated about fifty miles southeast of Albertville in Anniston on March 27. The farmer, Gervis Wood, told me he had never seen cuts or tears like that before.

"There was no blood on the animals or on the wet ground and only one print," he said, "that looked like one huge dog track." Researcher Tom Adams remembers that large "dog tracks" were reported near animal mutilations in the Canary Islands off the west coast of Africa in the 1970s.

Plate 48 - *Male goat found with testicles and penis removed on November 7, 1992, in Albertville, Alabama. Photograph by Andy Whitten, Albertville Police Department, Albertville, Alabama.*

On January 9, 1993, Chief of Detectives of the Albertville Police Department, Tommy Cole, found one of his own black Angus steers dead and mutilated at his farm. (Plate 49) The belly had a large excision from which very white tissue protruded. There was no blood at all, which was unusual. But a white color for that particular belly tissue was not abnormal, according to Crossville veterinarian Mike Creel, if an animal had gone into shock and blood had pooled in the internal organs.

Plate 49 - *January 9, 1993. Tommy Cole, Chief of Detectives, Albertville Police, standing next to one of his steers found dead and mutilated. Very white tissue protruded without blood. Photograph by Fyffe Police Officer Ted Oliphant.*

"Internal hemorrhage could account for it," said Dr. Creel. "What happens in the superficial belly tissue area as soon as the animal is in shock, all the superficial capillaries shut down. And it shunts all the blood to the vital organs — the heart, brain, lungs and liver. The blood would be shunted away from the stomach. So in looking at Detective Cole's situation, it could have been blood pooling internally."

But neither Dr. Creel, another veterinarian Roger Adams who examined the steer, Tommy Cole, nor anyone else knew what could have caused such trauma nor could they determine cause of death in the animal which Cole said was healthy until he found the steer in the pasture with the gaping tissue "white as snow." Rectal tissue had also been neatly excised, again without blood. According to Officer Ted Oliphant, at least two other Alabama mutilated animals were autopsied by two local veterinarians and neither could determine cause of death in those cattle either.

On January 29th in Dawson, Alabama, not far from Collinsville, a black Angus cow was found with its right jaw stripped of all flesh and its tongue removed. (Plate 50) The teeth were intact.

The rectum and vagina were also gone. Officer Oliphant found a putty-like substance on the right rib cage and on the ground five feet from the cow's head which he collected and asked me to help get to a lab for analysis. (Plate 51)

Plate 50 - *Black Angus cow found January 29, 1993, with its right jaw flesh and tongue removed in Dawson, Alabama. Photograph by Fyffe Police Officer Ted Oliphant.*

Plate 51 - *Cow hair and unknown substance from January 29, 1993, Dawson, Alabama mutilation.*

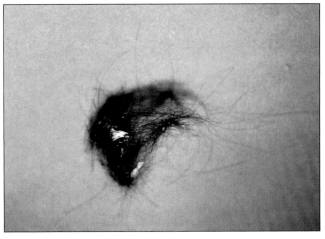

The scientist, who examined the substance and wishes to remain anonymous, sent me a report. He enclosed an analysis of composition (Plate 52) and a scanning electron microscope image of the substance. (Plate 53)

"... *Examination with a Geiger counter showed no detectable radioactivity. When a small piece of the material was placed in water, it did not appear to dissolve.*

"*We then examined the sample using a scanning electron microscope — and energy dispersive spectroscopy to determine the elemental content of the sample. Two sites were examined ... and the elements detected were primarily aluminum, silicon, titanium and oxygen. The titanium and oxygen levels relative to each other and to the aluminum and silicon differed some at the two sites. The technique does not necessarily indicate the relative amounts of each element accurately; however, I think we can say there are significant amounts of these four elements present in the sample.*"

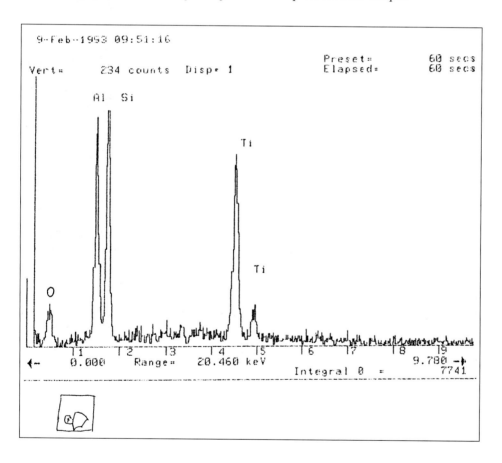

Plate 52 - *Analysis of composition indicating peaks in aluminum, titanium, silicon and oxygen.*

The scientist said the substance was not a naturally occurring mineral and was therefore manufactured. Paint products, for example, have titanium in them. But what manufactured product containing titanium would be found on the ribs of a mutilated cow?

Plate 53 - *Electron microscope image of unknown substance found on Dawson, Alabama mutilated cow.*

000001 15KV X30.0 1.00mm

In the 1970s when animal mutilations were being reported all over the United States, Canada and other parts of the world, a young heifer on the Hubert Herboldsheimer ranch near Sterling, Colorado, was found October 10, 1978, with a putty-like substance laid in two parallel lines on her back. (Plate 54) The cow also had a typical pattern of excisions: her lower jaw had been stripped of all flesh (Plate 55); two of four teats had been cleanly removed (Plate 56); and the rectal and vaginal tracts had been cored out. (Plate 57)

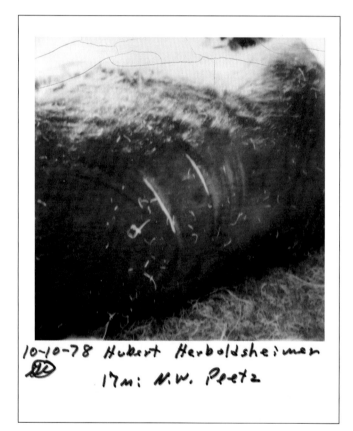

10-10-78 Hubert Herboldsheimer
17mi. N.W. Peetz

Plate 54 - *Unidentified putty-like substance laid in two parallel lines on back of young female cow discovered dead and mutilated near Sterling, Colorado on October 10, 1978. Polaroid photographs on both pages by Logan County Sheriff Tex Graves.*

Plate 55 - 1978
*Colorado cow's lower jaw
stripped of all flesh.*

Plate 56 - *Two of four
teats on Colorado cow
bloodlessly removed.*

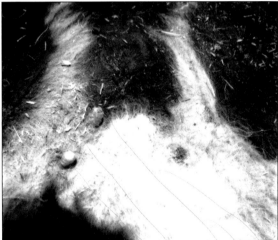

Plate 57 - *Rectum and
vaginal tract of
Colorado cow cored out.*

On February 4, 1993, a pregnant cow from Arab, Alabama, was found with her udder removed and her unborn calf's head partially out of her vagina. (Plate 58) The calf's left eye had been removed and a circle of flesh taken from around the empty eye socket. Unfortunately, no tissue samples were collected from either the calf or the cow.

Plate 58 - *February 4, 1993, Arab, Alabama cow and unborn calf dead and mutilated. Arrow points to missing left eye and circle of flesh removed from calf. Excised udder of cow can be seen in lower right hand corner. Photograph by Luanne Thrash, Investigator, Marshall County Animal Welfare Society.*

The Arab case reminded me of a pregnant cow found near Hope, Arkansas, in March 1989.[6] It was one of five cows found lying in a straight line, each with precise, bloodless excisions of tissue. One female had a large excision in her belly from which her unborn calf still inside the embryo sac had sagged onto the ground. (Plate 59) The calf was not cut, but its hair and the embryo sac were completely dry. When Dr. Altshuler examined tissue samples from the large excision in the cow's belly under a microscope, he could see that the hemoglobin had been cooked.

[6] *Chapter 5, An Alien Harvest* © 1989 and 2nd Edition December 2014 by Linda Moulton Howe, LMH Productions.

Plate 59 - *Pregnant cow, udder excised and unborn calf inside embryo sac had sagged onto ground, March 10, 1989, in Hope, Arkansas. Photograph by Juanita Stripling,* Little River News, *Ashdown, Arkansas.*

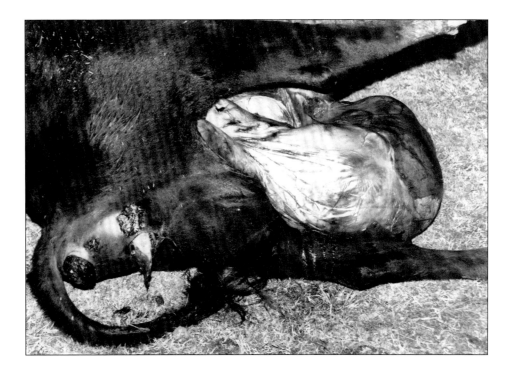

Also on February 4, 1993, around 12:30 p.m., Waymon Buttram in Geraldine, Alabama found one of his Angus cross Brahma cows dead with tissue excised from her left jaw. (Plate 60) She had calved six weeks earlier, weighed 1300 pounds and was considered healthy. Mr. Buttram had seen her alive and well at 10 a.m. the day before on February 3. Called to the scene were DeKalb County Sheriff Harold Richards; his Assistant Chief Deputy Dale Orr; Tommy Cole, Chief of Detectives in the Albertville Police Department; Sgt. Ron Ogletree, Post Commander of the Alabama State Troopers; and Fyffe Police Officer Ted Oliphant. (Plate 61)

Oliphant said, "When we cops entered Waymon Buttram's pasture, cows surrounded us twice, as if upset. We had to chase them away both times. Furthermore, for the following week after the discovery, the other cows defecated and urinated directly on the exact mutilation site, as if the smell would make what had happened go away."

Plate 60 - *Albertville Police Detective Tommy Cole examined cow discovered by owner Waymon Buttram in Geraldine, Alabama, on February 4. A "keyhole" excision of tissue had been removed from her left jaw. Photographs by Fyffe Police Officer Ted Oliphant.*

Plate 61 - *L-R: Dale Orr, Asst. Chief Deputy, DeKalb County Sheriff's Dept.; Harold Richards, Sheriff, DeKalb County; Tommy Cole, Chief of Detectives, Albertville Police Dept.; Sgt. Ron Ogletree, Post Commander, Alabama State Troopers, gathered to examine Waymon Buttram's mutilated cow, February 4, 1993 in Geraldine, Alabama.*

Unlike most other mutilations I have investigated, Mr. Buttram's cow had blood pooled in the jaw wound. Rick Sharpton, D.V.M., and the Director, Boaz Drug Laboratory, examined this animal. He concluded the jaw had definitely been cut with a sharp instrument and confidentially told a Fort Payne *Times Journal* reporter that he could not explain what had happened to Waymon Buttram's Angus cow.

Two days later on February 6, a Crossville, Alabama calf was found with a large section of back and rib hide removed, exposing bone and muscle tissue.

(Plate 62) Fyffe Police Officer Ted Oliphant said that a section of trachea and esophagus had also been surgically removed similar to the 1989 Red Cloud, Nebraska case in Plates 91-92. There was also a large hole on the cow's left side as reported in the Okemah, Oklahoma mutilation on Page 186.

Back even further on October 25, 1975, another calf with a similar excision was found near Sterling, Colorado, and reported to the Logan County Sheriff's office. (Plate 63)

Plate 62 - *Mutilated calf found on February 6, 1993, in Crossville, Alabama. Photograph by Fyffe Police Officer Ted Oliphant.*

Plate 63 - *October 25, 1975, at the Propst ranch in northeastern Colorado, a calf with rib cage excision similar to 1993 Crossville, Alabama calf. Photograph by Logan County Sheriff Tex Graves.*

Dr. Mike Creel, D.V.M., examined the Crossville calf. He has been a veterinarian for nineteen years practicing in the Crossville/Boaz area and said he was certain that predators were not responsible. While he was vaccinating young cows, he talked to me about the issue of predator attack, lack of blood at most mutilation sites and the discovery of high heat at the excision lines of some mutilated animals. (Plate 64)

"The Crossville calf had been dead for several days and the only thing I could determine was that it was not due to predation. Predators were not involved in the death of the calf," he said firmly.

"What convinced you it wasn't predator?"

"Generally, when predators attack a calf that age, they go for the rear quarters and for the nose. You usually find a lot of tooth marks around the hocks and nose of the calf. And that wasn't the case in this particular situation. After the animal had begun to decompose, dogs and other animals had come in and torn at the carcass. All I know is that predators weren't responsible for the calf's death."

"Could you determine if the cuts had been made with a sharp instrument?"

"No, I couldn't. It had been dead for five or six days."

Plate 64 - *Veterinarian Mike Creel vaccinating young cows in Crossville, Alabama, February 24, 1993. The heifer ran into the metal stanchion with such strength that the author laughed with Dr. Creel about how difficult it would be to simply grab a resisting animal. Photograph by Scott Vitatoe.*

I outlined for Dr. Creel the consistent pattern of mutilations worldwide as reported since 1967.

"Would you comment on this pattern of excisions from a veterinarian's point of view?"

"That would be quite difficult to comprehend in its entirety. This is new to me in this area."

"What about the fact that this same pattern of cuts is usually found on each reported mutilation?"

"That is bizarre, to say the least."

"It's not typical of predation from your point of view as a veterinarian for nineteen years?"

"I wouldn't think so."

I explained to Dr. Creel that the lack of blood from the beginning of the phenomenon in 1967 has puzzled law enforcement and ranchers. "Would you comment about how natural or unnatural the lack of blood at these excisions might be?"

"I've seen animals that have been killed by dogs or other predators and there has been quite a bit of blood. That's because the animal has been disabled and the heart is still pumping and you have open arteries and veins. So you have blood everywhere. Especially on snow-covered ground. I've seen that before. If the animal were killed and then someone came back later and removed these parts, then I wouldn't think you would see much blood unless they hit a major vessel. To cut off the parts that you're talking about would not cause lots of blood because the blood coagulates in the small vessels."

I told Dr. Creel about my work with pathologist and hematologist Dr. John Altshuler in Denver, Colorado since 1989, who has examined tissue samples from mutilations in various parts of the U. S. and Canada. In over thirty cases, he has found microscopic evidence that the hemoglobin has been cooked at the excision lines confirming that whatever made the excisions had to be very hot, at least 300 degrees Farenheit.

"Do you, as a veterinarian, know of or use any instrument that is portable for field surgery?"

"I don't know of anything. You're talking about electrocautery or something of that nature. That's something I would not have in my practice that would cut the skin of an animal like this," he said, gesturing to the cow in the metal stanchion. "That's leather. That would need something very hot to cut."

"Do you have access to laser equipment in your work as a veterinarian?"

"No, I wouldn't. I don't have anything like that in my practice dealing with cattle. We have electrocautery units for small animals for surgical procedures to deal with mucous membranes and soft tissues. Certainly nothing that I would have in my clinic would cut through the hide of a cow."

"Absolutely nothing?"

"I don't have anything in my practice that would cut through the hide of a cow and coagulate at the same time."

"Would that apply to other veterinarians in DeKalb and Marshall and other counties?"

"Yes. I probably do as much, if not more, large animal work than anyone. Most everybody here is a mixed practitioner and does both small and large. I do mostly large."

"What would a portable laser unit be like in size and power needs?"

"I'm not familiar with lasers. I don't use lasers in my practice."

"Not ever?"

"No."

"Do you know any veterinarian in Alabama who does?"

"No. We still use scalpels."

"So what is your comment about the pathology reports which have confirmed high heat at the excision lines of several animals found in remote areas?"

"Some kind of new instrument I don't know anything about."

On February 10, four days after Dr. Creel examined the Crossville calf, two cows and another calf were found dead in the same Grove Oak pasture. The owner estimated the animals had been dead a week, but there was no odor or decay. Only the calf and one black and white cow were mutilated. The other brown cow had one deep hole on her left side similar to Okemah, Oklahoma, on Page 185 and calf in Plate 62. The Alabama calf's genitals had been removed in a neat, bloodless oval cut and its small rectum cored out. The farm hands moved all three animals to one spot for examination. (Plates 66-67, 12, 15)

The black and white cow had an oval excision of its udder with a darkened edge. (Plate 15) Dr. John Altshuler and I have come to associate such discoloration with the use of high heat at the excision lines. In this particular case, though, no tissue samples were taken. Too often, mutilations are dismissed as disease, predator attack, or satanic cult without any medical examinations.

Fyffe Police Officer Ted Oliphant investigated the case and told me, "I was called out by Donna Saylor, who managed the Grove Oak farm. Tissue samples were not taken because the animals had been dead over a week.

"Veterinarians have been asked by police officers to look for heat exposure evidence in tissues of mutilated animals. But they have ignored the issue and we have had to go out of state to Colorado pathologist John Altshuler, M. D., in at least two cases. Further compounding the problem of getting facts, some sheriffs and police officers have taken an official position that 'mutilations just aren't happening,' an attitude that denies the evidence."

Plate 65 - The Weekly Post, *March 4, 1993, Rainsville, Alabama.*

Chief investigator says cattle mutilations are "just not happening"

By STEPHEN SMITH

DeKalb County Chief Investigator Mike James said in an interview this week that stories of strange mutilations of cattle in the last few months are unfounded, and that authorities have no evidence of any mutilation cases.

"This thing has really gotten blown out of proportion," James said. "It's just not happening in this county."

As late as last week, James was called out to a Sylvania farm to investigate a cow that was found dead by a farmer. A veterinarian examined the animal and concluded that it had died of natural causes and been eaten on by predators.

"It was just a dead cow eaten on by coyotes," James said of the Sylvania animal. "Our department has had no confirmed cases of a cattle mutilation. We haven't, the Alabama Cattlemen's Association hasn't, the State Department of Agriculture hasn't, and the state veterinarian hasn't." (partial text cont.)

"I've heard government cover-up, I've heard UFOs," he said. "It amounts to a great deal of publicity about something that's not happening.

"We're one step from someone getting hurt," James continued. "I've got people trying to buy high-powered guns, saying they're gonna shoot helicopters out of the air. I've got a friend in real estate who owns a helicopter, and he won't fly over this area."

At his request, James was faxed a copy of a magazine article from the Stockyards Division of the Alabama Department of Agriculture. In that article, author David Rorvik discusses a scientific study conducted by ex-FBI agent, Kenneth Rommel, Jr. In the study, backed by a government grant, Rommel concluded that all the mutilations occurring out West were nothing more than predators.

Plate 66 - *February 10, 1993, Grove Oak, Alabama, two cows and calf found dead in different parts of a pasture and moved together for examination. Only the calf and black and white cow were mutilated. Photographs by Fyffe Police Officer Ted Oliphant.*

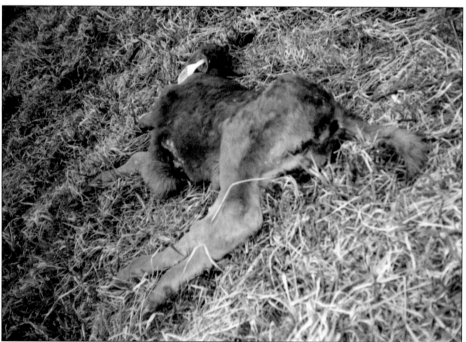

Plate 67 - *Grove Oak, Alabama steer calf found February 10, 1993, with its genitals and rectum neatly excised.*

Dr. Altshuler has also found tissue cut with a sharp instrument without heat. Why the difference, we don't know. But we do know that many mutilations are being dismissed as the work of predators, when microscopic examination of tissues can show that the predator explanation is not adequate. This happened when I was in Alabama.

My video crew and I had been waiting for a call from the local police about any new mutilation. By Thursday, February 25, 1993, heavy rain and snow were forecast, so that afternoon the crew went back to Chattanooga. At 5 p.m., I learned that there had in fact been a mutilation reported the night before at the Kenneth Hiland farm in Sylvania not far from Ft. Payne. The police with whom we were networking were not contacted, so we did not know about the mutilation until the next day when I was notified by Stephenn Smith of *The Weekly Post* in Rainsville.

I called Mr. Hiland and learned he was irritated that a vet called to the scene by DeKalb County law enforcement said coyotes or dogs had chewed off the cow's udder. Mr. Hiland told me, "It was definitely cut with a knife," but he went ahead and buried the cow to clear his pasture. I told him I was trying to get tissue samples from mutilated animals for medical study and asked him if he would dig the cow back up. I think because he was angry about the predator explanation, he agreed.

Then I had the problem of getting a camera, any video camera, within an hour. I also had to make emergency preservative fluid out of fifty percent rubbing alcohol and fifty percent distilled water. I called Stephen Smith and Carey and Teri Baker who publish *The Weekly Post*. Stephen said somehow he would track down a camcorder and we'd all meet at the Kenneth Hiland farm while we still had twilight.

By the time we got to the farm, it was nearly dark and sleeting. Mr. Hiland drove the digger and his son took the rest of us in his pickup truck to the place in the pasture where his dad had buried the mutilated cow earlier that afternoon. Stephen Smith did have a borrowed camcorder and Carey Baker ran it, but the only light we had was from the truck.

When the digger first hit the cow about four feet down, I thought of the hundreds of photographs I had seen since 1979 of mutilated animals and the dozen I had examined close-up. There was always an eeriness about the healthy-looking bodies marred by bloodless cuts. Kenneth Hiland tied a chain around one of the exposed legs and pulled the cow into the air and laid her down with her belly toward the truck lights. (Plates 68-69)

As I leaned close to look at the cut, there was no odor. The hide was not torn and the edges were smooth. The animals seemed so fresh, I could still sense the strength in her large, unmoving body, as if she would roll over and run away. At least this was one animal that was not going to be dismissed as predator attack without an examination of the cut. We used Mr. Hiland's knife to take two tissue samples from the belly excision where the udder had been. (Plate 70)

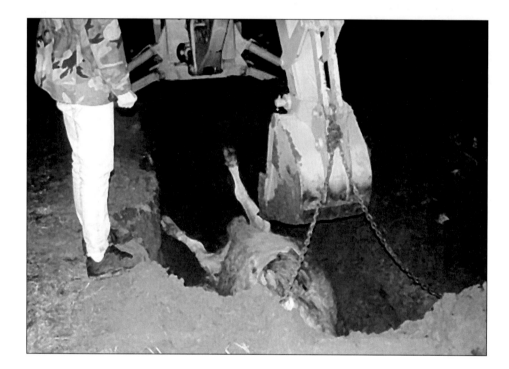

Plate 68 - *Cow being dug up at Kenneth Hiland farm, Sylvania, Alabama, February 25, 1993. Photograph by author.*

Plate 69 - *Kenneth Hiland explained to Linda Moulton Howe that "any 3-year-old could see the udder was cut off by a knife," in Sylvania, Alabama, February 25, 1993. Photograph by Stephen Smith,* The Weekly Post, *Rainsville, Alabama.*

Plate 70 - *Kenneth Hiland and Linda Moulton Howe removed two tissue samples from the udder excision line and placed each in its own container of solution that was 50% distilled water and 50% rubbing alcohol for shipment to pathologist John Altshuler, M. D. in Denver, Colorado. Photograph by Stephen Smith,* The Weekly Post, *Rainsville, Alabama.*

I received Dr. Altshuler's official report about the two tissue samples from the cow's belly. *(Appendix)* In part, it reads:

"1. The tissues submitted show borders that are consistent with sharp dissection.

2. There is no evidence of heat or cautery artifact, either by gross or microscopic examination.

3. There is no evidence to support the thesis that the edges of the tissues submitted are consistent with tearing or chewing as would be seen by predator attack."

I asked the Hiland family if they had noticed anything unusual in the sky above their farm at the time of the mutilation. The farmer's mother said that twice that week she had been awakened around 2 a.m., and both times from her window she saw a red-orange light the size of a full moon pulsing over the pasture. Her second sighting was February 24, the same day they found the mutilated cow.

Plate 71 - The Weekly Post, *March 11, 1993, Rainsville, Alabama.*

Lab tests show Sylvania cow was cut; predators not to blame

By STEPHEN SMITH

SYLVANIA — Laboratory results received this week on a cow recently found mutilated confirm a farmer's feelings that his animal was cut. The report stands in direct contradiction to what the farmer was told by local authorities.

Last week, *The Weekly Post* reported that a Sylvania man had found one of his cows dead with its milk sac and surrounding hide removed. Fairly certain this had been cut away, the farmer called his local law enforcement agency to report the incident.

Later that evening, a veterinarian arrived on the scene with Chief Investigator Mike James of the DeKalb Sheriff's Department. The veterinarian examined the animal and determined that it had died of natural causes and that the wounds were the result of postmortem attacks by predators.

The next day, the farmer, still unsatisfied with what he had been told, worked with Pennsylvania documentary film producer Linda Moulton Howe to secure tissue samples from his cow. These samples were sent for analysis to Dr. John Altshuler, a pathologist and hematologist in Denver, Colorado.

Dr. Altshuler's report stated that examination revealed that the cuts made to remove the tissue samples were the same type cuts which took away the animal's milk sac. "The mutilator and known man-made knife cuts could not be distinguished from each other," the report reads.

In conclusion, the report stated that "the tissues submitted show borders that are consistent with sharp dissection," and "there is no evidence of predator-type tearing of the tissues submitted."

This scientific proof that the Sylvania animal was not the victim of a predator is backed up by statements from Auburn University's Department of Zoology and Wildlife Sciences. "It would be obvious if a coyote had been tearing through," said Dr. Jim Armstrong, assistant professor and extension wildlife specialist.

"The wounds would not be similar to a smooth cut," Dr. Armstrong continued. "Coyotes bite through and pull to tear away the flesh. It would have a chewed on look."

Dr. Armstrong made a visit to DeKalb County earlier this week to view an animal found dead in a wooded area near Fyffe. The young calf had been dead for many days, and Dr. Armstrong stated that it was too decomposed to make a ruling on its injuries.

"I'm here as the skeptic," Dr. Armstrong said, "as the devil's advocate." With that objectivity in place, he viewed dozens of photographs taken of animals thought to have been mutilated in DeKalb and Marshall counties since last October.

"It's possible that a few of those animals could have been fed on by predators," he said of the photographs, "but for many of them there is no way a coyote or other predator inflicted those wounds."

Involved in an ongoing project to determine the actual-vs.-perceived damage caused by coyotes in Alabama, Dr. Armstrong is quite familiar with animals attacked by predators.

A copy of the photographs are being taken by Dr. Armstrong to a damage control agent with the U.S. Department of Agriculture, who is even more familiar with predator scenes than Dr. Armstrong himself.

"There are other scavenger animals, such as vultures, that will eat at the softer regions of a cow," Dr. Armstrong said, "but there's not gonna be these clean, surgical-type cuts."

A PROFESSIONAL OPINION—Dr. James Armstrong, assistant professor of Auburn University's Zoology and Wildlife Sciences department, examines a calf found dead at the start of this week in a wooded area near Fyffe. Dr. Armstrong is lending his expertise in wildlife and predator damage to those diligently searching for the truth behind the area's

Farmer wants answer to calf's mutilation; not satisfied with investigation

I left Alabama on Saturday morning, February 27. While I was in the air, another farmer named David McClendon of Crossville, Alabama found one of his 3-week-old male calves dead and mutilated. The penis, testicles and a very large section of hide had been excised from the belly, rectum and down the legs. All internal organs had been removed. Mr. McClendon first called the DeKalb County Sheriff's office. Assistant Chief Deputy Dale Orr and Crossville Police Chief Ron West went to McClendon's farm and Orr said it was predator kill. Mr. McClendon did not believe that explanation because he had never seen any predators in his Crossville area before and said there were no teeth marks on the calf. McClendon loaded the calf into his pickup and took it to the Fyffe Police Department. (Plate 72)

Plate 72 - *David McClendon standing next to the mutilated steer calf in his pickup truck at the Fyffe, Alabama Police Department, February 27, 1993. Photograph by Fyffe Police Officer, Ted Oliphant.*

Fyffe police officer Oliphant and I had talked about the importance of getting tissue samples analyzed, so while I was still flying home to Philadelphia, he made the 50/50 distilled water/rubbing alcohol preservative mixture and collected six tissue samples to send to Dr. Altshuler. (Plate 73) He told me that when he "looked into the rib cage and could see only a big, clean empty cavity, it was very intense." Oliphant also said a portion of the mutilator's cut had been notched like steps in a staircase.

Plate 73 - *Fyffe Police Officer Ted Oliphant excising six tissue samples from David McClendon's male calf for laboratory examination, February 27, 1993, Fyffe, Alabama. Photograph by Larry Williams, Fyffe Fire and Rescue.*

Under the microscope, Dr. Altshuler found evidence of high heat at the excision lines of all six tissue samples that Oliphant collected. (Appendix) How many other mutilations reported to Alabama law enforcement since October 1992 were also cut with high heat? Scientific and medical examinations are needed of each mutilated body to know for certain.

In late March 1993, about a month after the calf was found, David McClendon called Ted Oliphant to report a light blue helicopter hovering over his pasture. He told Oliphant that he grabbed his pistol and stepped forward toward the Bell Jet Ranger, which immediately took off.

It could be that some of the helicopters are government or military. I've been told by a confidential military source that certain frequencies are related to alien craft, that an agency in our government monitors those frequencies, and when detected, teams of choppers, jets, or vans equipped with radar and electronic gear are scrambled to interfere with and/or monitor non-human activities. But hard evidence is needed to confirm these allegations.

A colleague, Tom Adams in Paris, Texas, has researched the helicopter connection to the animal mutilations since the 1970s. He has contributed the following summary report for inclusion in this chapter.

Mysterious Helicopters
by
Tom Adams © 1993

Around the spring of 1973, events began to occur in the Midwestern United States which set the stage for an ongoing symphony of remarkable occurrences that resound to this day. Farmers in great numbers began to report the rustling and disappearance of livestock, which became linked to the appearance of unidentified helicopters. These helicopters, and the occupants thereof, paid an inordinate amount of attention to livestock, flying low over pastures and chasing cattle. There were even reports of farmers being shot at from the helicopters.

Later in 1973 and increasing into 1974, phantom helicopter sightings began to be associated, not with mere rustling, but with the mutilation-deaths of farm animals. These events reached a crescendo in 1975, as animal mutilations spread from the Midwest into every western state, other parts of the U. S., Canada and other countries. Accounts of unidentified helicopters associated with the mutilations increased with a complementary intensity throughout the year, with notable concentrations in Texas in the spring, Colorado in the summer and New Mexico in the fall. My files record well over 200 cases of helicopters near or over mutilation sites. This body of evidence, circumstantial though it may be, precludes invoking coincidence to explain away the helicopter and mutilation link.

These helicopters might be of several varieties and colors, and almost always without identifying markings (sometimes such markings appear to be covered or painted over). Although sightings of single craft predominate, there have been reports of from five to nine. These craft are frequently reported to be flying at abnormally low, unsafe or illegal altitudes and often at night without lights, save the occasional beam of light directed to the ground or on to herds of cattle.

At times the choppers appear very near mutilation sites, even hovering over an area where a mutilated animal is later found. Phantom helicopters have also been seen *shortly after* an animal mutilation has been reported. This has led to the speculation that, whatever or whoever is behind the chopper forays, they seem to possess some information or ability which allows them to anticipate mutilation-type events.

In the spring of 1975, livestock mutilations and helicopters were being reported over an extensive area of Texas. There were so many reports of unidentified helicopters flying low and harassing livestock in the Bosque County area of Central Texas that one Cranfils Gap resident requested an investigation from the Federal Aviation Administration. Documents obtained through the Freedom of Information Act indicate that the agency conducted a cursory probe. The closest military installations — the Army's Fort Hood and Bergstrom Air Force Base near Austin — denied having any knowledge of the helicopter flights.

A few months later, in the fall of 1975, mutilations and phantom helicopters moved into northeastern New Mexico with a flourish. The intensity of the reports of helicopters chasing cattle and landing on ranches across the high plains, and the accompanying public outcry, again prompted the Federal Aviation Administration to initiate an investigation. This time, unlike in Central Texas, the FAA publicly announced the onset of their study. Later, in response to numerous Freedom of Information inquiries, all relevant offices of the FAA denied any knowledge of an investigation into helicopter reports in northeastern New Mexico in late 1975, despite being furnished with a newspaper account announcing the start of the probe. What did they find? Apparently, reasons not to announce their findings.

Compared to the previous decade, in the 1980s the number of helicopter sightings associated with animal mutilations diminished, but never ceased for long. There were sporadic reports from Colorado, New Mexico, Wyoming, New Hampshire, and Alberta, Canada. In Marshall County, Alabama, in April of 1986, a female cow was found dead on the Vandervoort Farm near Guntersville. The heart, vagina and one teat were reported missing, with a small amount of blood on the carcass, but none on the ground. The following night, a helicopter could be heard flying low over the area.

From October 1992 into the early months of 1993, at least eleven animal mutilations were reported in Marshall County, Alabama, with additional cases in adjoining DeKalb County near Fyffe, a UFO "hot spot" of some renown. There were several reports of low-flying unidentified helicopters in both counties during this period, with most witnesses describing the choppers as blue and white. The Tennessee Valley Authority owns blue and white helicopters, but when police investigating the unmarked helicopters inquired with the agency, TVA denied any knowledge of their helicopters working in northeastern Alabama.

Not far away, in Lawrence County, Tennessee, a man reported that he was fired upon from a blue and white helicopter on November 10, 1992.[7] Milling company employee David Lopp told the Lawrenceburg Sheriff's Office that he had been sitting in his truck alongside a corn field that was being harvested when he heard, but could not see, a helicopter. He got out of the truck and observed a Huey or Jet Ranger-type helicopter rising above the trees. A side door slid open on the craft and what appeared to be machine-gun fire strafed the cornstalks just behind Lopp. He could barely hear the gunfire over the noise of the rotors. The chopper was not close enough for Lopp to have discerned identification numbers. In fact, he hit the ground as the shooting started. The aircraft left the area with a burst of speed.

On the night of June 6, 1980, a bull was killed and mutilated on a ranch in Saguache County, Colorado. Just before dusk, the rancher had observed a helicopter rising out of a field. He described it as a bubble-type chopper with beige-yellow side panels on a portion of the framework-type tail section typical of this helicopter model. There was another beige-yellow area on the back of the "bubble," where it met the tail section.

In 1993, this incident was explored further by writer Christopher O'Brien who was preparing a series of articles on anomalous phenomena in the San Luis Valley of Colorado. On January 21, he interviewed the family whose bull had been mutilated that night in 1980. The next day, January 22, a helicopter that looked exactly like the one described by the Saguache rancher flew low along the Sangre de Cristo Range and over O'Brien's house in Crestone, Colorado.

It should be recognized that the helicopter/animal mutilation accounts comprise only a small portion of all the animal mutilation reports. Yet, the "mystery helicopters" remain an integral and important part of the mutilation mystery. If we can ever begin to understand the origins and motives behind the phantom helicopter flights, we will be perhaps closer to understanding the enigma of animal mutilations.

[7] "Copter Fires On Man In Field," *The Tennessean*, Nashville, Tennessee, November 13, 1992.

The idea of "phantom helicopters" did not originate with the animal mutilation investigation. Reports of such craft have long been entangled with the UFO mystery, as well. As early as the mid-1960s, unidentified helicopters were reported in the wake of the classic Wanaque Reservoir sightings in New Jersey.

Science writer Lloyd Mallan exerted much effort to determine the origin of the helicopters; but, as usual, to no avail. In later years, ufologist Ann Druffel has written of UFO/helicopter reports in California and Connecticut in 1975. On Long Island, New York, in the late 1980s, there were numerous reports, not only of UFOs, abductions and animal mutilations, but mysterious helicopters, as well. In 1980, insurance agent John Cumby of Littleton, Colorado, called television producer-writer-director-editor-reporter Linda Moulton Howe when she was Director of Special Projects at the CBS affiliate in Denver. John reported to Linda that his family had watched a low-flying helicopter above their house turn into a black square and then a ball-shaped object before ascending straight up and out of sight.

In a report from British investigator David Rees, a Mrs. Clark of Barnehurst, Kent, in southern England, had an experience while gardening on the sunny afternoon of July 27, 1978. In her own words:

"I was startled suddenly by this helicopter just above the clothesline, which made me duck down and fall over. From this position on the ground, I looked up and saw two men distinctly. One was looking down at me, but the other, who was slightly behind, looked ahead. I got up, still looking at him and him at me. Then, I started to walk up the path, and from that moment, I did not think of it again and did not see it go. When my husband came home, I told him about this helicopter that was flying so low that it made me fall over. Then he started to ask me such questions as, 'Was I deafened by the sound?' and 'Did the rotors blow everything about?'

It was only then that I realized there must have been something strange about it, for when he was asking these questions, I realized that there had been no sound and no down-drafts from the rotors, which I had not noticed at the time. The two men looked like ordinary beings and so did the helicopter. The window of the copter was all-in-one and I did not notice any landing gear, skids or wheels. No markings at all."

Mrs. Clark estimated that the craft was as low as sixteen feet above the ground during the 30-second event. The color of the craft was described as a brownish-black and the two occupants were wearing what appeared to be brown leather helmets. England has had its share of phantom helicopter reports, including one with Oriental-appearing occupants similar to another such account in Montana in 1976. The autumn of that year, a hunter was alone at 3 p.m. in the Red Mountain area near Norris, Montana. He watched as an unmarked black helicopter flew over him and disappeared behind a nearby hill. He climbed to the top to see what was happening. The helicopter appeared to be a Bell Jet Ranger setting on the ground with its engine running.

Seven "Oriental-looking men with slanted eyes and olive skin" were walking up the hill "jabbering in an unknown language." They were dressed "like normal people" and the hunter yelled greetings and waved. The men then immediately turned around and ran back to the helicopter, got in and flew away. The confused hunter contacted Madison County Sheriff Roy Kitson, who had been frustrated by twenty-two confirmed animal mutilations between June and October that year along with many reports of silent, black, unmarked choppers over pastures.

The well-known American UFO abductee Betty Hill investigated numerous reports of unidentified helicopters in her area of New England in 1975 and 1976. Querying all possible origins for such craft, no civilian or military agency admitted responsibility.

In 1982, William Steinman was conducting on-site research for his book *UFO Crash At Aztec* and visited the scene of the alleged 1948 crash in Hart Canyon near Aztec, New Mexico. Two huge unmarked helicopters followed him, both into the canyon and out of it. After he returned home to California, Steinman was plagued for several months by helicopters flying low over his home.

Perhaps the most famous UFO/helicopter report is the Cash-Landrum encounter of December 29, 1980. Two women and a boy reported a diamond-shaped UFO accompanied by as many as twenty-three helicopters north of Houston, Texas. Many accounts of this case have been published, including one in my *The Choppers – And The Choppers.*[8] One military source claims to have participated as one of the helicopter pilots during the event. The active Army man said that in December 1980, he was stationed as a helicopter pilot at Ft. Hood near Waco, Texas. Between Christmas and New

[8] Revised Edition © 1992 by Tom Adams, P. O. Box 1094, Paris, Texas 75460.

Years, there was a special alert and he and several other pilots were told they would go on a mission to an area where each would be vectored in to a location where they would see an "unusual aircraft flying below radar," so the pilots would have to "go visual." Their mission, as he understood it, was to "force the object to land or keep it at a low altitude." The Ft. Hood helicopter pilot said that he was flying a Huey, but that there were also large Chinook choppers that had "contact teams in them and if the craft did set down, or crashed, the teams were to secure the area." He said there were a total of four contact teams in the Chinooks. At the vectored location, he said he saw "the biggest damn diamond I have ever seen in my life! I have no idea what the object was." As he and the other helicopters flew over the top of the object, he could see it "throwing off sparks like a Fourth of July sparkler." The "diamond" began to move away and the Ft. Hood choppers followed it for seven to ten miles at a very low altitude. Then the object stopped producing sparks and began to glow. At that point, it became stationary in the air. He and the other pilots received orders to abort the mission and return to their various home bases, implying that the pilots and helicopters were from several military points of origin.

Back at Ft. Hood, he was told the diamond craft was "an experimental aircraft gone astray, was outside its flight pattern, and had experienced problems." He and other pilots were told it had been crucial to insure that no civilians got close to the object. And yet, two women and a young boy were physically and mentally hurt when the aerial diamond descended over their car. In fact, the driver, Betty Cash, got out of the car to watch the diamond and suffered burns, eye damage and hair loss consistent with radiation sickness. In spite of persistent efforts by John Schuessler[9] to help the family and to find out what the government was doing with "twenty-three helicopters circling the diamond," explanations have not been forthcoming in this tragic and important case, considering the debilitating physical effects suffered by the witnesses.

A controversial videotape began making the rounds in ufology and on television in 1992. Mailed from Canada by someone calling themselves "Guardian," it showed what appeared to be a brightly-lighted disc-shaped object hovering just above the ground. Nearby could be seen a group of reddish, smoking flare-like flames. The tape included an obscure image of an alleged alien being with large slanted eyes, and the tape was accompanied by a series of question-

[9] "Cash-Landrum Radiation Case" by John F. Schuessler, P. O. Box 58485, Houston, TX 77258-8485.

able Canadian government "documents." But, as reported on NBC-TV's *Unsolved Mysteries* in February 1993, a West Carleton, Ontario woman, Diane Labenek, had apparently witnessed the incident depicted on the videotape. One night in August 1991, in her rural area not far from Ottawa, she observed the row of red "flames" and the object which soon moved into view and hovered alongside. The brightly-lighted craft was topped by a brilliant blue strobe light. United States Navy physicist Dr. Bruce Maccabee analyzed the videotape and reported that the strobe was unusual, not only for its color, but for the rapid strobing at seven cycles per second, compared to a common aircraft strobe of one to two cycles per second. After about ten minutes, the craft lifted up and out of sight and the "flames" suddenly went out. Mrs. Labenek later watched the videotape and described it as exactly what she had seen.

About ten minutes after the "flames" had gone out, a helicopter appeared and flew low over the site several times. Then it flew over the Labenek house before departing. According to *Unsolved Mysteries*, low-flying helicopters have been seen on several occasions over the West Carleton, Ontario, Canada area since the 1991 incident. Some choppers have been black, some green, some maroon – all unmarked and with dark-tinted windows. The Canadian military, through a spokesman, denied any knowledge of the helicopters.

Phantom helicopters have made unwelcome intrusions into the lives of persons who report memories of UFO-related abductions. These reports have increased at a significant rate in recent years. As with the helicopter/animal mutilation reports, this has reached far beyond coincidence. The most prominent, publicly acknowledged examples of abductee harassment are those of Betty Andreasson Luca[10] and her husband Bob Luca and Michigan abductees Shirley Coyne and her husband, George. Ed Conroy of San Antonio, Texas, author of *Report On Communion*, began to be plagued by phantom helicopters in 1988, while preparing his book on the experiences of best-selling novelist Whitley Strieber. Some of the choppers seen from his downtown office building appeared right at 4 p.m. and others at precisely 3:33 p.m.

In the November *1992 HUFON Report* (Newsletter of the Houston UFO Network, Inc.), ufologist and author Bill Hamilton writes of the abduction of a California woman in May 1991. She was reportedly confronted at her home in the Tehachapi Mountains by short, grey non-human beings; a human dressed in black; a man

[10] *The Andreasson Affair* © 1979 by Raymond E. Fowler and Betty Andreasson, Prentice-Hall; *The Andreasson Affair, Phase Two* © 1982 by Raymond E. Fowler and Betty Andreasson, Prentice-Hall; *The Watchers* © 1990 by Raymond E. Fowler and Betty Ann Luca, Bantam.

in "Air Force blues;" and a dog. Several hours of lost memory were only partially recovered under hypnosis, due to an apparent memory block. The woman believed she may have been to an installation located within the Tehachapi Mountains. Since that night, she has been visited by low-flying helicopters. One, described as a "military helicopter," hovered less than one hundred feet over her property.

Helicopter harassment of abductees has continued to accelerate. In late 1992, many people in widely-scattered parts of the United States began to exchange accounts on computer bulletin board services, such as Prodigy. Both abductees and non-abductees have filed reports, including that of the occupants of black helicopters taking photographs over homes and businesses on both the East and West coasts. Reportedly, one such individual was admonished by an intelligence agency friend to not speak so freely on this subject in his computer network communications.

The question has always been: Are these phantom helicopters real helicopters, operated by elements of the military-intelligence community? Or, are they yet another face of the phenomenon behind UFOs, designed to confuse and/or lay blame on human agencies?

There are helicopter reports which some feel suggest that many of the "choppers" are camouflage for an alien intelligence, particularly those that are completely silent. It's possible that the noiseless ones are an Earthly technology such as Active Noise Control (ANC)[11] which most of us know little about. Simplified, ANC incorporates the production of a second sound to mask or cancel out an initial noise. State of the art military technology might be quite superior to that which has been publicly acknowledged.

On the other hand, if <u>we</u> can do it, one could scarcely imagine the capabilities of a non-Earthly technology with a head start on us by hundreds, thousands or millions of years. So, while perhaps not a Rosetta Stone, solving the phantom helicopter enigma could bring us a significant step closer to understanding the larger phenomena that include worldwide animal mutilations and human abductions.

[11] "Noise Cancellation," *Wall Street Journal,* May 28, 1993.

Plate 74 -
The Weekly Post,
June 24, 1993,
Rainsville,
Alabama.

Plate 75 - *Cow found i*
n New Harmony,
Alabama, June 16,
1993, with excisions
of four teats, thin
circles of tissue
around each teat, jaw
flesh and rectal
tissue. Photograph by
Luanne Thrash,
Investigator,
Marshall County
Animal Welfare
Society.

Another mutilated cow found in New Harmony
Predators? Cattlemen say "No way"

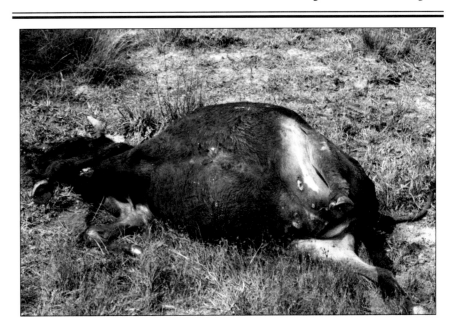

In June 1993, another cattle mutilation was reported in Alabama. On June 16, at 6:30 a.m., farmer Randall Armstrong of New Harmony, between Geraldine and Fyffe, discovered one of his cows lying on her right side. The hide had been stripped from her jaw, four teats had been removed along with somewhat circular, excisions of skin around each teat, and rectal tissue had been cut out. (Plate 75) Stephen Smith, reporter at *The Weekly Post* in Rainsville, began a large, two-page article about the mutilation: "A cow was found dead with several wounds in a south-DeKalb (County) pasture last week, and many farmers in that area disagree with investigators who claim that predators are responsible for what they saw."

Mr. Armstrong told Smith that he had to look for the rest of his cow herd and found them off in the woods. "They were scared of something, because when I came up toward them, they took off running." Mr. Armstrong was convinced someone had killed his animal and inflicted the wounds, so he called the DeKalb County Sheriff's Department. "They told me on the way to the pasture that more than likely it was caused by predators," Armstrong said. The veterinarian called to the scene was father-in-law to one of the police officers and was the same vet who told Mr. Hiland his cow had died of natural causes and coyotes had chewed off the bag – the same cow I dug up with Mr. Hiland and the pathology report confirmed the udder had been excised with a sharp instrument.

This time, the veterinarian said the New Harmony cow had died of bloat because she had grass in her mouth. Then predators had fed on the carcass. But Mr. Armstrong insisted there were no teeth marks. "I think she was hit by something when she was chewing her cud. She was not bloated when I found her and there was nothing wrong with her the night before. The blood around her jaw was still fresh. If a predator had done it, then there should have been fresh tracks around the cow, and there weren't any." It had rained and the ground was damp, so any fresh tracks would have been easy to see.

Word spread that another mutilation had been found and ten neighboring farmers with a combined experience of 300 years in raising cattle went to see Mr. Armstrong's mutilated cow. One farmer, Waymon Buttram, who had lost one of his own cows to the mutilators in February (Plate 60) said, "I see dead animals all the time and this is not predators doing this. Predators just don't do what I saw on Mr. Armstrong's cow. Something different is going on."

Luanne Thrash, Investigator for the Marshall County Animal Welfare Society, also examined Mr. Armstrong's cow. She said, "Anyone who says predators are doing this is either covering something up or really incompetent."

Other 1993 Animal Mutilations

On April 6, 1993, a steer weighing 700 pouns was found dead and mutilated in Blaine County, Oklahoma. A vet examined the animal and could not determine cause of death. Another mutilated cow was found the same day in Canadian County. South of Oklahoma City, in Moore, Oklahoma, a dog was found with its head cut off, three paws neatly severed and the heart excised, all bloodless. The head and paw excisions have been a repeated pattern in mutilated dogs throughout the U.S. since the late 1980s. Local law officials almost always assume such smaller animal mutilations are related to satanic cult activities, but are they?

A week later, Eloiso Rael found a 750-pound Charolais bull dead and mutilated in the Rael's Questa, New Mexico pasture. The genitals were gone and Mrs. Rael told me, "It looked like they had been burned off."

In April to May, the phenomenon moved to the western border counties of North and South Dakota. Davina Ryszka, State Director of South Dakota's

Mutual UFO Network (MUFON) called me about several new cases. On April 8, Mark Kelner who lives north of Buffalo Springs, North Dakota (Bowman County) found one of his young 250-pound calves dead with a "perfect five or six inch circle cut out of the hide near the back leg." Kelner said no meat was taken and there was no blood. The temperature was warm and he was surprised that the calf did not bloat and no wild animals came near the carcass. He told the *Nation's Center News* in Buffalo, South Dakota, "I also heard about some ranch and farm dogs that have been reported missing in the Reeder (Adams County, N.D.) area."

On May 14, 1993, Fred McPherson of Sturgis, South Dakota, found one of his calves with one eye, tongue and udder removed and "the rectum had been cut out in a perfect circle." The Meade County, South Dakota Sheriff's office was contacted, but no necropsy or other analysis was performed.

On Saturday, May 26, 1993, a three-month-old male calf was seen lying on its side (Plate 76) about 150 yards inside the Harding County line on the Alton and Darlene Finck ranch in South Dakota. The nearest town is Reeder, North Dakota. A neighbor reported the downed calf, but the

Plate 76 - *The South Dakota 3-month-old male calf lying where the Fincks found him on May 28, 1993, approximately 20 miles from Reeder, North Dakota. Photographs by Alton Finck.*

Fincks did not know there was anything unusual until Monday, May 28. Then they called both the Harding County and Perkins County, South Dakota Sheriff's offices. "There was a perfect circle where the genitals should have been," Mrs. Finck told me. The bottom lip, one ear, one eye, tongue and rectal flesh had also been cut away. (Plates 77-80)

The calf belonged to their son Tim, who was shocked by the excisions. He said, "Hide the size of a basketball was removed along with the testicles, penis, navel and rectum. There were no jagged tears like an animal might make. None of the meat was taken, either." The Perkins and Harding County Sheriff's deputies said the calf was an unusual case, but neither a necropsy nor pathology examination was performed.

Plate 77 - *Three-month old mutilated male calf, Alton Fincks ranch, Harding County, South Dakota, May 26, 1993.*

Plate 78 - *Circular excision removed genitals, rectal and leg tissue, Harding County, South Dakota.*

Tim Finck also learned that a rancher near Scranton had a calf mutilated in October 1983. There was no blood, no tracks and no sign of struggle. The owners, Mona and Wayne Johnson, told Tim, "It was really weird. Nothing would go close to the dead calf, not any birds, wild animals or other cows. It was spooky."

Two weeks later on Saturday, June 12, 1993, horse owner Sally Brown from Independence, Minnesota (West Hennepin County), found that one of her palomino colts had been killed "and its left eye had been removed with surgical precision taking a perfect four-inch circle of flesh around the eye, too," she said. (Plate 81) "There were no apparent wounds that would be the cause of death. Our vet, Dr. Charles Van Patten, said it was a very clean, sharp cut around the eye."

The police also reported that "the chestnut (normal hard callus) on the inner front right leg was cut away and there was some blood around that area." Dr. Van Patten told Sally Brown that it did appear that however the horse died, it died quickly. He also told her that he could not have surgically removed the eye and circle so precisely. He said whoever did this knew what he was doing and knew how to handle a knife.

In addition to the removed eye, Brown told me there were also half-inch long straight "slashes" on the horse's penis, anus and one of its front legs. The police report stated, "it was very obvious that these marks were not from any animal as they were very clean lacerations that resulted from a sharp knife. These cuts on the penis and anal area were not deep, but had just cut the surface skin."

Plate 81 - *June 12, 1993 male palomino colt found by owner Sally Brown on her Independence, Minnesota, horse farm. Photograph by West Hennepin Public Safety Department, West Hennepin County, Minnesota.*

Police checked the scene and found no area of entrance into the corral and there were no vehicle tracks coming up from the back side of the property. Even though there was no apparent bullet hole on the horse, police also checked for bullet cartridges on the ground, but could not find any.

Todd Boelter, a police officer with the West Hennepin Public Safety Department outside St. Paul, and Chief of Police Larry Bailey said they were investigating possible satanic cult involvement. But Boelter said they were puzzled by lack of tracks or any signs of struggle by the horse in the pasture.

The horse was sent to the University of Minnesota School of Veterinary Medicine for a necropsy. Their conclusion: unknown cause of death, followed by predator attack.

Police officer Boelter told me that four days later on June 16, a veterinarian brought a dog to the police department, alive but wounded. (Plate 82) There was a one-half inch wide and two-inch deep plug of tissue removed from the dog's left hip near the tail bone. The hole was dry and bloodless. The vet said, "The injury was possibly made by an electrical probe, like a cattle prod, because the injury did not bleed." The dog continued to heal after the veterinarian's report to police.

Plate 82 - *June 15, 1993, plug of tissue bloodlessly removed from dog with possible high heat by unknown instrument. Photograph by Minnesota's West Hennepin Public Safety Department.*

One week later on June 22, 1993, another mutilated horse was found in northern Colorado's Weld County, a county which has had dozens of mutilation reports since the 1970s. Mike Peters, reporter for the *Greeley Tribune* (Plate 83) wrote, "Well-known northeast Weld County rancher Doris Williams found her favorite horse dead and possibly mutilated Tuesday, June 22. It appeared one eye had been removed, and there were smooth cutting-type

Plate 83 - The Greeley Tribune, *June 23, 1993, Greeley, Colorado.*

Mutilation debate resurfaces

3 recent animal deaths investigated

By MIKE PETERS
Tribune Staff Writer

A controversial mystery has surfaced again among ranchers and state officials with the discovery Tuesday of a dead horse in northeastern Weld County and an accusation by the owner that her horse was mutilated.

Well-known northeast Weld County rancher Doris Williams found her favorite

this morning said the horse died of natural causes and are reluctant to call the death a mutilation. They say the damage may have come from predators eating the dead horse.

Williams, a former member of the Weld County Council and two-time county commissioner candidate, lives near Buckingham, 65 miles northeast of Greeley. She found her

ries at CSU for tests.

It appeared one eye had been removed, and there were smooth cutting-type marks around one ear and down the jaw. The skin had been removed from that area. It also appeared part of the tongue had been cut out.

While the edges of the skin appeared to have been cut smoothly by a knife, sheriff's

as an "unexplained death" until CSU experts examined the animal.

At CSU this morning, veterinarians who were performing an autopsy on the horse said it had died from a twisted bowel. Sheriff's spokesperson Margie Martinez said if a horse gets a stomach pain, it will sometimes roll on the ground continuously. "That could cause a twisting of the bowel and kill the horse."

Preliminary reports stated the veterinarians believe the cuts on the animal's head and neck

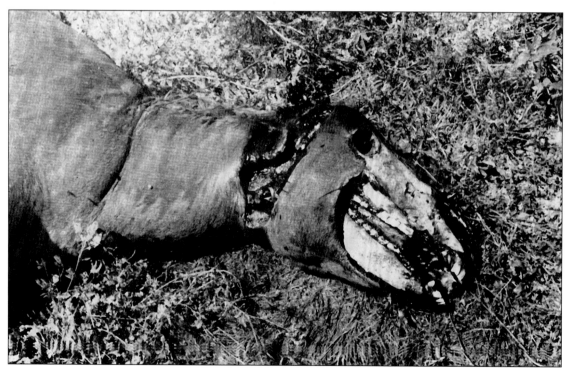

Plate 84 - *Fourteen-year-old gelding found June 22, 1993, by owner and horse raiser Doris Williams, New Raymer, Colorado. Photograph by Mike Peters, The Greeley Tribune.*

marks around one ear and down the jaw. The skin had been removed from that area. It also appeared part of the tongue had been cut out." (Plate 84)

Deputy Ron Richardson reported the incident as "unexplained death" and called for a county truck to take Doris Williams's horse to Colorado State University for tests. There, a pathologist said the horse had died of a twisted intestine and predators had eaten the head tissue. Mrs. Williams did not believe the report. She told me, "I have been raising horses in Colorado for over thirty years and I have never seen anything like this before."

It was the third alleged mutilation found in Weld County in May to June, 1993. One was at a ranch north of Mead, Colorado. Deputies said they found a cow with a missing calf embryo. "It looked like someone had cut out the rectum, uterus, and took the entire calf from the womb," said Deputy Duff Knott. "We didn't find a trace of calf anywhere."

Another mutilation had occurred a few miles south of Doris Williams's ranch in which the tongue, lips and female organs had been excised. Rancher Delbert Castor had also sent that cow to the CSU diagnostic laboratory. In his case, the lab *confirmed* cutting with a sharp instrument.

I called Dr. Altshuler in Denver after talking with Mrs. Williams and the next day, July 2, he travelled to Fort Collins to meet Doris Williams at the CSU lab and to talk with the pathologist. When Dr. Altshuler asked to see the photomicrographs of the intestinal tissue that confirmed cause of death, the CSU pathologist said no microscopic examination had been made. Dr. Altshuler was surprised and told me that from his pathologist point of view that would be equivalent "to reviewing a book you had never read."

None of the horse's intestinal tissue or other body parts, except the head, had been preserved. CSU had incinerated them. But Dr. Altshuler did examine the head tissue which was too decomposed to see definitely under a microscope whether the cuts had been made with a sharp instrument, high heat, or predator teeth. He did not think the tissue had the typical hardened and darkened edge we have come to associate with cuts made by high heat.

Doris Williams's horse, like Sally Brown's in Minnesota, remains a mystery in spite of laboratory reports of predator gnawing. From my own personal experiences with Alabama and other cases that were dismissed as predator attack and then later confirmed by microscopic examination to be cut by sharp instrument or high heat, I wonder about the cursory examinations these animals are given in the pastures and in the university laboratories. I remember talking with Elbert County, Colorado Sheriff George Yarnell about one of his own tests of accuracy for the Colorado State University diagnostic laboratory. It was around 1976 and Yarnell was frustrated by all the predator explanations coming back to him from the Colorado Bureau of

Investigation in Denver and the CSU laboratory in Fort Collins. So, from one dead cow he cut a piece of hide with his own hunting knife and notched it. He kept the notch as proof of his cut and sent the rest of the hide to CBI which sent it on to CSU. CBI relied upon CSU to confirm if mutilation cuts had been made with sharp instruments, predator teeth, or something else.

Sheriff Yarnell was angry when he received an analysis report that said the hide had been gnawed by predators. He called up Carl Whiteside, then head of CBI's animal mutilation investigation and asked, "What the hell is going on?" There followed a meeting in Denver with CBI investigators and a representative from the CSU pathology lab. The lab's only comment was, "We're human. We make mistakes."

Plate 85 - The Columbus Dispatch, *January 17, 1993, Columbus, Ohio.*

Horse mutilations anger owners, baffle police in England

Scripps Howard News Service

LONDON- Horse owners in Hampshire are on full alert after a third mare in a week fell victim to a sexual assault by animal "rippers," who have attacked almost 30 animals nationwide.

The latest attack, reported Friday night, took place at stables near Kilmerston, Hampshire, where the "ripper" got past prowling guard dogs to slash and sexually abuse a 23-year-old mare in foal.

Similar assaults took place earlier last week in Owlsbury, Hampshire; and Lacey Green, Buckinghamshire.

These attacks have been repeated in the past nine months 22 times in Hampshire, twice in Buckinghamshire and five times on the outskirts of Hull.

Stallions, too, have been attacked. Hampshire veterinarian Andrew Kennedy, who practices in the Meon Valley, which has seen the most attacks, and he has treated horses whose genitals have been shocked with electricity. Other stallions and geldings have been rectally assaulted, flogged and stabbed.

The sadism of the attacks has angered rural communities, and police admit they are baffled. So, too, is a battery of psychiatrists, psychologists, veterinarians and equine experts, each of whom has a different theory on who is to blame.

Until last year, western Sweden saw a spate of rippings, with 200 horses and cattle slashed. No arrests were made. Attacks have occurred in the United States - in San Diego, Arizona and Pennsylvania, where investigators point the finger at cults.

Professor David Canter, who heads Surrey University's psychology department and profiles sexual offenders sought by police, dismisses the cult theory.

"Belonging to a cult, however bizarre its practices, requires an intellectual framework and an ability to relate socially," he said, while the animal attacker "will be mentally, psychologically and educationally disadvantaged."

Canter said the attacked would "almost certainly" be male and young, and in his childhood may have shown signs of cruelty to animals. He is likely to be a menial worker with animals, he said.

While helicopters, bright lights, disks and animal mutilations were reported in Alabama, there were also reports from Hampshire, England of more than thirty horses found dead and oddly cut. Hampton veterinarian Andrew Kennedy from the Meon Valley reported that he "treated horses whose genitals have been shocked with electricity." (Author's emphasis.)

Police admitted they have been baffled and Professor David Canter, who heads Surrey University's psychology department and studies sexual offenders, dismissed the satanic cult theory saying, "Belonging to a cult, however bizarre its practices, requires an intellectual framework and an ability to relate socially, while the animal attacker will be mentally, psychologically and educationally disadvantaged."

12 *Extra-Terrestrials Among Us* © 1986 by George C. Andrews, Llewellyn Publications and *Extra-Terrestrial Friends and Foes* © 1993, Illuminet Press.

Author and investigator George Andrews[12] wrote from France about bloodless sheep mutilations. He said there have been reports there in 1993 and summarized other recent years:

"We had a flock of about 250 sheep mutilated and drained of blood in 1985, plus a flock of about 200 sheep that died under mysterious circumstances in 1986. The incidents near Cajuers military base in the fall of 1992 involved approximately 300 sheep.

It is as if periodically something somewhere in France needs a 'fix' of fresh blood and tissue, approximately the same amount being taken each time. If it was needed for some secret government project, it would be much simpler for the government to simply run a herd of sheep through the local slaughterhouse, telling the butcher how they wanted the sheep processed."

Nearly every type of domestic animal and wild game, including deer, elk and rabbits, have been touched by the mutilation phenomenon. Since the 1970s, there have also been waves of cat mutilations in Canada, California, and Texas. One cycle began in May 1992 in Vancouver, British Columbia, Canada. Typical was the purebred Russian blue cat that was put out in the evening and never came back. The back half of the cat was found three blocks from its owner's home without a trace of blood. It was the fourth cat found cut in half in a two week period. So far, the pattern has been that only half of the cats are found, either the back half or front half, but not both. By January 10, 1993, Vic Warren, Supervisor of Animal Control for the Vancouver City Pound, had opened a file on seven cats found cut in half. "They're clearly being butchered by someone - it's a real surgical job," he said. "All I hope is that these cats were already dead when they were cut in half."

In March 1993, Dr. John Altshuler in Denver received one of the Vancouver half-cats for examination and confirmed that the entire excision had been cut with high heat.

Similar reports of cats cut in half emerged in the summer of 1991 and spring of 1993 in Plano, Texas, an affluent suburb north of Dallas. (Plate 86)

I talked with Plano Police Detective Mike Box. In addition to the mutilated cats, he said by August 1991, they had missing reports on more than eighty domestic house cats with collars and I.D. tags. None of those cats were ever found. In 1993, other animals had disappeared from adjoining Creek-Forest neighborhoods. Detective Box and his department investigated satanic cult activities, but could find no hard evidence that connected them to the mutilated and missing cats and other animals, such as dogs. Thirteen years before in 1978, authorities in St. Catharines near Toronto, Canada, were also frustrated by more than one hundred missing cats and dogs and others found skinned and badly mutilated.

Similarly, by August 1989, sixty-seven cats had been found in Tustin, California. *The New York Times* reported on August 13, 1989, "Some of them (were) cut in half with what some say is almost surgical precision, others disemboweled or skinned." Janet Hampson of Tustin summed up the eeriness of it all: "There is never any blood at the scene, the animals are often dismembered with surgical precision and paws and other body parts are often left on the ground in strikingly similar arrangements. No one ever seems to hear anything, nor do dogs bark during the killing." She believes the cats are captured, taken elsewhere, their blood drained and organs removed, then replaced on their owners' lawns.

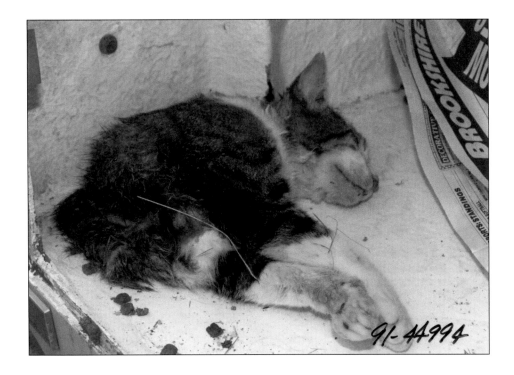

Plate 86 - *Half-cat photographed by Plano, Texas Police Officer for Incident Report #91-44994, August 31, 1991.*

RECENT WAVES OF MUTILATIONS

1989:	Idaho, Nebraska, Washington.
1990 - 1991:	Arizona, Arkansas, Canada, England, Illinois, Kentucky, Mississippi, Oregon, Sweden, Tennessee, Texas, Virginia.
1992:	Arizona, Canada, Colorado, Kansas, Missouri, New Mexico, Oklahoma, Sweden.
1993:	Alabama, Arkansas, Canada, Colorado, England, France, Germany, Minnesota, New Mexico, North Dakota, Oklahoma, South Dakota, Sweden, Texas.

1989

As Alabama was the focus of the mutilators in 1993, Idaho was the focus in 1989. There were so many cattle mutilations in southern Idaho that Bear Lake County Sheriff Brent Bunn told me, "We haven't seen anything like this since the 1970s." Sheriff Bunn sent me sixteen neatly typed *Investigation Reports* about cattle mutilations that were found in his county between May and December. Over half occurred in a remote valley called Nounan. Only eighty people live there. Ranching is their main income source and cattle are precious. Disease and predators are old and well-understood enemies.

What descended on Nounan, Idaho, in the summer and fall of 1989 was not understood – and it scared people. Bloodless, precise cuts and no tracks — that's what always bothers people. "There were no visible signs of the cause of death," Officer Gregg Athay wrote in his mutilation report. "It appeared that only the soft tissues (nose, lips and tongue) were gone off the head and four nipples off the bag. Again, there was no blood on the hair and ground." (Plate 87)

In 1989, residents of southern Idaho weren't alone in their fear and confusion about animal mutilations. William Veenhuizen woke up on July 27, 1989, to find his finest cow mutilated about two hundred yards from his farm house in Maple Valley, Washington, southeast of Seattle. (Plate 88) The six-year-old female was due to calve in about three weeks, the unborn calf still inside her belly. Mutilators had cut away a smooth oval section of the cow's mouth, removed a segment of jaw with teeth, excised the tongue, and cut out a large, hide-deep section of vaginal and rectal tissue.

Plate 87 - *Idaho rancher Steve Somsen next to his mutilated female cow found July 23, 1989. Photograph by Ellen Carney,* Idaho State Journal.

Something awakened Mr. Veenhuizen around 1 a.m. that morning, he remembered. He even put his shoes on and went outside, but he could not see or hear anything out of the ordinary. After sunup, when he discovered what had happened to his cow, he was so upset that he started keeping the rest of his animals inside the barn.

"A neighbor said to me that coyotes did it," he said, "but I told him that coyotes don't have that sharp a knife."

Bill Veenhuizen wasn't the only farmer in Maple Valley, Washington, having mutilation problems. On Sunday, November 11, two female sheep were found with their sexual organs removed. The Hicks-Raburn King County Police found small holes on the carcasses similar to BB gun pellet wounds, but no pellets were found. Similar "biopsy plug" removals have been reported in the necks of birds and other domestic animals. Perhaps

Plate 88 - *Pregnant cow owned by Bill Veenhuizen, Maple Valley, Washington, found dead with "keyhole" excision of jaw flesh, bone, teeth, tongue, and large hide-deep excision of rectal and vaginal tissue on July 17, 1989. Photograph by Bill Veenhuizen.*

that is what happened to the dog in West Hennepin, Minnesota. (Plate 82).

Also in November 1989, in Red Cloud, Nebraska, rancher Ron Bartels found a large 1,000-pound Chianina cow dead and mutilated. (Plates 89-90) A circle of tissue around the eye had been removed, a 4-inch straight vertical cut was in the throat, and a large triangular patch of hide had been removed from the belly, rectum and vagina.

The Franklin County Sheriff's Department investigated and veterinarian Carl Guthrie, D.V.M., was asked to do a necropsy. In his report (Plate 91), he stated that a 4-inch straight incision had been made over the cervical trachea. Inside the animal's neck, over eight inches of trachea and esophagus had been surgically removed. "The skin over the abdomen was excised in a clear, demarcated line, but no musculature disturbed," Dr. Guthrie wrote in his report. The rectum and vagina were cored out. Bartels told me, "After several days, there had been no predation and with the number of coyotes we now have in this area, they completely strip a carcass very quickly. But nothing touched that cow."

Plates 89-90 - 1,000-pound Chianina cow found in Red Cloud, Nebraska, November 27, 1989, with circular excision of tissue removed around eye, a 4-inch vertical cut in the throat, and large triangular patch of hide taken from belly, rectum and vagina. Photographs by Ron Bartels.

Plate 91 -
Veterinarian's
Necropsy
Report by
Dr. Carl
Guthrie, Red
Cloud,
Nebraska,
November
27, 1989,
about Ron
Bartels's
Chianina
cow.

Veterinarian's Necropsy Report

Owner _Ivan Schukei_ Address _____

Species _Bovine_ Breed _RWF_ Sex _Female_ Age _8yr_

No. Killed _1_ Weight _1000#_ Condition _Fair_ Time Since Death _~3day_

History, symptoms: Cow found dead in corn stalks; 1 eye missing; signs of possible predator strike/foul play.

Skin (including hair, external body orifices and subcutis): ~4" straight incision over cervical trachea ~8" of trachea & esophagus missing; skin over abdomen was removed in a clear demarcated line — No musculature disturbed

Respiratory System (nasal cavity, larynx, trachea, bronchi, lungs, pleura): Old fibrin scars from resolved pneumonia

Cardiovascular System (myocardium, pericardium, endocardium, valves, blood vessels): Normal

Hematopoietic System (spleen, lymph nodes, bone morrow): Normal

Digestive System (oral cavity, teeth, tongue, salivary glands, tonsils, pharynx, esophagus, stomach, small and large intestine, liver, pancreas, peritoneal cavity): Rectum - removed;

Musculoskeletal System (muscles, bones, joints): Musculature over upper hind limbs has been removed

Urogenital System (kidneys, ureters, bladder urethra, ovaries, uterus, vagina, vasa deferentia, seminal vesicles, prostate, penis, prepuce): missing

Nervous System (brain, spinal cord, cerebrospinal fluid, meninges, peripheral nerves): N. Examined

Endocrine System (pituitary, pineal, thyroids, parathyroids, thymus, adrenals): ——

Special Laboratory procedures and results:

Conclusions: There were definite signs of suspicious acts to the body of this cow — the nature in which the skin was severed & removed was not characteristic of a predator strike; however I am unable to determine whether these acts occurred before/after death of the cow.

Diagnosis:
  1. Cause of death of animal:

  2. I am unable to determine cause of death because: Post mortem changes

Veterinarian _Carl A. Guthrie D.V.M._ Address _405 N. Elm Red Cloud, NE_

Insurance Company Representative _____ Date _1/27/89_

2057

▲

173

1990 - 1991

In 1990 to 1991, while I was producing *Earth Mysteries: Alien Life Forms* in Atlanta and then working as creator and supervising producer of the Fox network hour special, *UFO Report: Sightings*, based on *Earth Mysteries*, I received mutilation reports from Oregon, Virginia, Arkansas, Kentucky, Tennessee, Illinois, Arizona, Texas, Canada, England and Long Island, New York.

On April 21, 1990, at Sound Beach, Long Island, two rabbits were found a few hundred feet from each other, dead and mutilated. No blood, no tracks. One of the rabbits was headless (Plate 92) and one had the now classic removal of eye tissue around an empty eye socket. (Plate 93) Long Island investigators sent Dr. John Altshuler both rabbits intact. In all the excision lines, Dr. Altshuler found evidence of high heat. (Plate 94)

Plate 92 - *Headless rabbit found at Sound Beach, Long Island, New York, on April 21, 1990. Photographs by John Altshuler, M.D.*

Plate 93 - *Second rabbit with right eye and surrounding eye tissue removed, found a few hundred feet from first rabbit at Sound Beach, Long Island, New York, on April 21, 1990.*

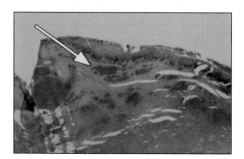

Plate 94 - *Photomicrograph of Sound Beach, Long Island rabbit tissue. Yellow arrow points at cooked hemoglobin.*

In Oregon near Portland in October 1990, investigators Carlo Sposito and Keith Rowell examined a two-year-old Hereford steer, (Plate 95) the fifth mutilation in the same pasture on the Richard Fazio ranch within four months.

Plate 95 -
Two-year-old Hereford steer, the fifth mutilation on the Richard Fazio ranch within a four month period ending in October 1990. Photograph by Carlo Sposito.

Plate 96 -
Uniformly serrated edge of mutilator's excision in steer found October 1, 1990, near Portland, Oregon. Photograph by Keith E. Rowell.

Sposito and Rowell took photographs of an unusual serrated cut that was similar to another serrated cut found on a mutilated cow near Great Falls, Montana, in 1975. (Plates 96-98)

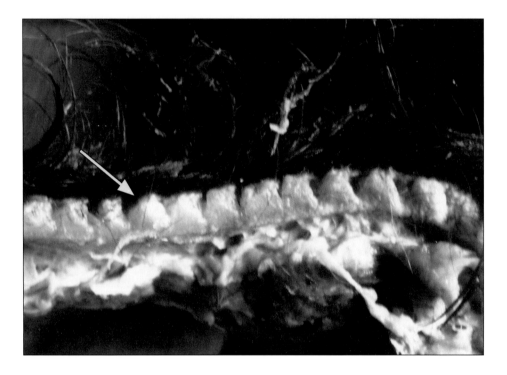

Plate 97 - *Close-up profile of 1990 Oregon steer's serrated excision cut with high heat. Photograph by Keith E. Rowell.*

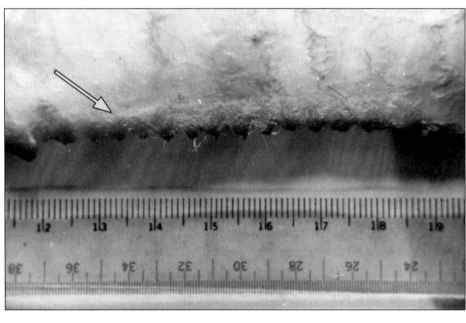

Plate 98 - *Close-up profile of 1975 Montana mutilator's cut with similar serrated edge. Photograph by Cascade County Sheriff Deputy Keith Wolverton.*

Sposito sent tissue samples to Veterinarian Madeline A. Rae at the Veterinary Diagnostic Laboratory College of Veterinary Medicine, Oregon State University, Corvallis, Oregon, and to Dr. John Altshuler in Denver, Colorado. Dr. Rae filed a formal Report of Laboratory Examinations (Plate 99) in which she concluded: *"The notched edge does exhibit a band of coagulation necrosis consistent with a heat-induced incision, such as with an electrosurgical unit. ...It is not possible to tell whether this lesion was caused by a laser."*

Plate 99 - *Report of Laboratory Examination of 1990 Oregon steer by Veterinary Diagnostic Laboratory, Oregon State University, Corvallis, Oregon.*

VETERINARY DIAGNOSTIC LABORATORY   Accession Number: D91-08123
   College of Veterinary Medicine
   Oregon State University
   P.O. Box 429
   Corvallis, Oregon   97339-0429   (503) 737-3261

REPORT OF LABORATORY EXAMINATIONS

Specimens
submitted: FIXED TISSUE
Animal ID: HEREFORD CROSS STEER
Species: BOVINE
Mail to - Owner: Age: 2 YEARS
    RICHARD FAZIO   Sex: MALE

Date Specimen Received: 02/12/91
Preliminary Report On:
Final Report On: 02/22/91

Communications: |_| oral |XX| phone

Submitted by: RANDY LEE DVM

Dr. Lee by MAR on 2/13/91

PATHOLOGIST REPORT:

HISTOPATHOLOGY: Sections of skin from a steer are examined. All sections display moderately severe post-mortem autolysis. The notched edge does exhibit a band of coagulation necrosis consistent with a heat induced incision, such as with an electrosurgical unit. Numerous bacteria are present on the skin, except in the area of coagulation necrosis. This is consistent with a specimen collected via electrosurgical excision.

DIAGNOSIS: Coagulation necrosis of the skin.

COMMENT: It is not possible to tell whether this lesion was caused by a laser. It does appear consistent with a heat-induced injury.

SIGNED: *Madeline Rae, DVM*
     Madeline A. Rae, DVM / SPS   mar

Another veterinarian in the fall of 1990 was puzzled by the death of a 500-pound Charolais bull calf found September 23, 1990, in Madison, Nebraska. (Plate 100) The tissue around the penis had been removed bloodlessly with a sharp instrument leaving the organ intact. The rectum had also been cored out.

Dr. David Camenzind, D.V.M., wrote a report about the case in which he stated:

> *"The calf was found lying out in a pasture with no signs of struggling. The caudal end of the scrotum was sharply removed with the testicles intact and remaining on the carcass. A 10-inch circular area was cut out in the perineal region, extending about 6 inches deep, removing the skin at the base of the tail, anus and surrounding tissues down to the ischium of the pelvic bone. The accessory sex gland appeared to be removed also, but the penis remained intact."*

Plate 100 - *Charolais bull calf found September 23, 1990, in Madison, Nebraska. Tissue around penis and rectum had been bloodlessly removed with a sharp instrument. Photograph by Dan Long.*

In January 1991, thirteen dogs were found mutilated in Lynchburg, Virginia, exactly as the April 1993 case in Blaine County, Oklahoma. Their heads and paws had been neatly cut off and Lynchburg Police Commander Gary Reynolds said, "It was kind of methodical the way they had been laid out. But we've had no evidence of satanic sacrifices within the city of Lynchburg in my sixteen years with the police department."

Then on February 4, 1991, James Thorne of Green Forest, Arkansas, found his second cow mutilation in three months and his fifth mutilation since 1978. (Plate 101)

Plate 101 - *In this same pasture in Green Forest, Arkansas, farmer James Thorne found the fifth in a series of mutilated cows on February 4, 1991.*

Deputy Sheriff Archie Rousey of the Carroll County Sheriff's Office examined the 18-month-old heifer who had never calved. (Plate 102) The deputy told me the entire udder had been removed in a "somewhat circular cut" and he did not understand what had happened because "it was so abnormal." The entire tongue and portion of jaw flesh had been excised.

Plate 102 - *Deputy Sheriff Archie Rousey, Carroll County, Arkansas Sheriff's Office, and Green Forest farmer James Thorne on February 4, 1991. Photograph by* The Star Progress, *Berryville, Arkansas.*

Dr. John Altshuler confirmed that the excisions on the Green Forest cow had been made with high heat. But the local veterinarian in Berryville, Arkansas, Dr. Alan Honnicutt, diagnosed the cause of death as black leg, a bacterial infection. Dr. Altshuler and I independently called Dr. Honnicutt to discuss cell changes indicative of high heat. The veterinarian said, "I don't know about that," and apparently did not want to know, because despite the hard medical evidence that the hemoglobin had been cooked at the excisions, Dr. Honnicutt insisted the animal had died from the clostridium bacteria associated with black leg.

When I asked him if clostridium bacteria can set in *after* an animal's death, Dr. Honnicutt admitted that it could after an injury to a cow, such as a bruise or cut. I asked him if it were possible the heifer had suffered the mutilation excisions and death prior to the onset of the bacteria's growth. He said it was possible. But in his official report to James Thorne, Dr. Honnicutt never discussed the discovery of cooked hemoglobin and said the cow died of black leg, a cause of death that James Thorne rejected completely. "I've seen cows die of black leg, and they don't have neat cuts taken from their tongue, jaw and belly!"

Unfortunately, many veterinarians have chosen not to discuss the mutilations publicly. One in Wyoming told me quite frankly that if he talked to me on television about the inexplicable removal of the optic nerve in one mutilation case, his veterinarian colleagues would ridicule him. But he had no medical explanation for how the optic nerve had been removed nor how a small, cone-shaped plug had been removed from the cow's skull without causing any bleeding in the brain tissue underneath.

On April 21, 1991, two newborn calves were found twenty miles apart in Kentucky, each mutilated like the other. (Plates 103-108) Steve Wesolowski, a detective with the Greenup County Sheriffs Department, wrote that "the tan calf belonged to Deputy Ted Howard of our department. The calf was less than 24 hours old. White powder was found on the calf and at four points (on the ground.) The tan calf was found on top of the hill at Mr. Howard's residence with its eyes, penis, rectum, guts, tongue and blood missing. The ears of this calf were slightly cut."

The other 24-hour-old calf was a black Angus. Officer Wesolowski said, "It is estimated that it (black calf) was killed about the same date. The body parts taken on this calf were one eye, one ear, penis, rectum, guts, blood and tongue. This other calf was also found on top of a hill with what appears to be the same type of powder which was used on and around the tan calf. The hooves of both calves were extremely clean, as if they had been polished."

Plates 103 - 108: *Black calf in left column; tan calf in right. Both 24-hours-old, twenty miles apart and nearly identical excisions. Photographs by Greenup County, Kentucky Sheriff Deputy.*

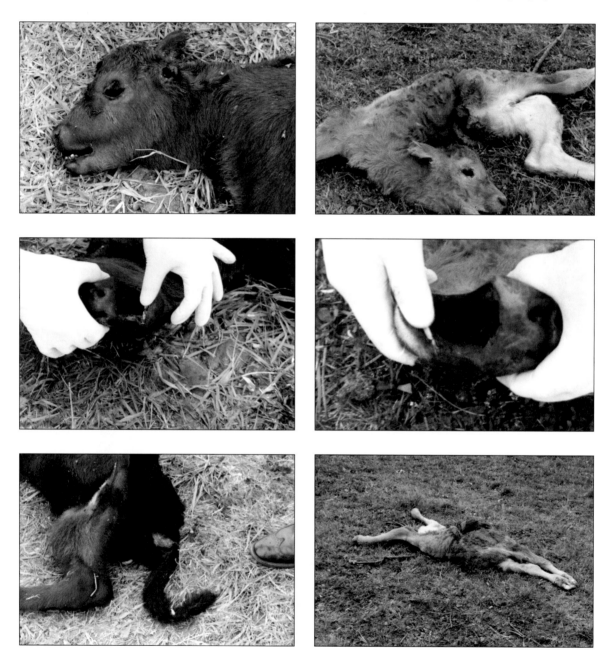

1992

In the cold winter nights of December 1991 to January 1992, the unknown was again haunting Oklahoma, Kansas and Missouri leaving dead and mutilated cattle in its wake. One couple, driving down a country road after dark, saw two, bright objects moving low in the sky.

"As one got over the road above us, it blinked out," said Mike Markum of Cement, Oklahoma. "The other object stopped and started. That's what caught my attention. We heard no sound."

Markum and his wife reported they saw several "sparkler-like balls" going over their house at low altitudes. One shot off at tremendous speed and left a green trail.

I received calls and letters about several mutilations in Oklahoma where MUFON investigators Richard Siefried, Jean Waller and Chuck Pine helped me research the situation. On February 1, Pine visited Grant County Sheriff Archie Yearick in Medford, Oklahoma. The sheriff said he was very puzzled about the mutilations. "If satanic cults are involved," he asked, "why aren't there any tracks at the mutilation sites?" He said he had filed five mutilation reports in his county and had learned about a new one over the border in Caldwell, Kansas, that morning.

Plate 109 - *Mutilated steer found in Caldwell, Kansas on January 31, 1992. Jaw flesh, bone and teeth had been excised in an oval cut. Photograph by Chuck Pine.*

Plate 110 -
*Genitals of
Caldwell, Kansas,
steer removed in
bloodless round
excision. Photograph
by Chuck Pine.*

So, Pine traveled with a police officer to see the steer and to collect tissue samples from four different excisions on the animal's head, genitals and rectum. (Plates 109-110)

I arranged to ship the tissues to Dr. Altshuler, who found that the hemoglobin in these excisions had been cooked by high heat as he has found in so many other animals.

Two more steers were found mutilated in Calumet, Oklahoma, near El Reno. The first was found by Robert Jacobs and his son Travis Dean on the morning of February 6th. That evening, Travis took his girlfriend, Julie, back to the field to show her what had happened. It was about 8:15 p.m. and a light appeared above the field. Travis said, "It was about ten times brighter than a star. As we drove closer, we began to see different colored lights on the edge. They were red, yellow, blue and white. They flashed at random, not sequentially."

Within three-quarters of a mile from the object, Julie became frightened and asked to go home. The object rose higher in the sky and followed them.

"We were doing about 80 mph," said Travis, "and by the time we reached town, it had gone past us!"

After dropping Julie off at her house, Travis picked up his father and went back to the field where they saw the light again over the pasture. Robert Jacobs said he could clearly see the different colors flashing on the object. They tried to approach it in the pickup, but the light moved away and disappeared. In a few minutes, the light reappeared moving to the southeast and disappeared again.

On March 3, 1992, back in Okemah, Oklahoma, after midnight, three men saw a grey, diamond-shaped object with "windows" land and then take off. They estimated the diameter to be over thirty feet. A week after that, a cow was found with its udder cleanly and bloodlessly excised from the belly. There was also a large hole on the cow's left side. "Like a bullet hole," one investigator said, but there was no exit hole and no bullet. There was also blood on the ground near the cow's head, which is not typical in the mysterious mutilation phenomenon.

On March 4, Benton County Sheriff Danny Varner went to meet Bill Cowger at Tyson's Hog Farms near Hiwasse, Arkansas. An 8-year-old cow was lying on her right side. Her left eye was missing, the tongue had been removed and a large piece of hide measuring 20 by 30 inches had been excised between the cow's back legs, taking the udder with it. The cut was only hide-deep. The muscle tissue underneath was untouched. (Plates 111-113)

Plate 111 - Cow's missing left eye, March 4, 1992, Benton County, Arkansas. Photographs by Deputy Sheriff Danny Varner.

Plate 112 - Benton County, Arkansas cow from which tongue had been removed deep within the throat in clean, vertical cut, March 4, 1992.

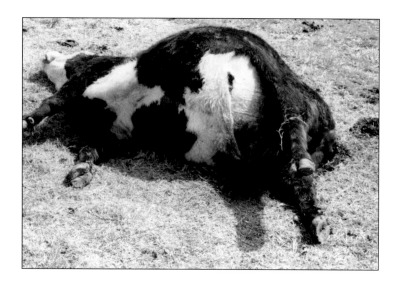

Plate 113 -
*Udder removed
in large oval
cut, hide-deep
and bloodless,
March 4, 1992,
Benton County,
Arkansas.*

Sgt. Varner wrote in his investigation report: "I found the cow's tongue had been removed by someone (using) a very sharp instrument. The tongue was cut diagonally from side to side, approximately 6 to 8 inches from the cow's front teeth. The cow's left eye had been removed. The cow's udder and hide were removed by a very sharp instrument, no damage was done to the stomach wall and the cuts looked to be that of a surgeon."

In February to March 1992, eleven mutilated cows were reported in Webster County, Missouri, east of Springfield. (Plate 114) At the same time in Northview, people were seeing strange lights. The Highway Patrol said so many people were parking along the I-44 Northview exit to look for UFOs, it was a safety hazard.

Tissues from several mutilations were sent to Dr. Altshuler. He found evidence of high heat at the excision lines and a hardened, "plasticized" edge which is not consistent with typical laser surgery. Furthermore, a portable laser powerful enough to cut cowhide requires an electrical generator the size of a large freezer.

"If you could afford such a laser, why would you lug it out to a field in the middle of the night where a farmer might take a shot at you for messing with his cows? Why not just buy your own cow?" Duane Bedell asked. He is Co-Director of the MUFON chapter in Webster County. "And how are the cows killed without a struggle and no tracks and no blood?"

One farmer, Joe Bouldin, said his cow's throat was slit, the esophagus removed and the teats neatly sliced off the udder. "But there were no marks on the ground anywhere. It's real mysterious," Bouldin said. A necropsy revealed most of the blood had been drained from the cow. But the ground was dry.

"How do you drain a cow of blood without spilling any?" Bouldin asked. "I've never carried a gun before in my life," Bouldin said, "but now we are carrying a loaded gun in our truck. That's about how I feel about all this."

Another troubled farmer was Edwina Ragsdale. She said, "It's just like the cows were embalmed. We went out there last week (February 1992) and there was a faint smell of decay, but they should have been deteriorated by now."

Plate 114 - News-Leader, *Wednesday, April 8, 1992, Springfield, Missouri.*

Odd cattle deaths intrigue Webster County residents

Chris Bentley

Joe Bouldin doesn't believe in UFOs. And he doesn't give much credence to talk of Satanic cults.

But something mysterious killed and mutilated one of his cows three weeks ago on his farm south of Northfield.

And the two suspects at the top of the rumor mill in Webster County are UFOs and cults.

Bouldin's cow apparently died with no sign of a struggle. Then its throat was slit, its esophagus was removed and its teets were sliced off at the udder. Oddest of all: its blood was gone. And there were no tracks near the body.

Other animals would not go near the dead cow. It has not decayed as quickly as animals usually do, says Bouldin, 54.

"It's real mysterious," he says.

His is one of 11 cows that have been mutilated in Webster County over the past two months. The Webster County Sheriff's Department and the Missouri State Highway Patrol are investigating.

Sheriff Bill John said last week he believes the mutilations are part of cult activity he thinks exists in the area.

The Highway Patrol doesn't ascribe to any particular theory, spokesman Sgt. Terry Moore says.

There is a third group investigating the mutilations, too. It's the Mutual UFO Network Inc., the largest international organization dedicated to researching evidence of UFOs.

Many of the Webster County mutilations match classic cases that have occurred all over the world in the vicinity of sightings of mysterious lights in the sky, MUFON members say.

Of course, people have been seeing strange lights in the sky over Northview

since late last year. So many people park along the I-44 exit to Northview to look for UFOs that the Highway Patrol says they are sometimes a safety hazard.

None of the investigating agencies will release names of farmers whose cows have been killed. That would violate the farmers' privacy, they say.

But in addition to Bouldin's cow, two cows died mysteriously in February on the farm of Phillip and Edwina Ragsdale just east of Marshfield.

One died with no sign of a struggle, and two patches of skin were cut from its stomach. The other died after an apparent struggle and was not mutilated at all.

Predators and scavengers like coyotes and possums in the area did not touch the bodies, either. The bodies also did not decompose as quickly as normal.

"It's just like they were embalmed,"

says Edwina Ragsdale. "We went out there last week and there was finally starting to be some flies on them. There was a faint smell of decay, but they should have been deteriorated by now."

She won't offer a theory.

"UFOs or cults — they both scare me to death," she says.

Bouldin says he doesn't much like either theory, but he's leaning toward the cult, "just because I don't believe in UFOs," he says.

He admits, though, the cult explanation leaves questions unanswered.

For instance:

■ How were the wounds made? They were straight and precise, with dark

Story concludes on Page 8D
(Expert says conventional weapon couldn't have caused cattle deaths.)

8D Wednesday, April 8, 1992

FROM PAGE 1D

▶ Mystery/Webster Countians ponder strange cattle deaths

edges that apparently had not bled.

Local investigators for MUFON took tissue from nine of the slain cows in Webster County, including Bouldin's and Ragsdale's. They sent them the samples Dr. Robert Altshuler, a pathologist in Colorado.

Altshuler's conclusion: The wounds were made by a precise high-heat instrument like a surgical laser beam.

But because of differences in carbon readings and the polarity of cells near the wounds, he told local MUFON members a conventional laser wasn't involved.

"Basically, he said there is no known technology that could produce these wounds," says Duane Bedell, co-director of the MUFON chapter in Greene, Christian, Webster and Polk Counties.

Bedell points out that the smallest surgical laser is the size of a refrigerator and costs thousands of dollars.

"If you can afford one, why would you lug it out to a field in the middle of the night where a farmer might take a shot at you for messing with his cows? Why not just buy your own cow?" he says.

John Nolen, an investigator for the Webster County Sheriff's Department who checked out Bouldin's cow, says it looked like it could have been cut by a sharp hunting knife.

He also says he's heard of cases where coyotes or other predators

slashed a cow's throat with their teeth as cleanly as if it was cut with a knife.

But Bouldin said MUFON investigators used knives to cut away the wounds for tissue samples. Comparing their cuts to the wounds convinced him the wounds weren't made by a knife, he said.

■ How was his cow killed without a struggle?

"Even if you shoot a cow in the head, it'll kick," Bouldin says. "There wasn't even a blade of grass broken near this one."

Nolen says the lack of struggle doesn't mean anything, though.

"Some will struggle, some won't," he says.

The Highway Patrol took blood samples from Bouldin's cow and others to check for tranquilizers or other drugs that could have made a cow drop in its tracks.

The state crime lab should send back results in a month or two, Sgt. Moore says.

■ Why were there no tracks near the cow's body?

Bouldin says the field was covered with manure from about 100 cows he kept there.

But he, Nolen and Bedell agree there were no tracks — from people, predators or vehicles — near the dead cow. Ragsdale says there were no tracks near her cows, either.

The night Bouldin's cow died, March 10, temperatures dropped to about freezing, National Weather

Service records show.

The ground could have frozen for an hour or two before dawn, so tracks wouldn't show up.

Nolen checked the area carefully for other clues and says he did not find any signs of trespassers in the area. A fence nearby didn't have any drops of blood or scraps of cloth on it, he says.

■ Where did the cow's blood go?

Bouldin says there was only about a quart of blood left in the cow. Ordinarily a cow has about six gallons of blood, he says.

But the ground was not soaked with blood.

"How do you drain a cow of blood without spilling any?" he asks.

Bedell says the disappearance of blood is one of the classic signs of mutilations associated with UFO sightings.

As for Bouldin, he still doesn't believe in UFOs. But he knows one thing: His family is scared.

"Let's put it this way. I've never carried a gun before in my life, in my truck. But now we are carrying a loaded gun in our truck. That's about how I feel about it," he says.

Chris Bentley is a News-Leader reporter.

Cattle Mutilations

13 65 125 **MARSHFIELD** 44 **Northview** **Springfield** 60

In the past two months, eleven cows have been found killed and mutilated on farms in this area of Webster County. Authorities are searching for clues. Rumors credit either UFOs or Satanic cult activity for the slayings.

SOURCE: News-Leader research   The News-Leader

When asked what she thought was responsible, she said, "UFOs or cults — and they both scare me to death."

I have also seen an "embalmed" animal. In May 1980, when I was producing the TV documentary *A Strange Harvest*, a Colorado Springs rancher found one of his horses dead and mutilated. As often happens, mutilations aren't reported for several days. In this case, the crew and I filmed about twenty days after the horse was first found dead. The weather had been warm, but there still were no maggots. When we cut into the horse's flanks to take tissue samples, the muscle was bright red. I asked a local veterinarian if that were normal. He said there should have been tissue deterioration.

By April 1992, mutilations were reported in Liberty, Mississippi, and Leduc, Alberta, Canada. In Liberty, two cows had been found with half the face hide removed and tongues cut out. Then a 3-day-old calf was found with its head and hind feet missing, all bloodless and trackless. Two more cows in Liberty were found dead and mutilated by the end of the summer.

In Canada, ranchers Dorthea and Roman Verchomin of Leduc, Alberta, discovered six mutilated cows between April 14 and July 16, 1992. All six of the cows were found lying on their right side. The chronological list is: 1) April 14, 1992, 20-year-old Holstein milk cow; 2) June 14, 1992, 250-pound Charolais Hereford calf; 3) June 21, 1992, 250-pound Hereford heifer calf; 4) June 24, 1992, 250-pound Hereford heifer calf; 5) June 28, 1992, 800-pound Hereford milk cow; 6) July 16, 1992, 800-pound Hereford milk cow.

The two-year-old milk cow found July 16th had its rectum cored out and one teat cleanly removed from the udder, "like it was burned off," Mrs. Verchomin told me. Part of the tongue and several teeth were gone. On the left side of its neck was a 4-inch slit with a 1-inch-wide and 2-inch-deep hole in the middle of it. No necropsy was done, but I couldn't help wondering if sections of trachea and esophagus were also removed as in the Crossville, Alabama calf and the cow in Red Cloud, Nebraska?

"I have never seen cuts like those that were on that cow," Mrs. Verchomin said in a phone call. "I followed the cuts with my finger. They were harder than the hide and every two inches there was a slight rise like a scalloped edge. The rest of the cows became very upset when they found her. Their eyes rolled around and they bellowed and stampeded."

Mrs. Verchomin is convinced after years of farming that no predator could cut cows that way.

"Coyotes don't even come onto our property," she said, "and they haven't bothered the herd in the past."

Tissue samples from the mutilator's excisions were sent to Dr. Altshuler. He confirmed a darkened and plasticized edge and under the microscope the cells revealed exposure to high heat.

England 1992 -1993

Strange animal deaths were reported to me in both 1992 and 1993 while I was in England. In August of 1992, I visited Roger Harley and his wife at their East Kennett farm near Alton Barnes. We drove to a hillside pasture where fifteen sheep and two cows died one by one over a two week period in May. (Plate 115)

Plate 115 -

Roger Harley at the hillside location on his farm in East Kennett, Englandwhere fifteen sheep and two cows mysteriously died one by one over a two week period in May 1992.

Photograph by author.

The animals were not cut. Roger Harley said his father was the veterinarian who examined some of the animals, but did not autopsy any of them. His father's conclusion upon visual inspection without necropsies was, "Probably massive heart attacks." As improbable as that seems, if true – why?

In the summer of 1991 near the same pasture, a dumbbell formation was found in wheat. The Harleys walked to see it with their Australian sheep dogs that stay close wherever they go. But the dogs would not follow them into the formation. They whined and stayed outside the flattened plants. The couple said they had never seen the dogs do that before and asked me, "What do the dogs sense that we don't?"

Law enforcement investigators in Idaho and Colorado tell stories of tracking bears, wolves, or coyotes up to about twelve feet from a dead and mutilated cow. Normally such large predators would have devoured the carcass, but the tracks stopped and formed a frenzied circle without ever going to the body. What do both predators and dogs sense that we do not?

On August 16, 1993, I drove beyond Ringwood, England, an hour south of Wiltshire, to meet newspaper reporter David Haith, who works at *The Advertiser* in Poole, Dorset. George Wingfield had talked with Mr. Haith about the horse slashings in Hampshire and about my research of the mutilation mystery. Mr. Haith was doing his own research in southern England and had learned about three calf mutilations, all in one week in early July.

We met and drove together out to a farm owned by Carol and Brian Cherrett of Motcombe near Shaftesbury. Six weeks before, the couple had found two of their four-month-old calves dead and mutilated in the same pasture about three hundred yards from the Cherrett's home. (Plate 116) The first was female; the second male.

Plate 116 - *Brian Cherrett pointing to pasture site near his Motcombe, England home where mutilated calves were found the first week of July 1993, and the rest of his herd "went mad" afterward. Photograph by author.*

"One ear had been slashed off (each) and the tail area had been completely cut around like you cut out an apple core," said Mrs. Cherrett, who discovered the first one.

"How was the ear cut?" I asked.

"In a diamond or oval shape," Mr. Cherrett said, "and it was really a clean cut on both calves."

Mr. Cherrett discovered the second one two days later. He said, "There was a cut where its testicles would have been and another on the inside of its leg. The tail and ear were missing. And that rectum was cored out, too, clean as can be. There's no doubt it was deliberate. I would just like to get my hands on whoever did it." (Plate 117)

Plate 117 - *Male calf mutilated like other male and female calves in Motcombe, Dorset, England, the first week of July 1993. All three had tails removed. Photograph by Brian Cherrett.*

The Cherretts were also puzzled about how the ears they had tagged for life were gone, but the identification tags were on the ground.

"The ear was gone, but the ear tag was there next to each animal. When you put those tags in, they are locked metal. There is no way you can pull them away. You'd have to take ear tissue with the tags, but there was no blood, skin or nothin' on either of the tags." (Plate 118)

I told the Cherretts that in the early 1980s, I received an ear tag in the mail from a rancher in South Dakota who was also confused about how the tagged ear was taken from his cow in a mutilation, but not the tag.

Plate 118 - *Metal identification tag that had been punched in excised ear and was found on ground next to mutilated steer calf at the Cherrett farm in Motcombe, England, the first of July 1993. Photograph by author.*

"Did you notice anything unusual about the rest of the herd?" I wondered, thinking of the unusual behavior of cows around mutilation sites in the past.

"Two days after we found the second one," said Mr. Cherrett, "something happened and they all started to go mad. We were in a nearby field turning hay. We heard terrible bellowing, the sound cows make in a slaughter house just before they die. We could see half a dozen cows standing in a circle with their heads toward each other, all making a terrible noise. Then all the rest of the cattle in the field (about forty) charged towards them. So, I jumped off the tractor, went over the fence and ran toward the cows, but I couldn't see nothin'. Then all of a sudden all the cows were charging toward me. So, I turned and ran and jumped up on my tractor."

"Have you ever seen six cows come together in a circle with their heads down bellowing?" I asked Mr. Cherrett, knowing he had farmed for almost thirty years.

"No. Nothin' like that has ever happened before or since."

Like the Green Forest, Arkansas case in 1991 (Pages 179-180), a veterinarian in the Dorset town of Gillingham attributed the death and missing tissue to black leg and predators. That vet examined the steer at the request of the Gillingham police. Mr. Cherrett did not know if any tissue analysis or other tests had been done. He had not received a written report from either the police or the veterinarian.

"That calf did *not* die from black leg," he told me with the same irritation I have heard from other farmers who don't like illogical explanations for animal deaths that puzzle them, especially when they have experience with natural animal disease, death, and predators.

In England, dead cows are stripped of hide and the meat is fed to fox hunting hounds. Mr. Cherrett said he tracked the skinned hide to one of the Hunt clubs and discovered two small puncture marks about half an inch wide "just under the front leg." Puncture marks resembling biopsy plugs have been found on mutilated animals over the decades. In one Colorado case, the in vestigating sheriff probed a stick in a quarter-inch-wide by one- inch-deep hole in a mutilated cow's shoulder. He told me at the site there was no evidence of a bullet. Yet, the next morning's newspaper said the cow had been shot.

On Sunday morning, July 4, 1993, Gordon Wing and Charlie Riggs, who run Forest Lodge Farms at Motcombe, found two more dead calves. "One had been sick with pneumonia, but the other had been perfectly fit," said Mr. Wing. "It was stretched out on the grass with its neck and ears cut out" like the Cherretts' calves.

The ear tag on Mr. Wing's calf had also been removed from the missing ear and was on the ground.

"We are afraid that what has been happening elsewhere to horses may now be happening to our calves." Mr. Wing was referring to the more than two dozen reported "horse slashings" in England, (Plate 119) another dozen in Germany and about two hundred horse attacks reported to police in western Sweden. Those were described by *Fortean Times* in its August 1992 issue as "cut with a sharp, scalpel-like instrument, in or beside their sexual organs. The wounds were often thirty centimeters long and five or six centimeters deep. About half the animals were so severely maimed that they had to be put down.

Plate 119 - *Front page,* Leicester Mercury, *August 13, 1993, Leicester, England.*

Thugs launch callous attack on pet horse

A DISTRAUGHT horse owner today branded vandals "callous thugs" after they savagely attacked her family's much-loved pet.

Leicester mother-of-seven Mrs Paula Calver discovered her four-year-old mare Goggin had been brutally attacked and injured early yesterday morning.

Her daughter Hannah is pictured comforting the shocked horse.

The mare, which gave birth to a foal just 12 weeks ago, was found in her field at Groby with six deep wounds on her neck wounds Mrs Calver

described as 'puncture marks'.

In addition an eight-year-old gelding also owned by Mrs Calver's family suffered a blow to his nose.

"We found both the horses in a very distressed state when we went to feed them yesterday morning," said Mrs Calver who lives on Leicester's Mowmacre estate. "It was a mindless and brutal attack."

Mrs Calver and her husband Gary called a vet out to the injured horses.

The couple, who have seven daughters aged between three and 12 years, have only owned the mare and gelding for four months.

As mutilation reports have accumulated in my files since 1979, I remember the Air Force intelligence officer at Kirtland AFB in Albuquerque who told me in 1983:

"That documentary you did (*A Strange Harvest*) upset some people in Washington. They don't want UFOs and animal mutilations connected in the public's mind," implying to me that was a truth the government was hiding.

After my book *An Alien Harvest* was released in June 1989, I received a letter from a security guard in Denver, Colorado. He described a night in August when he was patrolling the grounds of a large corporation west of the city. From his truck, he could see a large circle of lights in the dark sky. The lights remained stationary over a pasture a few hundred feet from where the guard watched. He never phoned anyone because he was afraid if he uttered the word "UFO" he might lose his job. But the next morning, he felt guilty as he watched a farmer gather up two dead and mutilated cows from the pasture where the lights had hovered overhead. He asked me, "What kind of technology are we talking about? I never took my eyes off those lights. There was no beam, no sound, nothing. How did they do it?"

Not only how, but who — or what — is killing and mutilating these animals — and why?

My first effort to introduce the animal mutilation phenomena to national television was in *UFO Report: Sightings* on Fox, first broadcast October 18, 1991. That night, I was out of town speaking at a conference and an unidentified man left a message on my phone answering machine. He said:

> "I think the information you presented was good, but you are off the track on a few things.
>
> (Bob Lazar)[13] mentioned that the aliens were hundreds of years ahead in technology. Actually, it would be more like thousands of years.
>
> The ships don't have windows as we know windows to be. The craft are smooth and metallic colored.
>
> They have no intention of hurting anyone.
>
> There will be increased sightings, very, very increased sightings in the future.
>
> The blood from the animals that you were talking about is not being used to make things compatible with people, as it is being developed for, shall we say, to save the animals against radiation poisoning.
>
> The government does not have ships in working order, but does have the remains of some. There was a survivor (alien), but I don't know if that person is still living.
>
> The truth of the matter is that if the reason for their visiting the planet were revealed, the public could not handle it."

[13] *A scientist who had first worked at Los Alamos Laboratory in the mid-1980s and later, from December 1988 to March 1989, was allegedly hired through EG&G in Las Vegas and Office of Naval Intelligence to study a silver disk "not from this earth" hidden in an engineering bay inside the Papoose Mountain range at Nellis AFB, Nevada.*

What is it that the public cannot handle that has perpetuated an apparent government policy of silence?

Is there one major intelligence behind all these events? Or are there competing species from Somewhere else out there — maybe even species in conflict?

Some researchers are convinced that humanity is property, that we belong to Something else that experiments with and tests us like lab animals, communicating with and controlling us by various frequencies of light and sound. The implication is that the chronic harvest of genetic material from Earth life, both humans and animals, is related to an alien experiment dating back to mankind's origins that might involve the aliens' survival, as well as our own.

In the next chapter, some possible insights into these questions emerge from the alleged physical encounters, memories and strange dreams of people who feel they have encountered one or more alien life forms that interact with life on our planet.

Plate 1 - *Artist's sketch based on the eyewitness account of Ron and Paula Watson of Mt. Vernon, Missouri, who described their daylight sighting through binoculars. Two small, silver-suited beings stood over a black cow near their farm house on a July morning in 1983. The Watsons said "a Lizard Guy and a Bigfoot" stood on either side of a cone-shaped object that had a mirrored surface. "The trees, grass and sky reflected in a perfect camouflage," Ron said. The beings "floated" the black cow into the cone-shaped object and disappeared. The owner confirmed his black cow was missing and never returned.*

FACT

Since the 1960s, hundreds of people have complained of missing time events, often associated with unidentified bright lights, in which minutes to hours are inexplicably lost from a person's life. The phenomenon has come to be known as the "UFO abduction syndrome."

FACT

A 1992 Roper survey about "Unusual Personal Experiences" of people in the United States suggested to some analysts that perhaps 2% of the population has experienced the UFO abduction syndrome.

FACT

"Anomalous trauma victim" is a phrase sometimes used by psychiatrists, psychologists and other mental health professionals to describe patients who report experiences with odd lights and missing time. Often people report disturbing memories of non-human beings that perform physical examinations and extract human tissue, fluid, sperm or ova.

FACT

Non-human entities seen in broad daylight have been reported in the United States by a Waco, Texas rancher; a farm couple in Missouri; a mother and son in New Mexico; a boy in Georgia; and in many other countries.

FACT

Animals, alive or dead, are sometimes reported by anomalous trauma victims who either see animals in "glass cages" as if on exhibit, or see them hooked up to tubes and wires as if being tested, or see the same excised body parts that have been reported missing in worldwide animal mutilations.

CHAPTER 3

HUMAN ABDUCTIONS
AND EYEWITNESSES

"The Roper Survey conducted between July and September 1991, suggests that hundreds of thousands, if not millions, of American men, women and children may have experienced UFO abductions, or abduction-related phenomena."

JOHN E. MACK, M.D.
PROFESSOR OF PSYCHIATRY
HARVARD MEDICAL SCHOOL

Since the 1960s, the same decade that animal mutilations were first reported in the media, another strange phenomenon has emerged: the UFO abduction syndrome. It touched general public consciousness when *Look Magazine* and writer John Fuller disclosed the Betty and Barney Hill case.[1] Psychiatrist Benjamin Simon, M.D., used hypnosis to penetrate the amnesia that both husband and wife experienced on September 19, 1961. The Hills had been on vacation and were driving back in the late evening through the White Mountains to their home in Portsmouth, New Hampshire. Betty noticed a light in the sky that was big, bright and moving. As the light moved toward them, Barney Hill stopped the car and got out. Fuller wrote, "The huge object — as wide in diameter as the distance between three telephone poles along the road, Barney later described it — swung in a silent arc directly across the road, not more than a hundred feet from him. The double row of windows was now clear and obvious."

The rest of John Fuller's book details the trauma that the couple experienced: amnesia, physical body marks, headaches, repeated nightmares, anxieties and separate hypnosis sessions with Dr. Simon. In six months of hypnosis from January to June 1964, Betty and Barney Hill independently recounted their experiences with non-human beings that took them from the car aboard the round craft and subjected each to physical examinations

[1] *Look Magazine,* October 18, 1966, excerpt from The *Interrupted Journey* by John Fuller © 1966, Berkeley Publishing, N.Y.

2 *"Unusual Personal Experiences - An Analysis of the Data from Three National Surveys,"* Conducted by the Roper Organization © 1992 Bigelow Holding Corporation, Las Vegas, Nevada.

and extractions of tissue and fluids. Although "shared dreams" was suggested as a possible explanation, the psychiatrist's formal diagnosis was "emotional disturbance created by an experience with an Unidentified Flying Object."

Thirty years later in July to September 1991, a Roper survey[2] concerning "unusual personal experiences," was conducted. John Mack, M.D., Professor of Psychiatry at Harvard University and investigator of anomalous trauma in the UFO abduction syndrome, said the survey "suggests that hundreds of thousands, if not millions, of American men, women and children may have experienced UFO abductions, or abduction related-phenomena." Anomalous trauma refers to the shock that many people report after an alleged encounter with non-human beings in which the person describes, either consciously or under hypnosis, a "medical exam" by alien life forms. That exam, as reported, often involves the removal of tissue, fluids, ova or sperm from the human abductee.

Dr. Mack appealed to mental health professionals who have "maintained an arms length attitude toward this phenomenon" to become familiar with the abduction syndrome, which he broke down into four categories: "1) The physically and emotionally intrusive abduction phenomena themselves, which may have recurred repeatedly during the lifetime of a particular abductee; 2) The personal isolation the experiencer has undergone, reinforced whenever their communications are misunderstood or treated as a form of strangeness or evidence of mental illness; 3) The shattering of socially agreed upon or consensus definitions of reality, which abductions bring about and that abductees, like ourselves, must undergo in their confrontation with this phenomenon; 4) The fact that the trauma, whatever its source, is not over; i.e., abductees cannot prevent its recurrence or protect their children and other loved ones from its effects."

In addition to their own physical examinations by alien beings, some abductees have also reported seeing Earth animals in glass cages as if on display, or hooked up to tubes and machines as if being tested, or even have watched excisions of the same body parts found missing in the worldwide animal mutilation phenomenon.

One such case began in May 1973. A family of five from a suburb outside Houston, Texas, traveled together in a car to go play bingo. It was a clear night and on the way back home, Judy Doraty noticed a bright, blue-white light pacing the car. She pointed it out to her brother-in-law, her sister, her teenage daughter, Cindy, and her mother. Eventually, they stopped the car by the side of the road in farmland outside the city to watch the light more carefully. Judy got out of the car. Then she remembered getting back into the car feeling nauseous and very thirsty.

When the family finally reached another relative's home, the time was later than expected. To the group's amazement, the light appeared there, too, and came down low over a nearby field showing what appeared to be a row of lighted windows in a round object. Judy began screaming at all the children and her daughter, afraid they were going to run toward the open pasture where the object seemed to be headed as if to land. Even then, she was surprised at her reaction, not understanding her hysterical fear. Suddenly, the disk rose and "shot up to sit next to the moon like a star," Judy and Cindy said later.

After that night, Judy suffered terrible headaches and vivid dreams that panicked her. Finally, she sought medical help in 1978. That led to hypnosis with a medical doctor to relieve her blocked memory about that disturbing night. In the first session, Judy described seeing a small animal rising in a pale yellow beam of light into the sky.

Judy and the doctor contacted individuals and groups trying to learn more about unexplained lights. They shared the hypnosis tape with the Aerial Phenomenon Research Organization (APRO) in Arizona. In 1979, when I began producing the documentary film *A Strange Harvest*[3] about the animal mutilation mystery, Jim Lorenzen at APRO contacted me because an animal was involved. He sent me the audiocassette and as I played the tape in my office at Channel 7 (CBS) in Denver, Colorado, I felt intuitively there was truth in her description of the beam of light lifting the animal. An advanced technology that could lift heavy animals, even 1800-pound bulls in a beam of light, could explain the lack of tracks and other evidence which has haunted law enforcement for decades.

When I first reached Judy by phone, she still had severe anxiety about the 1973 incident. There was even anguish in her voice when she told me she could not remember much more than what was on the tape. At the time, I did not discuss the animal mutilation subject of my documentary because I did not want to alarm her further. I simply said I hoped we could learn more about the animal in the beam of light.

In addition to the light, Judy Doraty had remembered a strange face which she had drawn and APRO had sent to Dr. Leo Sprinkle, a psychologist who was then Director of Counseling and Testing at the University of Wyoming in Laramie. Dr. Sprinkle had investigated the UFO human abduction syndrome since the late 1960s, was an APRO consultant and had helped dozens of traumatized people. He had also worked with me on a case in Wyoming in which a rancher and cousin watched a 300-foot-long, orange glowing craft hover above his cattle. That rancher had two mutilations, a missing cow, and apparent abduction experiences with missing time which Dr. Sprinkle had helped him explore and better understand.

[3] *A Strange Harvest* Emmy award-winning documentary film by Linda Moulton Howe © 1980 and 1988, McGraw-Hill and LMH Productions.

Leo Sprinkle is an honest man who has tried all his life to help other people and I trusted him.

It took two months to convince Judy Doraty that she could trust both of us to protect her identity. (Judy Doraty is not her married name.) Arrangements were made to fly Dr. Sprinkle and my cameraman with me to a southwest location to meet Judy. In that four hour hypnosis session conducted March 13, 1980, before our camera,[4] she finally recalled the May 1973 evening in greater detail. Not only did she see a brown and white calf rise in a pale yellow beam of light, but she watched two "little men" (Plate 2) excise tissue from the calf's eyeball, tongue and testicles and then lower the calf back down in a beam of light onto the pasture, dead and mutilated.

[4] Complete hypnosis transcript included in Appendix of *An Alien Harvest* ©1989 by Linda Moulton Howe, LMH Prods.

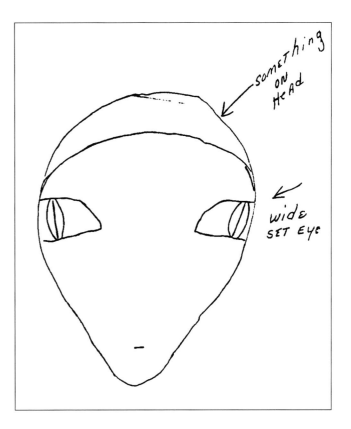

Plate 2 - *Sketch by Judith Doraty received September 24, 1979, by psychologist Dr. Leo Sprinkle after her first hypnosis session with a medical doctor. In 1980, Dr. Sprinkle, then Director of Counseling and Testing at the University of Wyoming, did a second hypnosis session in which Judy remembered "two little men" who excised tissue from a calf's eye, tongue and testicles.*

Judy had the impression that it was important for the calf to be alive with its heart beating while the excisions were made.

In that hypnosis session, Judy also saw her daughter, Cindy, on a table surrounded by more strange alien beings who were putting instruments into Cindy's mouth. Judy Doraty was so upset at the sight that she began to pound the chair arm and came completely out of her trance state to yell, "No, I don't want to!" at Dr. Sprinkle, meaning she did not want to see what was happening to her daughter. Leo Sprinkle told me then he assumed both mother and daughter had been abducted together and Cindy's experience was equally important.

Afterward, I asked Judy if we could contact Cindy, who was then twenty-two and married, to see if she would also undergo hypnosis to explore more details about the 1973 experience. Two witnesses at a single abduction event provided an unusual and valuable opportunity to see how closely their experiences might match, or differ. But, Cindy was afraid, Judy was protective, and both mother and daughter resisted the suggestion.

However, ten years later in 1990, while I was working on projects at CNN and WATL in Atlanta, Judy called me. She said her daughter, then thirty-two and divorced, had moved back to Missouri where Judy was living and finally wanted to learn more about what happened in Texas in 1973.

Judy Doraty told me she had never shared her experiences with her daughter because she hoped that one day Cindy independently would be able to corroborate what happened. "After I was regressed in the 1978 and 1980 hypnosis sessions," Judy said, "more than anything else I wanted confirmation from someone else that I wasn't going crazy, that what I remembered was the truth. I went to great lengths to not talk to my daughter, Cindy, about those sessions or what happened. I even locked tapes and books up at my house so Cindy wouldn't see them. I figured that if she ever agreed to hypnosis herself and described any of the same things, that would prove to me that I saw what I know I saw. And without hearing anything about my story, when Cindy finally did do hypnosis with John Carpenter in 1990, she came up with the same things I had before. That meant a lot to me. I always wanted only the truth to be told about what happened and that people would believe me and not make fun."

After talking with both Judy and Cindy, I organized a videotape crew and traveled to Springfield to record Cindy's first hypnosis session which began on the evening of August 6, 1990. Conducting the session was John Carpenter, M.S.W., a psychiatric hypnotherapist who has worked in a major Springfield hospital for more than a decade.[5] Occasionally, he has used hypnosis in therapy sessions with other human traumas. He took an active interest in the UFO human abduction syndrome in 1988 and began applying his professional skills to recovering experiences from periods of amnesia or "missing time."

We all met Cindy for the first time that August night in a small office that John had arranged for his own private work time outside the hospital.

[5]B.A., Psychology, DePauw University, Greencastle, Indiana, May 1977; Masters in Social Work (M.S.W.), Washington University, St. Louis, May 1979; trained in clinical hypnosis at the Menninger Clinic, Topeka, Kansas, April 1980; Past member of the American Group Psychotherapy Assoc. and American Assoc. for Marriage and Family Therapy; earned the distinction of ACSW (Academy of Certified Social Workers) in 1983 and Diplomate in Clinical Social Work in 1993; is a Licensed Clinical Social Worker and psychiatric hypnotherapist in a Springfield, Missouri hospital.

Cindy was taller than I expected, about five feet seven. Her mother is about five feet one. Cindy's hair was short and a reddish-brown color that exactly matched her eyes. She was thin with a pretty face that was brightened by the gold dress she wore. John used a reclining chair upon which he placed a fuchsia-colored sleeping bag for Cindy's comfort. (Plate 3)

Plate 3 - *Cindy Tindle with John Carpenter, M.S.W., psychiatric therapist, and his assistant Carla Vincel, during Cindy's first hypnosis session, August 6, 1990, in Springfield, Missouri. Photograph by author.*

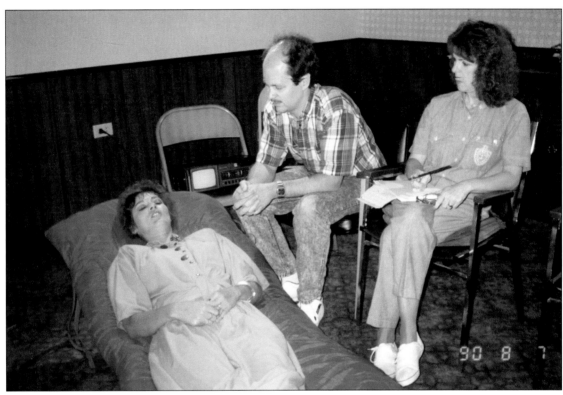

Before the session began, I talked with Cindy while she was having a cigarette. She was nervous, as most people are before trying hypnosis, and she was skeptical.

"I think my mom's full of it about all this light business, but I've got to prove it for myself. I don't think anything happened in Texas and it bugs the hell out of me that mom still talks about that stupid light. Even Jerry (her uncle) thought it was a helicopter!"

Cindy was so nervous that it took John Carpenter a long time to help her reach the deep relaxation in which hypnosis functions. The state of mind is not sleep, but more like daydreaming when a person is in deep internal concentration reliving an earlier event to solve a problem or plan a goal. In that state, sights, sounds, smells, tastes and tactile sensations of the relived event can be recalled.

▲

203

The following are excerpts from Cindy Tindle's first hypnosis session conducted by John Carpenter. Cindy's comments are in italics.

I just see this big ol' light right down in front of the car, coming down from out of the sky in front of the car. ... It's moving around. From left to right. It's like I'm sitting in the car and it's like a spotlight hitting the ground. And it's going in front of the car from left to right.

Did it ever touch the car, the light itself?

Oh, yeah, I think so.

Picture how that looked when that happened.

I think I'm still in the back seat. Everyone's getting the heck out of the car!

Fast?

Yeah, I think so.

What do you hear?

My mom hollering, "Oh, shit!" ... I don't know what Jerry is doing. I know I'm kind of scared because I was afraid it was going to crash into the car or something. I could tell by everyone's reaction that there is something wrong. But I don't know...

Did it change color at this point?

It's – no, it's still a blue-white light, bright, bright.

Move a little step forward in time.

Wow, I think I'm standing next to my mom outside. I said, "Hey, Mom, check that out!" But I don't know what it is. I don't know – it's like I'm holding her hand and walking up with her some place. But I don't know where it's at. It don't make sense. I don't remember getting out of the car.

Can you feel where people are?

I can see the spotlight out in the field now. I guess I must be out of the car on the passenger side. ... I'm just watching the light reflected on the ground, like it's looking for something.

There are several minutes in which Cindy is confused about how she got out of the car and walked with her mom across the field.

Can you look to your left and see the car over there?

Yeah, but it's far away. A lot further than what I thought. But I don't know how in the heck I got where I'm at. ... But I'm just looking at this light trying to shade my eyes. It's real bright ... and feels real warm on my skin.

Can you feel your feet on the ground in the field?

Yeah, it's kind of dry dirt and tumbleweedy-type stuff out there.

Can you remember walking through it?

Yeah, vaguely, but I don't know why I'm walking out there. I think I was holding on to my mom's arm, but I don't know where everyone else is. I don't know why we're there.

Just look at her for a moment, and tell me how she looks.

(Sudden breath and sound of fear in her voice.) Scary! She doesn't look right. I don't think it's my mom! I don't think – they're screwin' with my mind!

(Became very agitated and breathed hard.)

OH, THESE CHARACTERS ARE SCARY LOOKING! (Spoken loudly)

Tell me what you see.

How did they ever get me out there?!

Nice and slow, just stay like a camera, taking pictures with your mind and describe just the details. You don't have to know why.

But I thought it was my mom!

I know. They're scary-looking, you say?

It's my mom, but it's not my mom.

What makes it look different from your mom?

The way they act. It's just the way they are.

John Carpenter relaxed Cindy more deeply and asked her to freeze the moment in time so that she would not move forward too quickly and become emotionally overwhelmed.

Now you can safely and peacefully look around and see what's around you, and how many, as you scan 360 degrees, or as much as you can. And nothing is moving, everything is frozen in time like a snapshot. Let's see little by little what is there.

There's one leading me by the arm. And there's two more over there. He's got me by the arm. Like how I was holding my mom's arm, he's got one arm. It's like I'm being escorted, sort of.

Let's stop and take some mental pictures and describe what these things look like.

I can't see them. Just figures, I don't see no face. Just two bodies. ...

But are they like tall, six foot ...?

About as tall as I am.

How tall are you then (age 15)?

About as tall as I am (now about 5'7").

So you can look them right in the eye?

I don't know. I'm not that close. I'm just standing there. But the one who has me is shorter because I thought it was my mom.

How tall is your mom?

5'1" or 5'2".

Take a good look and see how the face looks different from your mom's.

It looks like it's got a wig on, like short, brown hair. I don't know. Oh, boy, it looks almost unreal. It looks almost buggy – like a bug!

What kind of bug?

Oh, Lord! It's got big eyes.

What color?

Black.

What color are the pupils?

I don't think they have any. I don't know. I can't really tell. They have slits for a mouth. And he's got hold of my arm.

Take another look and describe everything you see.

It's like a light coming down underneath this thing, ...

What color is that light?

That's like a yellow. ... Underneath that thing with the lights. ... Like it's searching for something. The spotlight is still looking. But there's another light (yellow) and that's where the two guys are.

When you look at those two guys, how do they seem to appear?

They're skinny. And they are standing with their legs spread apart.

They are not moving?

No, they are just standing there.

Keep your eyes on them and see now what kind of action takes place next.

I'm being led up to where they are at.

Move slowly and know I am with you this time and I will help. We'll go nice and slow... Are your feet walking on the ground step by step?

Yeah, I'm going with them.

And you see their feet moving on the ground as well?

They sort of walk real short, stubby steps.

Is it smooth?

No, not really. It's almost kind of <u>mechanically</u>. ... I'm taking one step for each of their two. It's almost like their ankles instead of moving with their legs as a stride, it's mostly moving from the knee down.

Like the upper legs don't move?

No, they move, but it's a choppy, it's almost like they walk mechanically, like leg, knee, ankle.

What does it remind you of?

Like a robot. But I don't think it's a robot. It's just the way they walk, I guess.

Are they barefooted?

No, I don't think so. They have that jump suit on.

Take a quick look at one of these, maybe the one that has your arm. And see which one that seems to be.

The one that's got me by the arm is the one that scared the heck out of me. It's got the <u>snake eyes</u>, but why he's wearing a brown wig, I don't know!

Let me know if you smell anything that goes along with this? Any particular odor or fragrance?

Moisture. There's a lot of moisture in the air. It's almost like I'm getting mist right on me.

Is someone doing that?

It's in the light, I think.

The light is hitting you now?

Yeah, I'm getting close to it and I can feel <u>moisture from the light</u>.[6]

Is it the big yellow light coming down from underneath?

[6] In a second hypnosis session, Cindy remembered understanding the moisture was a disinfectant. "It was killing. I guess they don't want to get germs from us. It's like a purifier."

Yes.

Stop for a second and look up and see where the yellow light comes from?

I'm not close enough to see it.

What is the search light doing? Does the search light find something?

Oh, my land! Yeah!

What did it find?

They're pulling up a cow! It's a baby calf. (Plate 4)

Hear, listen, what do you hear?

It's moving around, but I don't hear anything.

You can see the cow moving?

Yes. It acts like it's bawling, but you can't hear it.

How are they taking the calf?

It's just like I'm being led up there and those two guys are waiting on me and this other person. The spotlight is going to the right and the calf is going up on the left. Oh, this can't be feasible! This isn't right.

What?

They can't be doing this.

Why not?

Because, this just don't happen! ... It's a calf about half way up, up in the air. And it's in this light and it's moving around. It's trying to get away, trying to get out, it's scared. I guess it's afraid it's going to drop. Its feet are kicking. I could see its mouth. It acts like its crying, but I can't hear it. ... I'm watching it go up and I can almost see – it's like it gets up so high and then it's gone. Disappears.

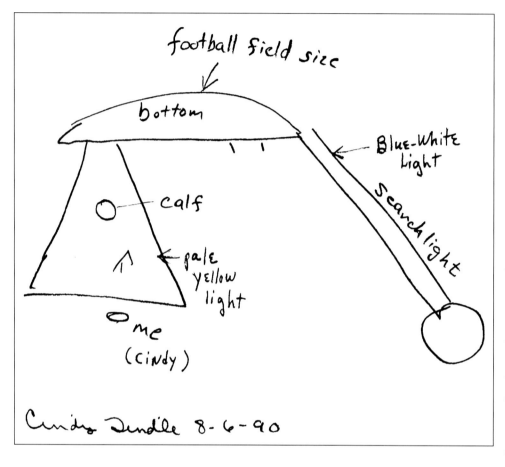

Plate 4 - *Cindy Tindle's drawing after the August 6, 1990 hypnosis session in which she recalled seeing a brown and white calf rise in a pale yellow beam of light into a disk-shaped object. Another blue-white spotlight searched the ground. May 1973 incident, Houston, Texas.*

After that, Cindy described suddenly finding herself surrounded by blackness, "like I'm in space, in a transition." Then she sees a room.

Everything is rounded, kind of. I don't know what this is. I've never seen anything like it. It's steel grey. Cold. Dingy or dark or shadowy light.

Do you smell anything?

It's kind of sweet, smelly air. I've never smelled it before.

You're looking around, what other shapes can you make out?

There's one of those — whatever they are!? He is looking down into a light. He looks like a bug!

Why?

He's got a head like a bug.

What shape?

It's real rounded with a pointed chin, like a cartoon bug character, is what they look like. Like an ant sort of. ... They're like sticks – built real skinny! (Plate 5)

Plate 5 - *Cindy Tindle's drawing of "stick" figure with "a head like a bug" that she saw looking into a lighted machine "like a TV screen." Drawn after August 6, 1990 hypnosis session.*

Do you see a hand?

No, not really, more like claws really. I don't know how they can hold up their heads? ... It's just – he is looking down into this light ... like a screen of light – almost like a TV-like thing.

What color?

A blue-white light. I'm sitting on this platform-type table, type thing. I don't know why I'm sitting there for. I'm staring at him because I'm trying to figure out what the heck is going on here.

What is he wearing?

I don't see any. He's just so skinny.

Is that what you meant by stick-like?

Yeah.

What color?

Grey , kind of a greyish color.

Dark, light, what kind of shade?

Metallic grey .

Shiny?

It's just dull, he's almost the same color as the interior. He's looking into this screen like he's – but I feel like there are two of them coming up on the side of me.

While you're on the table?

Yes. I can kind of see these two guys – I don't know who they are.

They look like all the others?

They all got basically the same kinds of heads.

What color hair?

I don't guess they have hair.

So, you're sitting on the table and the two are there. Follow the action like a movie camera and record the scene, telling me what you see.

They pushed me down, one of them did.

Did they do that roughly or gently?

They just walked up and pushed me on the chest area. And it was more or less like telling me that I needed to lay down. ... I wonder where I'm at? Where's my mom?

That's what I was wondering. There was a calf ...

I don't know where the calf is. I don't know where anything is. I'm just there.

Do you try to ask them anything? Do you try to communicate?

They've got me strapped down!

I thought you laid down willingly?

I tried kicking one of them.

You're still pissed off?

I was scared, I was scared! I don't know what they are doing to me.

When did you try to kick him? Describe the scene.

They're grabbin' at my hand. Three or four of them.

Can you see the hands now?

They look like mittens. (Plate 6)
This one looks different than the one looking in the screen.

Plate 6 - *Drawing of an alien hand that "looks like mittens" by Cindy Tindle after her August 6, 1990, hypnosis session.*

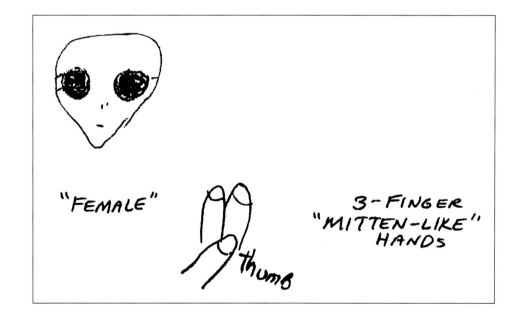

"FEMALE"

thumb

3-FINGER
"MITTEN-LIKE"
HANDS

What looks different?

These others aren't skinny like he is.

What do these look like?

They are short, got the same kind of face basically.

Take a good look at that face. What shape are the eyes?

They all got big eyes, all of them do. They still look like a bug.

Perfectly round eyes?

No, they're almond-shaped.

And they go back straight toward the ears?

I don't think they have ears.

But they do go straight back that direction?

They are bigger in front and slant toward the back on the side of the head.

Are there pupils?

No. Wait a minute, <u>they look like a snake!</u>

In what way?

The pupils – or like a cat's.

Any color?

They look like a snake's eye kind of, they've got the long pupil in them or something like that. Yeah, they look just like a snake or lizard or something. … He's standing by my knees and looking at me directly. (Plate 7)

From there?

Yes, that's how close he is. They're big (eyes.) He looks pissed.

Plate 7 - *"Snake-eyed" being that "glared" at Cindy and which she tried to kick while under examination on a table. Drawn after August 6, 1990, hypnosis session.*

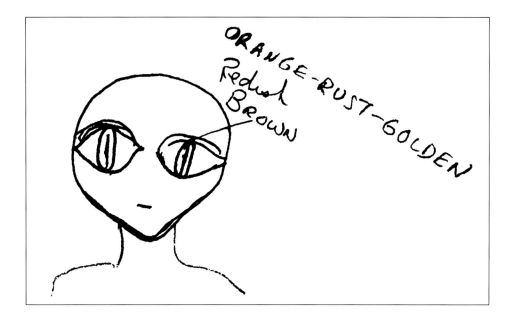

How can you tell?

Just by the look. He just doesn't have no emotion. He's unemotional. He's glaring at me. Staring, but I don't know why. ... They were trying to get me to lay still. And I kicked one of them. I'm kicking at them.

What is he doing that you want to kick him?

I don't know. I don't want to give him a chance to do anything. But he's... I'm screamin' "NO!" at them.

What happens?

Nothing.

Like they didn't hear you?

Yeah, they don't care.

What are they doing now?

He's pulling at my face for something. He's like trying to hold my face still. I thought he was going to try and kiss me, but I know he's not going to do that. But I don't want him to grab my face. I'm fighting them, I'm trying to get them off of me because I don't know what they are going to do to me!

▲

Let's see how your face felt at that moment, what kind of touch or feel came to you?

I think they are amazed at my teeth because I had braces. … They keep pushing my cheeks together – like… I don't know what they are doing. Like it hurts on the inside of my mouth. Pushing my mouth up against my braces and it's hurting.

Then what do they do?

I don't know, I'm trying to fight them off because I don't know what they are going to try to do to me.

Are you swinging at them with your arms?

Trying.

What happens when you try? Can you move your arms?

No.

How does it feel when they touch you anywhere, especially your face?

They're not rough. I think basically they aren't trying to hurt me. But I don't want them touching me because I don't know who they are and they are scary to me.

And you feel their touch on your face and it's not rough.

No, I think they just want to look at my teeth.

Do you see any particular things in their hands?

They put something on my forehead.

See if you can see it as it went toward your forehead. Get a glimpse.

It looked like the size of a quarter.

What was it?

A probe of some kind. I don't know what it is.

Made of cloth or cotton?

No, that metal stuff. It's like everything is made out of the same thing.

Is it skinny, fat?

It has like a long tubing on it, real skinny about the size of a cigarette, but longer and at the end it has a round disc about the size of a quarter.

Is it sharp or smooth?

No, it's dull, like a finished surface.

Touch your head with your hand where you felt it touch you. (She motions to the center of her forehead)

And when it touches you, how does it feel?

I feel like I go out. Relaxed or out. Almost like a sedative thing. ... And they are pressing on my stomach. But I've got my panties on.

Where do they touch you on your stomach? Move your hand to that pressure?

(And she moves her hand near right hip) *By my hip bones. And up here by my belly button. Because there are three of them, those little guys. ... This one blinks. It blinked at me.*

Does the blink go from side to side? Or top to bottom?

It goes straight down and up.

All the way from the top to bottom and then all the way back up?

Yeah, almost mechanically.

When it's all the way down, is that when the cat eye looks black?

No, when it's up, it's black. When it closes, it's almost the same color as the skin, a 'shroomy-looking (mushroom) yucky color, it's almost like – their skin don't even look normal. It looks fleshy, but I don't know if it is or not. Because they don't act real.

So it's black when it's open and skin colored when it's closed.

Yeah, kind of a brownish-beige color.

When does it look like a snake eye?

That was the other one... the one down by my feet.

The one that was glaring at you?

Yeah.

Was there anything different about that one, the snake eyes?

He just looks mean, cold.

What is he wearing?

It looks like a jump suit.

Is there any kind of marking on it?

Just a rounded neck.

And it's plain all over?

Dingy grey.

Does anyone have any decoration on what they have?

Not that I can tell. This one up here (Plate 8) *and the one down by my knees and feet, they're two different, completely different. But they both have the same shaped heads.*

Describe that shape again.

It's real big at the top and kind of goes to a point at the bottom.

They all have the same shaped heads? And you see some differences?

Yeah, definitely.

And those are?

The eyes, this one is soft, it may have feeling and emotion.

Which one is that now?

The one standing up here toward me, toward my arm.

Plate 8 - *Cindy Tindle's drawing of a being with "soft eyes, it may have feeling and emotion," that she felt was quite different than the snake-eyed being that glared at her.*

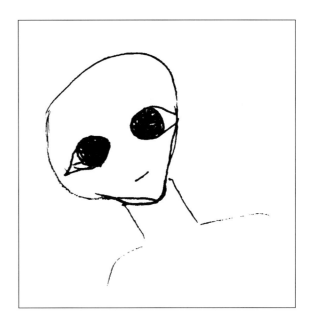

You felt pressure around your belly button and abdomen. Pick one and tell me what happened.

Nothing that I know of except they are poking on me. ... I guess they have mittens on? I felt them going up my arm like this and it's almost like this one is still standing here, I don't know what it's doing. One is moving up my arm.

When you feel that kind of touch, is it gentle?

Yeah, but it's quick. They know what they are looking for, but I guess I don't have it. I don't know how to explain it. They know what they are doing, I guess. ... I think they're amazed with my braces. They got this real long thing. I don't know what it is.

What does it remind you of?

A sewing machine foot. It's shaped like the letter "L" but it's real long, probably about 4 or 5 inches.

So what do they do with it?

They just stick it down my throat. (She is gagging)

You know they didn't hurt you. Let's go through it quickly. What did they do?

I started gagging. I guess they're trying to hold my tongue down. I don't know how the hell they got into my throat, but they did. ... They are scratching on the inside of my throat. I don't know what they are doing, like checking my tonsils? I don't know. They are just there. I guess they are just doing what they got to do. They are checking my neck. Turning my head from side to side. ... They want me to sit up. They are poking me on my back ... and I just know to sit up.

The one you kicked, was that the regular crew there?

That was the one that looked cold.

Oh, you tried to kick him.

Yeah, he was down by my leg. But I don't know which one had me by the arms. I think the nice one – it was like one was nasty and one was nice; one was hard-looking and one was soft-looking; one was emotionless and one acted like it had emotion. I don't know if it did or not.

Did they ever communicate?

No.

Did you hear any sounds between each of them?

Clicking?

Can you imitate it?

(She clicks with her tongue.)

Was it fast or slow?

Kind of fast, but not real fast.

Is it constant?

Just when they are moving around working on me. I don't know if they are talking back and forth or what? But it's a clicking sound. Weird, I mean they scare me.

What happens after you sit up?

I can see my mom looking in the window! She's screaming!! How in the world is she in the window? She's screamin', "That's my daughter!!"

This moment was apparently the same event that so disturbed Judy Doraty ten years before in the hypnosis session with Leo Sprinkle that she began to pound the chair and cried out, "No, I don't want to!" Dr. Sprinkle prompted her to go on, "You see Cindy on the table. What happens next?"

Judy cried, tears streaming down her face. "I'm just afraid they're going to hurt her."

"You're afraid, but you let yourself go ahead. Let yourself go on through the experience."

Judy did not speak for many seconds as if watching inside her mind. Then she said more quietly, "They put her to sleep, I guess. ... They're just examining her, I guess. But I'm so afraid they're going to cut her or something!"

Dr. Sprinkle asked her, "Do you say anything?"

Judy sounded irritated. "They don't listen. They just ignore me and just go about their work as if it's nothing. They don't seem to have any emotions. They don't seem to care. I thought they were going to harm her. That they were going to do to her what they did to the animal."

Dr. Sprinkle asked her what had happened.

"They just take some samples from her ... just scrapings like ... they go inside her mouth. I can see her lying there and they just kind of scrape little pieces off." Judy's hand moved to her opened mouth as if she had a utensil scraping inside her cheeks.

"They reassure me that she's going to be all right. But I don't believe them."

"They tell you everything's going to be all right, but you don't know whether to believe them or not?"

"I just don't. I feel like maybe they just want to be left alone. You know, they were very busy doing their work real quickly. ... They didn't have any emotion or feeling. They couldn't seem to understand why I would even be upset."

"Just like it was routine ..."

"Yes."

"Business for them?"

"Like a laboratory animal or something."

Judy earlier had watched the small, grey beings excise tissue from the calf. "It's taken into some sort of chamber. It's a little round, tiny room. And I get nauseated at watching how they excise parts. It's done very quickly, but the calf doesn't die immediately. For some reason, the calf's heart isn't taken. I don't know. It seems like it's still living and that upset me very much. And then I can see the calf being lowered, like it's being dropped back down and when it's on the ground it's dead. I can see that it's not moving."

As she watched the grey beings, she said "They work very quickly. ...It has to be done very quickly or it loses something. They take the probes and insert them in the different areas. (The tissue was) laid out nice and smooth. It glistens. And there's needles in it, or what appears to be like needles. It may be probes. But it has a tube connected to it. And the same thing with what appears to be testicles ... the same with the eye. And the tongue.

"Every part that's significant, the skin, there's sometimes teeth, sometimes tongue. There's eyes, there's ears. Tail sections. Reproductive organs. Cows' udders. This is not done in only cattle. This is done in almost every animal you can think of. ... They take these parts and they're tested in some manner. There's a fluid extracted and there's fluid put in. They look at how far down it (what the non-humans are tracking or extracting) is in the reproductive system of animals. ... It's like a movie screen, but it's not a movie screen. But they can project something there if they want to see it."

"...They knew exactly what they were doing. ... For some reason they projected that it was necessary that this be done. You know, that it was for our betterment, for the betterment of mankind that this was done. That they were more or less watching out for us."

The beings told her they were "stationed here" and had been testing our soil, water, vegetation and animal life for quite some time. Judy received information about our nuclear testing in space and underwater and a consequential poisonous contamination of earth water. She did not understand the connection. "It's like if we continue like we are now, it's going to involve not only us but possibly other ... and they're trying to stop something that could cause a chain reaction. And maybe involving them." The beings told Judy they take "every part at some time or another" from animals. "The most important is the reproductive system. That they keep a closer watch on because they can tell how far down it is (changes due to the unidentified poison) and if it affects the offspring. With each offspring, they say (the changes) get more prevalent."

Cindy Tindle's Second Hypnosis Session

John Carpenter did a second hypnosis session with Cindy a few days later and she saw more details about a laboratory-like room filled with bottles and animal parts. One of the aliens with the "long snake eyes" was there and she could see a lighted screen that reminded her of the other TV-like machine monitored by the "stick being" and perhaps the same "movie screen" that her mother described. The snake-eyed being, Cindy felt, "does not like me — he's glaring at me. These are the ones that walk that broken gait."

In the laboratory , he also saw "funnels down into the floor" which was similar to her mother's description in the 1980 hypnosis session of "basins" built into the room in which she watched the calf tissue excised. Cindy thought the floor basins were "there for being cleaned, or somethin', cause I guess they spray it down." Also in the laboratory was another of the large-eyed beings that felt "soft" to Cindy, not as threatening and more emotional.

Oh, my God, she's ("soft" female) *got a scalpel. ... I guess she's got three fingers. ... It's like a thumb and two .. she's like very much in charge.*

Watch the scalpel-like instrument and see what she does.

It looks like a tongue. Like she's scraping the hide off of a tongue.

You mean like a regular human tongue?

Yeah, but it looks mighty big. ... Oh, Lordy, I hope it ain't the calf, cause it's not like a big cow's tongue. It's bigger than ours, it's real long.

Is she carefully slicing?

Just exactly like you would be peeling a carrot, (but) there's nothing coming off. She's just scraping it with this scalpel. ...Actually, she wanted to check my mouth again.

And you're just standing there?

Yeah. She's pushing on my cheeks like how they (beings who first examined Cindy) were trying to do. ... I'm leery because I don't want her to cut my tongue out.

What does she do after she scrapes the tongue?

There's little test tubes which fit, slip into the walls ... and she's stickin' these things down in those slots.

Kind of look around, see if you are aware of any other parts.

Yeah. Dog's snout ... just the mouth area.

The whole snout. And how do you know it's a dog's?

Cause of the teeth. ... it looks like it's been bleached, the bones. The bones were just like they were ... immaculately clean. ... But I don't know where the rest of the face is. (It looks) almost like you could just glue it right back on and it would fit perfect. (Plate 9)

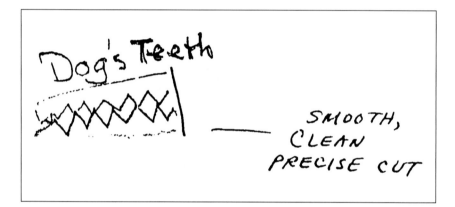

Plate 9 - *Cindy Tindle's drawing of the dog's snout that was vertically cut "smooth, clean, precise," which she saw in the laboratory along with the pig fetus, long tongue (perhaps calf's) and two dead birds, completely feathered.*

Any other interesting parts?

I'm wantin' to say a pig fetus. ... Looks like a pig that's still in the bag, sort of, but it's in a jar with gel or somethin'.

John Carpenter asked her how big it was and Cindy said it was about four or five inches long. She also described two birds lying on a table. "They still have their feathers and everything else on 'em. And it's just kind of heebee jeebee 'cause I know they're dead. ... One looks like just an old sparrow, and the other one, I think, it's a bluejay."

Carpenter asked how tall the "soft" female was that squeezed Cindy's cheeks. Cindy said "about bust height, if not a little shorter" which would have been about four and a half feet to Cindy's five-foot-seven. "She's like the stick person, almost ... and her skin feels clammy. It looks like bone with skin stretched over it." And yet when she described the female's hands, she said the being had "a very fat thumb and then very fat fingers. It's almost like a mitten."

Variations in alien physical characteristics as described by abductees have puzzled researchers for years. In the beginning, it was thought that perhaps the alien intelligence disguised itself with "screen memories" that covered up their actual appearance for unknown reasons. Now the abductees themselves insist that there is more than one physical type and that there might even be a caste system among the alien species that most resembles insects with a "hive mind." Bees and ants, for example, have a hive mind. Each "unit," whether a worker, drone, queen or other, has specific work assignments which contribute to the whole hive. Individuality, as we know it, is not recognizable within a hive species. Perhaps the variations in "nice" or "mean," as Cindy perceived, could be related to the hierarchies of caste roles within the alien hive species. Perhaps some are specifically programmed to better relate to very emotional and individualistic *Homo sapiens sapiens.*[7]

Worldwide animal mutilations have been reported publicly since the fall of 1967, and probably go back to at least the early 20th Century based on local lore in the U. S. and Australia. The shared experiences of Judy Doraty and Cindy, her daughter, in 1973 are important because they were both conscious eyewitnesses, along with three other family members. They all saw a moving, strange aerial light that behaved similarly to the Betty and Barney Hill 1961 unidentified aerial craft and abduction incident in New Hampshire, along with so many other reports.

Cindy and Judy were also eyewitnesses allowed to watch a calf taken from a pasture in a pale yellow beam of light. Judy observed the actual excision of tissues while Cindy saw the neatly severed animal parts during their simultaneous abduction experience aboard the non-human aerial craft. Those memories were somehow suppressed by the alien beings, who apparently induced amnesia in Judy and Cindy, but pieces of memory seeped anyway into their dreams and nightmares. This pattern of experiences with non-humans that induce amnesia that is followed later by emerging bits of memories occurs chronically in the UFO abduction syndrome. Why does the alien intelligence even bother to blank human memories? Do the alien beings deliberately allow some of the experience to be remembered consciously? Or is their mind control technology imperfect?

In keeping with the inconsistencies of the phenomena, some people remain totally conscious and report their memories of encounters without hypnosis. The following section includes conscious eyewitness reports.

[7] *Out There: Remote Viewing of High Strangeness Material"* by Shelley Thomson © 1992 for the 9th International Conference on Shamanism and Alternate Modes of Healing, Berkeley, California.

Plate 10 - *Seated L-R: Judy Doraty and her daughter, Cindy Tindle, with television producer and author Linda Moulton Howe standing. Back yard of Judy's home near Springfield, Missouri, in May 1991, for production of the FOX television special* UFO Report: Sightings *(October 1991) created by Howe, who was also Supervising Producer. Photograph by John Carpenter.*

Eyewitness Reports

When I began research for my documentary *A Strange Harvest* in 1979, I did not set out to do a film about a UFO connection. But that's what I kept hearing from law enforcement and fully conscious eyewitnesses, who had seen orange, silent, glowing objects the size of football fields hovering above pastures where mutilated animals were later found. Or had seen beams of light shining down from "silent helicopters" that lighted pastures "brighter than daylight," and the next day mutilated animals were found where the beams touched the ground.

Then there were the broad daylight eyewitness reports of strange craft and/or non-human creatures involved with animals. Ranchers and other eyewitnesses have seen small, grey or grey-green creatures with or near animals that are later found mutilated or never seen again.

Back in 1975, Missouri horse farm owner Karl Arnold and his son were driving home one night. The road to their house passed between two large, grassy pastures. As Arnold turned into the driveway, he and his boy were shocked to see a small, grey-suited entity whose head was encased in a clear bubble standing near the gate (Plate 11) Karl hit the brakes and the being *slowly faded away* in the air.

That same year, he and his wife saw a silver disk in their horse pasture that left a ceramic-hard circle of dead grass and soil. Nothing grew there for two years. In that pasture, they found *five* of their horses and newborn foals dead and mutilated. Karl Arnold said the tissue on one 24-hour-old foal had been "surgically cut so clean it would be like a hot knife through jello — it was so smooth." (Plate 12)

Plate 11 - *Small, grey-suited being that Missouri horse farmer Karl Arnold and his son encountered at their pasture gate one night in 1975. Artist renderings by Lisa Dusenberry.*

Plate 12 -
Silver disk seen by Karl Arnold and his wife in their Missouri pasture. Ceramic-hard circle of dead grass and soil remained for two years.

On a July morning in 1983, Ron and Paula Watson of Mount Vernon, Missouri, were puzzled by bright, silver flashes in a pasture across the road from their farmhouse. Ron got binoculars that the couple shared back and forth. Each could see two small, silver-suited beings "running their hands" over a black cow that was lying on its side, not moving. (Plate 13) Paula thought the cow was alive, "but paralyzed somehow." She could see in the binoculars that the small beings moved their hands in odd, jerky movements, and then suddenly the cow rose straight up from the grass and floated with the beings into a cone-shaped craft in the background. Ron said that the object was nearly invisible "because the surface was like a mirror and reflected all the leaves, grass and sky like perfect camouflage."

Standing by a ramp and dark opening into the craft was a tall, green-skinned "lizard man," who glared with eyes slit by vertical pupils like a crocodile's or snake's. (Plate 14) On the other side of the craft was a taller, hairy creature the couple referred to as "a Bigfoot-type" that also had yellow vertical slits in round, green eyes. (Plate 15) As soon as the beings entered the craft with the black cow, it disappeared, popping invisible without motion.

The owner of the field told Ron and Paula later that one of his black cows was missing. The couple tried to explain what they had seen, but the farmer didn't want to listen. The black cow never did show up.

During August 1990 production of my television program for the FOX station in Atlanta, Georgia, *Earth Mysteries: Alien Life Forms,* Ron and Paula worked with an artist I contacted to depict what they had seen. (Plates 13-16)

Plate 13 - *Artist rendering for author in August 1990, by Hingwah Hatch, based on eyewitness account of Ron and Paula Watson, Mt. Vernon, Missouri.*

Plate 14 - *"Lizard Guy" seen by Ron and Paula Watson standing next to cone-shaped craft in the pasture where two, small, silver-suited beings levitated a black cow. Drawing by Hingwah Hatch for author, August 1990.*

Plate 15 - *"Bigfoot" seen by Ron and Paula Watson standing near cone-shaped craft with the "Lizard Guy" as if guarding. Drawing by Hingwah Hatch for author, August 1990.*

Plate 16 - *Paula
Watson giving
details to artist
Hingwah Hatch
about "Bigfoot" that
she and her husband,
Ron, saw in July
1983. Photograph
by the author,
August 1990.*

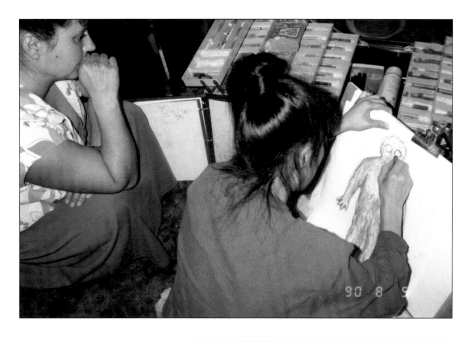

Plate 17 - *Ron and
Paula Watson
during production
of* Earth Myster-
ies: Alien Life
Forms *in
Springfield,
Missouri, August
1990. Photograph
by documentary TV
producer and
author Howe.*

Eventually Ron and Paula Watson sought out John Carpenter to help them with anxieties and insomnia from other strange experiences, but Carpenter said they placed little importance on the cow incident. "Neither had heard about animal mutilations nor did they realize their sighting in the pasture was so uncommon," explained Carpenter. "The couple did not understand what had happened to the cow. Paula had a peculiar and intense reaction to seeing those beings in the pasture. She pleaded with Ron not to go any closer across the road because she was afraid their whole family would be taken." Later, under hypnosis with John Carpenter, Paula realized that she had recognized the beings involved with the cow abduction because she had already been abducted by them just days earlier, but without any conscious memory. Her phobic response to the daylight encounter then made sense emotionally because the prior contact had remained submerged in her subconscious.

In the spring of 1980, a Milam County, Texas rancher watched one morning as two, four-foot-tall creatures with large, slanted black eyes carried a calf between them. He said they were "the color of mesquite trees in the spring," which is a dark green color. He was terrified and ran away. Three days later, he had the courage to go back to the scene with his wife and son. There they found the mutilated calf's body. The hide was completely intact and included the hooves and the skull bone, but no other skeletal structure, muscles or internal organs. The hide was turned inside out and folded neatly on the ground next to the backbone from which all the ribs had been removed. That rancher asked me, "Who would do this? And what are they trying to tell us?"

In May 1980, Myrna Hansen and her five-year-old son were driving home to Cimarron, New Mexico, when they saw two white-suited "men" working on a cow in a pasture next to the road. The cow was bellowing in pain. Hansen stopped and yelled for the men to quit hurting the cow. The next moment, she and her son saw two enormous and brightly lighted objects in the sky in front of their car. Together, mother and son were transported to an underground facility. Her son remembered most of the experience consciously, but his mother needed hypnosis to penetrate her amnesia. Dr. Leo Sprinkle was contacted by Albuquerque, New Mexico, investigator Paul Bennewitz. During the subsequent hypnosis session, Hansen thought she recognized some of the mountain terrain as surrounding the area of Roswell, New Mexico.[8] There, she was subjected to a painful vaginal exam by both small, grey beings and very tall, jaundiced-looking, hairless humanoids that seemed to be in charge. Afterward, she walked through an underground cavern with a large river flowing through it. There were rooms

[8] Appendix 13, Page 353+, *An Alien Harvest, 2nd Ed.,* © *2014* by Linda Moulton Howe. 1989, LMH Prods.

and in one, the mother saw a humanoid figure floating in a vat of reddish liquid she thought had something to do with blood fluids and tissues removed from animals. She also had the impression that the fluid was a "treatment" — or even sustenance — for the immersed being.

Both Cindy Doraty and Myrna Hansen were examined in their abductions. Cindy saw short creatures with "snake eyes" and stick-beings with large, dark, teardrop-shaped eyes; Myrna saw both small beings with large, dark eyes and others with "red glowing" eyes. She was also calmed by the very tall, hairless humanoids. During a very painful exam, perhaps ova were removed from Myrna's ovaries. Cindy's stomach was pressed externally, but the aliens' main focus was her mouth and she thought "they were amazed" with her braces. In a later hypnosis session, Cindy recalled that the aliens considered her thirteen year age "too young" for whatever they needed.

Dr. Sprinkle also did the hypnosis session with Myrna Hansen and talked with her son. In his notes from conversation after the session, he quoted Myrna and her boy as saying, "They (aliens) mean to control Earth, but maybe they don't treat everyone like (Myrna) was treated. Mother feels programmed, but has fought hard at times to deal with UFOLK. Dream of "mind control" over Earth plus "threat" of loss of mind or loss of son. ... Concern about Earth's plight!"

Judy Doraty also received communication about problems for the Earth's future. She understood that the "little men" were tracking a poisonous substance and its spread through their study of Earth animals and possibly abductions. But she felt that whatever was going to happen in the future would affect the aliens, too, and they were concerned about our survival as well as their own. Perhaps part of the story we are not understanding is a symbiotic relationship between Other Intelligences and us. Perhaps one hive species lives underground on our planet and has for eons, harvesting from the surface to suit its needs. Now that humans are seriously threatening the Earth's environment, perhaps we are also threatening the alien harvests.

Or does Something in this galaxy —or another galaxy, universe, dimension or timeline — travel to and interact with Earth specifically to harvest fluids, tissues and genetic material from animals and humans? If so, why here? What does this planet have that an advanced life form does not have somewhere else? And why all the secrecy and deception?

Some abductees feel that the real purpose of the animal mutilations and abductions is to create a part human, part alien hybrid species. A few men and women even report being shown what they call "baby things." [9] (Plates 18-19) Such concepts are repugnant to us, and most people reject it all as impossible. But our human denial might even help the non-human intruders.

[9] *Intruders, The Incredible Visitations At Copley Woods* © 1987 by Budd Hopkins, Random House.

If genetic material is what the alien intelligence wants, why does it need so much over so many years? Why can't They manufacture whatever is needed without harvesting us? And why do They leave animals to be found with excisions that cause fear and anger? Like the Milam County, Texas rancher asked, "What are they trying to tell us?"

Plate 18 - *Drawing of "baby thing" by Jeanne Robinson of Springfield, Missouri, who has experienced abduction trauma since she was four years old.*

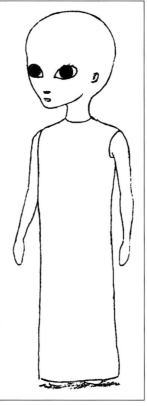

Plate 19 - *Drawing of older "hybrid" by a California female abductee, who believes this is a 4-year-old male created from one of her ova taken during an abduction. "His eyes," she said, "have a steel blue iris and he has cigarette-paper-white skin covered by a linen-colored gown."*

Motives for Animal Mutilations and Human Abductions

The motive issue is complex because the aliens themselves seem to use secrecy and deception about what they are doing and why. Mental communications, automatic writing, or even face-to-face encounters leave human abductees with many different impressions and messages about what's going on.

One perspective about different alien types and agendas in the animal mutilations and human abductions comes from a 36-year-old single mother, who lives in Springfield, Missouri. Jeanne Robinson (Plate 20) remembers a "skeleton with large dark eyes" standing at the foot of her bed when she was four. When she was twelve, walking in the woods near her home, a light that looked like a tornado funnel "sucked" her up into a white room where she was put on a table. "That was the first time they did a gynecology exam on me," Jeanne said. "... They put this thing into me and it was such a shock because I didn't realize they could put anything into me like that. Bein' twelve, I was pretty naive."

Plate 20 - *Jeanne Robinson, June 1993, Springfield, Missouri. Photo © 1993 by author.*

Jeanne Robinson was afraid she was going crazy. Budd Hopkins, well-known UFO abduction researcher, referred her to John Carpenter who lived only forty minutes from her home. Every two or three weeks for over a year, Carpenter explored Robinson's traumatic memories in fifteen hypnotic regressions. Despite the sometimes disturbing information that was revealed, the sessions helped Jeanne gain a sense of control, self-esteem and confidence.

Carpenter also arranged for her to undergo a series of psychological tests (MMPI-1, MMPI-2, MCMI, IQ, TAT, Rorschach, Sentence Completions, Proverbs, and House-Tree-Person drawings) to confirm her sanity. She was "within the normal ranges on all tests" that were performed by a psychologist who had no knowledge of Robinson's experiences or beliefs. Another independent study by the Center for UFO Studies (CUFOS) indicated that she was not "fantasy-prone." In fact, she was seen as more honest and sincere than the average person.

John Carpenter had worked with nearly one hundred people since 1987, who had described encounters with non-human entities and he said about Jeanne Robinson: "Although there is no hard evidence to support her accounts from age four through her thirties, many correlations are evident when compared with other abduction reports I have studied."

Jeanne remembers having been taken repeatedly since she was four by small beings that have grey skin and enormous black, almond-shaped eyes. (Plate 21)

Plate 21 - *Grey-skinned being with enormous black, slanted eyes seen repeatedly by Jeanne Robinson since her first abduction in 1958, when she was four years old. Drawing by Jeanne Robinson.*

She thinks it is possible the small grey beings are biological androids who work for others she described as looking like praying mantis insects. (Plate 22)

She has also encountered a "lizard guy." (Plate 23) Its physical appearance frightened her, but she also wondered if it were "possibly a different type of hybrid?" — created like the "baby things" for specific tasks.

In dreams, she has also seen blond, "Nordic-looking" humanoids she associates with the alien mystery and is confused about their relationship to all the others. According to Jeanne, *something* out there communicates with her telepathically, even when she is doing chores at home. Intuitively, she suspects the praying mantis types. She will get an urge to sit down with paper and pen and "thoughts that aren't my own rush into my mind." If she writes quickly enough, she says, she gets most of the ideas on paper. Otherwise, it evaporates from her memory. An environmental scientist in New England,

Plate 22 -
Drawing by Jeanne Robinson of "praying mantis" female that seemed "in charge" during one of her abductions.

who says he has been abducted, described his telepathic communication with alien beings in the same terms: If I don't immediately write down the thoughts in my head, I forget them."

The following are excerpts from Jeanne Robinson's correspondence to me about her telepathic communication with what she considers to be a non-human intelligence. It has given her unproved insights about different alien types and the motives for animal mutilations and human abductions.

Plate 23 -

"Lizard Guy"

drawn by Jeanne

Robinson based

on what she says

have been

physical

encounters with

this green-

skinned, yellow-

eyed creature.

"Mouth was

scary. Don't

know if it was

teeth or possibly

a breathing

apparatus, but

was a definitely

frightening

appearance.

Intensely cold

stare."

1990 - Jeanne Robinson's Telepathic Communications

> *"The* 'Greys' *are variable. They are manufactured replicates which serve as workers, decoys, lab keepers and envoys. There are also communicators who assist in the calming of the test subjects as well as attempts in communication with the individual.*
>
> *"The* 'Praying Mantis' *type are the ancients. They are a rare branch of the same species. The 'Great Mother' of many species. Supervisor of exploration and research. Purity of the species is extinct. The genetic ancestry is passed on in hybridization of compatible bipeds.*
>
> *"The* 'Reptilian' *are sentry/workers. The species are treatied (have a treaty) with the Greys as a combined work force within the craft. The Reptilians are not as intellectually complex, but have great body strength and warrior ancestry. The reptilians are what your dinosaurs would be had they survived the global upheaval and* <u>evolved as planned</u>*." (Author's emphasis.)*

Jeanne commented here: "My own feelings are there are some Greys who never have any telepathic contact. They seem automatic. There is usually one who communicates. The others do exams and so forth. My experience with Praying Mantis types was seeing one that watched over everything. I felt a feeling of great age and an impression of royalty, almost. Like she presided over everyone." (Plate 24)

Here telepathic communication about different alien types continued:

> *"The beings whom you describe as the* 'Nordics' (blonds) *have been among your people for many thousands of years. Their early settlements on your world gave them the opportunity to create a lasting co-existence with the humans. They are your early ancestors. Because of this implantation, they can work and study your kind with little fear of detection.*
>
> *"Their goals are different from ours. We need your kind to survive.* <u>We must use your genetics to reproduce</u>. (Author's emphasis) The blond ones have maintained their sexual abilities. They are more concerned with your spiritual evolvement. They are of an emotional, more gentle race. Their nature baffles us as much as the unrestrained emotional behavior of humans. However, we co-exist together in the study of your people, many times contacting the same individuals who are the subjects of study.*
>
> *"Several of the telepathic communications you have received are from the blond ones. They share the knowledge of communication through the biological transceivers. You will know which type of message has come from our kind. We prefer to share the more technological implications of our contact.*

Plate 24 - *Drawing by Jeanne Robinson of a grey being she called her "familiar buddy" who sometimes wore a collared cloak. Behind that entity, Jeanne drew one of the smaller types she thinks are biological androids programmed to do work for the advanced insect-type species that "preside over everyone else."*

"*The blond ones will answer the inquiries that concern spiritual understanding as it relates to universal concepts.*

"*These 'Nordics' have told some of your kind that they are from the Pleiades. They originate from this region, but prefer secrecy as to the specific location of their solar system.*"

About animal mutilations, the telepathic thoughts continued:

"*We use substances from cows in an essential biochemical process for our survival. The material we use from cattle contains the correct amount of protein substances needed for biochemical absorption. ... While we respect all life, some sacrifices must be made for the preservation of other species. In most instances, your people do not grieve over dead cows as they do dogs or people.*

"Increase in tissue sample collection of bovine species. Similarities in genetic make-up of human tissue. Samples extracted for varied uses. Pollutants registered in areas selected for study. Absorption of harmful substances revealed in tissue of mucous membranes. DNA uses also to be increased in collected data. The cellular tissue and organs <u>extracted by concentrated beam of photon energy</u>.[10] (Author's emphasis.) *Fluids extracted and circulatory system infused with hydrostatic substitute.*

"Tissue from selected bioplasms are collected, stored and processed for many uses. Bovine tissue most easily processed for replication. Tissue synthesized and expanded in symbiotic culture. Pollution levels in mucous membranes registered and analyzed for signs of genetic deviation caused by increased radiation bombardment. Continued sampling will increase as the need increases.

About human abductions, the telepathic communication said:

"Polymorphic indoctrination will continue. Speciation is necessary to guarantee continuation in the event of catastrophic annihilation. Necessity supersedes diplomacy.

"Intricate design of molecular substructures of DNA composition relays inherited deficiencies as well as positive traits and physical type. Genetic splicing of individual chromosomes within DNA matrix can be used to eliminate unfavorable traits and physical flaws which make a stronger race. The improved product can then pass on advanced biological systems to future generations which effectively evolves the species.

"Genetic alteration increases intellectual capacity of a larger percentage of the brain than the amount currently in use. By choosing the chromosomes which control the areas of specific interest, it is possible to achieve varied results. While the life span could be lengthened ten-fold, it is not advised. That is until your kind can adequately provide for the needs of the population already in existence."

[10] See Jim Marrs account in Chapter 2, Pages 102-103.

November 8, 1992 - Jeanne Robinson's Vivid Dream
About An Animal Mutilation:

Jeanne remembered a vivid dream and wrote it down, including her own confusion noted with question marks in parentheses. Throughout the group of UFO abduction syndrome experiencers, vivid dreams are sometimes thought to be an interface for communication with the non-human intelligence.

I asked John Carpenter to comment on the current professional perception of dreams. He wrote: "Although dreams are accepted as either meaningful or meaningless expressions from the subconscious mind, the field of psychology regards them as internally generated for the purpose of either safely revealing (perhaps metaphorically) unresolved feelings or regurgitating random stimuli or events from the individual's life. However, there are indications that a number of credible people have psychic impressions in dreams — often precise and detailed predictions that come true within a very short time.

"The nature of all possible sources for input into the dream world remains an open question. If there is any credence to the process of "channeling," then other sources of mental stimulation might exist and even affect the process of dreaming. It is worth considering when one recognizes the extremely high correlation among thousands of abduction reports of telepathic communication rather than audible or verbal communication.

"The following dream of Jeanne Robinson's is not proof, but one can consider all possible sources of information input, including an alien intelligence, which might be more than the human mind's need to resolve puzzling questions."

Jeanne Robinson: *"What I had flashes of was a large room with a raised platform where the animal lay. I felt it was a male. I don't remember udders. When I first saw it, there were bright strobe-like flashes of light. I feel I was told that these lights were purifying the animal, neutralizing germs and bacteria, yet allowing the bacteria to be measured. What I mean is the bad stuff (germs) remained in the tissue, but was no longer dangerous. The animal was twitching violently, almost convulsing. There was no other movement and I feel it was dead at that point. Next was the removal of the blood.*

A tube-like thing was stuck into the animal on the upper inside of the hind leg, near the hip joint, right side. A computer-like screen had an image of the animal like a CAT scan/x-ray type thing. The heart pulsed like it was beating, but I'm not sure there was life. Perhaps it was a reaction

▲

to the procedure. The extraction tube was hooked into a large container that seemed to be a robotic-type machine. There were Greys working the equipment. There was one who seemed to be explaining things to me. The CAT scan (Computed Tomography) thing could be manipulated to specific organs. The targeted areas were highlighted or outlined.

Then a Grey took what looked like a light pen, a tube with a light on the end, and pushed it up near the tail. When he removed it, the light was visible on the body. Somehow it was activated and began to move around the outside of the rectal area disappearing into the body. There was a burning smell, like burning hair and other nauseating mixtures of odors. On the monitor, a black dot moved over the highlighted area. The tissue was pulled out and placed in a shallow container. It's unclear to me right now on the details of how or who pulled it out of the animal, but the tissue (rectum) was placed in the container that was taken to a window-type fixture. The container disappeared into the window like it was on a conveyor or something. It seemed to be about a foot or so of rectum/intestine. A pinkish-grey color. It seems like there were contents inside the removed tissue, but that's hazy.

I feel I was instructed to insert the light into the jawbone area to remove the tissue there. They pointed out the spot to push it into and there was an indentation in the pen that I pressed to release the light. This time the light lengthened into a line of light which sliced through the tissue taking also the back two teeth on the left side as well as the skin and jaw flesh.

I believe it was explained to me that the jaw tissue and rectal tissue would be compared to see the contaminants in the body, and by measuring the two from the entrance area (mouth) to the exit area (rectum), the Greys could judge what and how much was absorbed and what was not.

The left eye was also removed and I was told that the beings catalogue DNA from the eye.(??) I don't remember any other aspects of being on the craft other than being brought into the room just as the steer was dying.

I feel I left the house from Stacie's (Jeanne's daughter) room upstairs. It had to have happened in the early morning hours of September 24 (1992), because I didn't go to bed 'til around 2 a.m. I woke up at 6:30 a.m. sleeping through my alarm (or else the alarm didn't go off). I rushed to get to work getting into an argument with Stacie before I left for work and she went to school. I was very anxious at the beginning of work (I only had one cup of coffee so it wasn't caffeine.) I felt the urge to go into a fetal position (?) to sort of crawl into myself to hide from the anxiety. When the memories started coming to me, the anxiety faded away. The animal was brown with a white face."

Is there one major intelligence behind the worldwide animal mutilations and human abductions, crop circles and lights in the sky? Or are there competing intelligences from somewhere else — maybe even intelligences in conflict? Why is it so difficult for the general population to accept the many eyewitness reports about the phenomena?

Both animal mutilations and human abductions are difficult subjects because no one likes the idea of a non-human intelligence having the ability to pick up people and animals in beams of light, subject them to examinations, and harvest blood, tissues, sperm and eggs. Abductees report that in addition to biological harvesting, the aliens also study our emotions and mental reactions. If so, the experimenters might need to remain hidden. Otherwise, they could interfere with their own investigation because their public presence among us might overwhelm normal human social functioning.

The next chapter outlines different alien types synthesized from dozens of drawings and reports sent to me over the past decade. Some might be "screen memories," manipulation of the abductee's mind to create an image overlay that disguises the alien's true physical appearance. Others might be biological species with independent consciousness and purpose, or biological androids programmed to do work for another intelligence that might exist elsewhere in this universe, or even outside this dimension. Whatever the truth, the consistent patterns of descriptions from people all over the United States and other parts of the world merit reporting.

Plate 25 - *Paula Watson's sketch with artist Hingwah Hatch in August 1990, based on memory from her own abduction July 1983, prior to cow's abduction from the pasture across the road in Mt. Vernon, Missouri.*

Plate 1 - *Strange, tall beings accompanied by symbols of unidentified circular and zigzag objects, a snake, and tiny bird-like creatures flying around one being's "antennae," and hieroglyphs were painted with dark red pigment on sandstone in the Horseshoe (Barrier) Canyon of southeastern Utah where the Colorado and Green Rivers meet. Archaeologists are uncertain about who created the many haunting figures more than a thousand years ago. Drawing by E. Wesley Jernigan from* Indian Rock Art of the Southwest © *1980 and 1992 by The School of American Research, Santa Fe, New Mexico.*

Beings other than human, tall and short, have been painted, carved, or sculpted centuries ago in canyons, caves, and statues in parts of the world as diverse as the American Southwest, Peru, Australia, Middle East, and Europe. Eyes are often depicted as much larger than human eyes, and heads are often much larger or longer than normal human scale.

The mysterious Sumerians, as far back as 4,000 to 5,000 B. C., had sophisticated mathematics and had evolved the oldest known wedge-shaped cuneiform script from primitive hieroglyphics. The skeletons from the Royal Cemetery at Ur had very large, long and narrow skulls. Large noses were another notable Sumerian feature. The gods, who interacted closely and physically with the Sumerians, were depicted as very tall with huge eyes and dome-shaped heads that were covered with ropy or ribbed headdresses.

The Bible in Genesis, Chapter 6, Verse 4, states that after the creation of humankind in the Garden of Eden, "There were giants in the Earth in those days, and also after that, when the sons of God came in unto the daughters of men, and they bore children to them, the same became mighty men which were of old, men of renown."

The prophet Ezekiel in the Bible's Old Testament, Ezekiel 1, Verses 4 - 7, described encountering a round ball of orange light ("fire enfolding itself") from which four unidentified "creatures" emerged that had "the likeness of man," but their feet were straight "like the sole of a calf's foot" and they "sparkled like the color of burnished brass."

The UFO abduction syndrome in the modern age has produced reported encounters with non-human beings in broad daylight, both tall and short, that most often have large black eyes, or eyes "like a snake or cat" with vertical pupils. Some people have described "legs that run into straight feet, more like hooves." Other humanoid beings, tall and short, have been described by abductees as "glowing" or "surrounded by light."

CHAPTER 4

OTHER BEINGS

"After a year of the most intensive search ever mounted to detect radio signals from extraterrestrial civilizations, astronomers from the University of California, Berkeley, have picked up 164 signals — out of 30 trillion recorded — that 'bear further investigation.' This doesn't mean that E.T.s have been found, only that these anomalies have not yet been otherwise explained."

TIME MAGAZINE
JUNE 21, 1993, PAGE 19
COMMENTING ON A NASA PROGRAM

Communication and physical contact with other beings has been ongoing for years, according to many people affected by the UFO abduction syndrome. But the official social and political attitude into the 21st Century has been that we humans are alone in the universe. NASA's Search for Extraterrestrial Intelligence (SETI) program that listened for certain frequencies had been the only respectable public focus for questions about extraterrestrial life until congressional funding cuts in the fall of 1993. Ironically, Other Intelligences might have been coming and going here on a regular basis with or without SETI's knowledge. Several people, like the Watsons and Karl Arnold in Missouri and the Milam County, Texas rancher, insist they have consciously seen non-human creatures or beings. What they observed resembled what other people have described, either from their own vivid recollections, dreams, or abduction encounters with glowing lights, beams, silver disks and non-human entities.

One 1992 incident on an otherwise normal morning in Salem, Oregon, was recounted for me in a letter from Helen Harris. Her life has been devoted to her husband and their family. The only unusual aspect has been psychic talent that has produced accurate premonitions. In that way, Mrs. Harris is familiar with the concept of telepathic thought and has been open- minded about other life forms in the universe. She has also read about UFO and abduction phenomena, but did not expect *physical* interaction with an alien being.

She wrote to me:

"August 13, 1992, was a hot day in Salem, Oregon. My husband left for work shortly before 7 a.m. As soon as he left, I opened the three doors to the outside to capture the early morning cool. The doors remained open. I was home alone with one cat and one dog.

At 9 a.m., I was seated at the dining room table facing the living room with the kitchen on my left. Out of the corner of my eye, I saw motion and turned towards the kitchen where the movement was. Through the window of the open back door, I could see the top of a hairless, greenish-grey head. The figure of an E.T. walked rapidly into the kitchen, a matter of three or four full steps. It stopped at a storage cabinet that sits mid-kitchen. It stood still, facing towards the bathroom for approximately six to ten seconds. It never turned or faced me directly. I had a full side view of it both when it was walking and when it stopped and stood still. It was a solid form, as solid and seeable as a human or animal would have been walking into the kitchen and coming to a halt. There was nothing subjective about this encounter. (Plate 2)

As soon as I saw the head through the window of the open back door, I used telepathy. Mentally I said, 'Hello. What do you want? Can I help you?' No reply. The fact there was no reply was more perplexing than the fact there was a solid, alien body fully visible in my kitchen. I suppose a normal person would have run screaming out of their house. The thought did occur to me, but I didn't.

The alien figure, after coming to a halt and just standing there not moving for several seconds, disappeared. It did not fade. It was just there and then not there.

During this encounter, other than turning my head towards the kitchen and my body slightly, I did not move physically. My participation up to the time it disappeared was strictly mental. Physically, I did not notice any change of energy in the house, no odor and no sound of footsteps.

If there was any rise and fall of the alien's chest, such as breathing, it escaped my notice. What I did see was that the figure had eye 'pans,' but I never saw an eye. (As if deeply recessed or perhaps with lids drawn over eyes.) The back of its head was more elongated than bulbous.

When the figure disappeared, I remained seated for awhile, probably less than a minute. I noted it was 9 a.m. About the time I stood up to walk into the kitchen to get a cigarette, the dog walked into the kitchen side of the bathroom door. He had been in the bedroom. He did not react in any way. I have no idea where the cat was during all this, but I do know the dog seemed unaware of anything happening out of the normal.

At approximately 9:20 a.m., I was again seated at the dining room table, but with my back to the kitchen writing a letter. My left arm was extended on the table, wrist exposed. An alien hand attached to approximately twelve inches of arm appeared as rapidly as the full figure had disappeared, and the middle or left finger of the three-fingered hand touched my wrist (Plate 3) and immediately disappeared. The touch was very painful. A cross between an injection and electrical shock. It burned. The pain did not last over three seconds.

The alien hand was narrow. Don't remember seeing knuckles like human knuckles. The skin was mottled. There was no sensation of texture to the skin, but only being touched by the area where, if human, the pad of the fingertip would be.

The fingers were long in proportion to the length of palm. The ends had no fingernails. I have an impression, but am not completely sure, that the fingertips may have had an extended flap of skin that came to a point. The 'flap' did not flop limply. It appeared rigid, but for some reason the impression I'm left with is the finger bones do not have the length that the covering skin has.

The arm terminated ... period. What can one say? So many inches of arm, a hand attached, suddenly appearing. The arm terminated. Visually it didn't appear to be attached to an invisible body. There was no 'blank' space with an arm and hand coming out of it. There was no feeling of a body standing next to my seated self. No stir of air, no odor, no sound.

(Two days later) there was a round circle, 1/4-inch in diameter of whiter skin than the surrounding skin tone. Inside this circle of discolored skin was a red mark the size of your average straight pinhead, offset towards the top of the circle, but not touching the edge of the circle. From the red mark was a red line which radiated towards a surface vein, but visually the red mark line did not appear to enter the vein. It is still barely visible today, February 19, 1992 (the date of her letter). It has never been sore to the touch. Putting pressure on it or rubbing it doesn't hurt.

Linda, I was strangely calm during the intrusion, surprised, but not overly alarmed. The little guy walked in, did his work, and that was that. Now you see him, now you don't."

Plate 2 - *Small non-human being described by Helen Harris of Salem, Oregon, as having green "pebbly, but not exactly reptilian, skin." Daylight, physical encounter was August 13, 1992, at 9 a.m. Drawings by Helen Harris.*

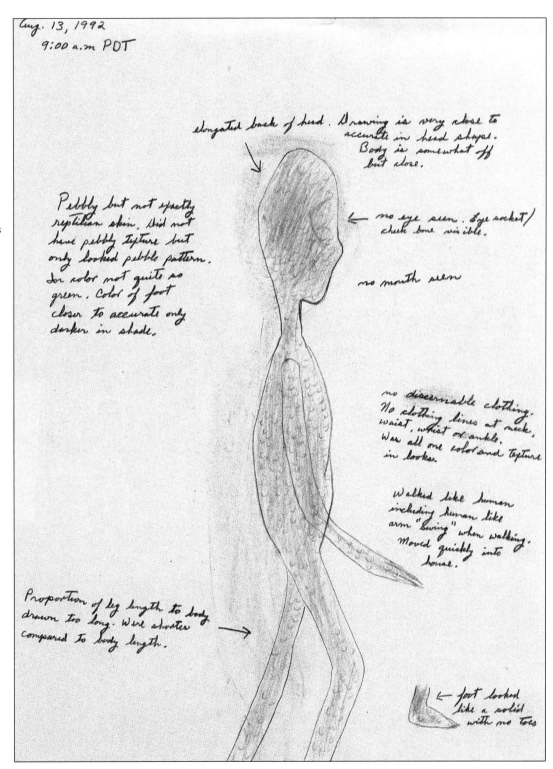

Aug. 13, 1992
9:00 a.m PDT

elongated back of head. Drawing is very close to accurate in head shape. Body is somewhat off but close.

Pebbly but not exactly reptilian skin. Did not have pebbly texture but only looked pebble pattern. In color not quite so green. Color of foot closer to accurate only darker in shade.

← no eye seen. Eye socket/ cheek bone visible.

no mouth seen

no discernable clothing. No clothing lines at neck, waist, whist or ankle. Was all one color and texture in looks.

Walked like human including human like arm "swing" when walking. Moved quickly into house.

Proportion of leg length to body drawn too long. Were shorter compared to body length. →

← foot looked like a solid with no toes

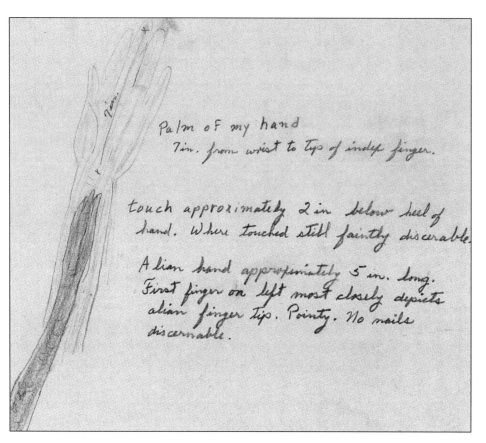

Palm of my hand

7in. from wrist to tip of index finger.

touch approximately 2 in below heel of hand. Where touched still faintly discerable.

Alien hand approximately 5 in. long. First finger on left most closely depicts alien finger tip. Pointy. No nails discernable.

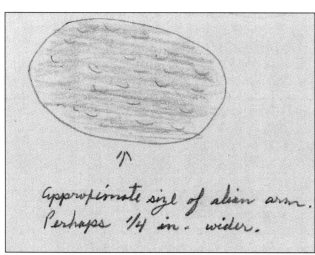

Approximate size of alien arm. Perhaps 1/4 in. wider.

Plate 3 - *Small alien being's hand touching Helen Harris's wrist as it suddenly appeared, as if attached to invisible entity. Also, estimated actual size of being's arm in second sketch. Drawing by Helen Harris.*

Mrs. Harris's sketch of a green, "pebbly, but not exactly reptilian, skin" reminded me of the Milam County, Texas rancher's description of the two small, green-colored beings that carried the calf that he later found mutilated. Or the green "lizard guy" the Watsons saw in the pasture where the black cow was taken. (Chapter 3) If, as some abductees insist, the various small beings are biological androids programmed for various work purposes, it is possible to speculate that the varying color shades from grey-white to grey to beige to green are a function of various metabolisms and/or abilities to interact or not interact with the light spectrum of our sun. Most encounters have occurred at night when there is no sunlight. Perhaps some beings, such as the greener ones, are constructed in such a way that they can better tolerate Earth sunlight. Perhaps those creatures contain the chlorophyll-like fluid mentioned in alleged government autopsy reports. There are also reports of very tall humanoids, six to eight feet, that have a greenish-yellow or pale-colored skin with a jaundiced yellow tinge.

In addition to letters from people throughout the United States and other countries, I have also received off-the-record information from military and intelligence sources who claim firsthand encounters with alien beings. Over time, a repeating pattern of non-human types has emerged. This chapter is an attempt to outline some of those non-human beings that have been described. The depictions could be extraterrestrial biological entities, inter-dimensional entities, time travelers, advanced holographic projections, "screen memories" planted by alien technologies that can manipulate human minds in order to disguise the non-human actual appearances. All of these? Or other possibilities?

Screen memory has long been a recognized, but confusing, factor in the human abduction syndrome. For example, after their encounter with the bright light in May 1973, Cindy Tindle and her mother, Judy, returned to their relative's home outside Houston, Texas. Cindy remembered being upstairs with her cousin in a bedroom where they watched the lighted object "go up and sit beside the moon." At that distance, it looked, she said, "just like a star." But when John Carpenter hypnotized her in 1990, Cindy realized that looking out her cousin's window was not possible because that house did not have a second story and her cousin's bedroom did not even have windows. The hypnosis had penetrated an apparent screen memory that had disguised a round room in the craft or other location as a second story bedroom in her cousin's house which did not exist.

When the illusion lifted during hypnosis, Cindy could see "a bald-headed man" who was short and wearing a "shiny spacesuit, kind of a golden color." (Plate 5) He was not like the "big-eyed one" she called a "stick figure."

The now-revealed bald-headed being was not like the other snake-eyed one similar to what her mother had seen. And not like the kinder one. (Plate 4) "He's different (bald-headed entity)," she said. "It's almost like he's an Oriental-type. You know how an Oriental person's eyes are slanted? But his are real long ... they're only open like so much (horizontal slits). And the center is going up and down, the pupils," meaning vertical pupils.

"The head is almost like brainy. ... It's almost like a mushroom, he looks like his head's been blown up, and it's veiny up underneath. The veins are coming up to the surface. ...He's also got the pointed, petite chin (and) little bitty lips. ... The skin is kind of a browny, almost looks like a mushroom color. Even the texture of it looks like a mushroom sort of. Beigy, browny, spotty." Cindy watched him work with tubes in a place that reminded her of a laboratory and sensed a puzzling familiarity about him. He did not scare her.

Plate 4 - *Beings drawn by Cindy Tindle and her mother, Judy Doraty. L-R: Cindy's "kinder female" with large black "teardrop" eyes; the more robust snake-eyed one; the bug-eyed "stick figure;" and another snake-eyed being drawn by Cindy's mother, Judy Doraty, that was excising tissue from a calf in the craft where Judy and Cindy ended up together after Judy saw a calf rise in a yellow beam of light from the pasture near Houston, Texas, in May 1973.*

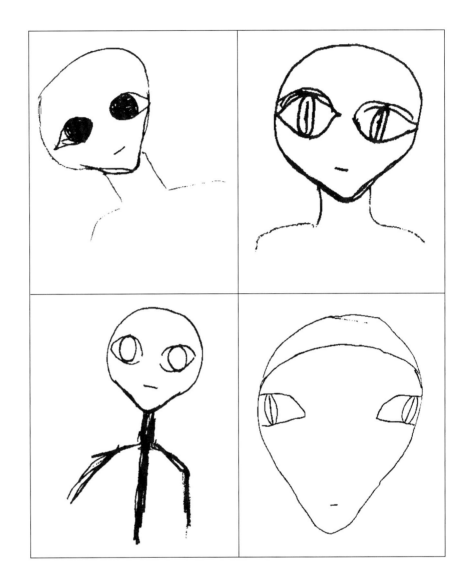

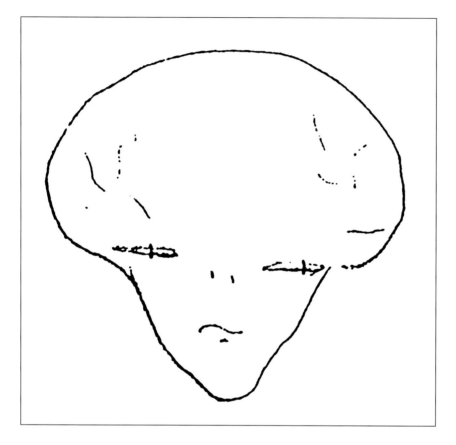

Plate 5 - *Cindy Tindle's August 6, 1990, drawing of "bald old man" with long, narrow "Oriental eyes." She saw him working with tubes in a round, laboratory room during the May 1973 abduction with her mother, Judy Doraty, outside Houston, Texas.*

Cindy's drawing of the Oriental-type being was similar to another sketch made in the year 1919 by occult researcher Aleister Crowley. (Plate 6) Crowley was born in 1875 in Warwickshire, England. He became associated with occult teachings, and Adolph Hitler hired Crowley during World War II for his knowledge of magical devices and ritual. He became a drug addict and died in 1947. Earlier in his life, he had been initiated into the Hermetic (alchemical) Order of the Golden Dawn on November 18, 1898, which, according to Crowley's biographer Kenneth Grant, "was the inner Mystery School of the Order that formulated itself in the outer world as the Theosophical Society."

The term *theosophy* is derived from the Greek *theos* "god" and *sophia* "wisdom" and is generally translated as "divine wisdom." Theosophy emphasized mystical experience, that God must be experienced directly in order to be known at all. Supernatural or extraordinary occurrences that lead toward the achievement of higher psychic and spiritual powers were of deep interest with the goal of recognizing the god force beyond, and inclusive of, all duality.

Plate 6 - *Drawing by
Aleister Crowley of
"Lam, an extra-
terrestrial" intelligence
with whom Crowley
said he was in astral
contact in 1919," as
re-printed in* The
Magical Revival
© *1991 by Kenneth
Grant and Skoob
Books Publishing,
London.*

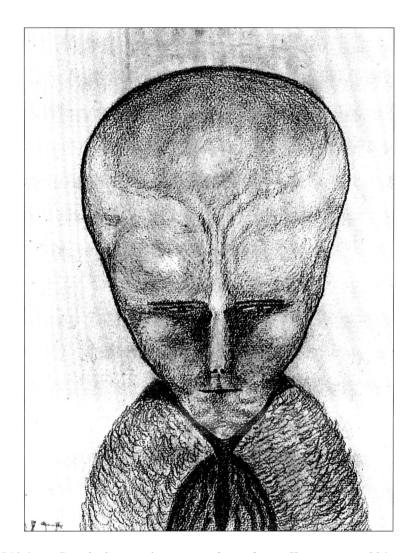

[1] Occult tradition
places this under-
ground residence
of the Hidden
Masters in the
northern and trans-
Himalayan region
of the Gobi desert.
Shamballah is said
to be one of seven
sacred centers on
the Earth, including
Cairo, Egypt;
Sumer (southern
Iraq); British Isles;
southern tip of
India; the Andes of
Peru; and northern
California.

One of Aleister Crowley's pursuits was astral travel, an effort to extend his non-physical self over distances and to travel in other planes of reality. Crowley said he encountered an "extra-terrestrial" being he called Lam while astral traveling, perhaps induced by magical ritual, and sketched him. The being allegedly communicated information to Crowley about many subjects related to the unseen. One of those subjects might have been Shamballah[1] thought by some to exist beneath the Himalayan range in Bhutan, Tibet and Nepal.

There have long been legends about a highly advanced intelligence living there underground. Could the similarity between the 1919 Englishman's drawing and the 1973 Texas teenager's sketch relate to an underground species that lives in some kind of symbiotic, but covert, relationship with life on our planet's surface? What is the relationship between the "Oriental-types" and the more commonly described "Greys?" Cindy's hypnosis sessions suggested that the various types[2] she encountered, including the "Oriental being" and the glaring "reptile," worked together in the same craft, or facility.

What reality do the various descriptions of other beings in the abduction syndrome represent? Are there a variety of biological species from somewhere else in the universe coming and going on our planet? Abductees say there are also different dimensional realities occupied by other beings. Assuming extraterrestrial and inter-dimensional origins are both possible, I do not know if described differences are real species differences or different models for different work purposes for one or several dominating intelligence/s, or disguises such as "screen memories" – or some other existence beyond my understanding.

Even abductees are not certain about the nature of the intelligences involved in their lives, but after fourteen years of interviews and having seen many drawings, different descriptions of other beings begin to break down into repeating patterns. The following list is summarized from more than twenty abduction cases and is representative of others I have researched. The stories behind some of these drawings will be explored more deeply in Volume 2, *High Strangeness*.

Different Alien Descriptions

Small Greys, No Hair
Three to four feet tall, with grey skin "much like the slightly wrinkled or pebbly surface coating of some refrigerators," one abductee said. Over the skin, leotard-type body suits are variously described as a shiny silver, black, dark blue, maroon or "grey like the skin." (Plate 8)

Some people remember patches or symbols, usually on the left side

[2] Two alleged extraterrestrial life forms, according to some abductees and other sources, originate from the binary star system Zeta Reticulii 1 and 2. It's a wide binary system of two yellow G-class stars, both of which have a visual magnitude of 5.22 and both are similar to Earth's sun. The stars are gravitationally bound. From Earth, Zeta-1 Reticuli is 39.16 light-years distant and Zeta-2 Reticuli is 39.24 light-years.

Plate 7 - *"Patch on left breast area of small, grey humanoid. Light colored, tight-fitting uniform/ jumpsuit." Drawing by adult female Jeanne Robinson, Springfield, Missouri, 1991, who has had numerous close encounter and abduction experiences since age four.*

Plate 8 - *Small, pale grey being described by Paula Watson, Mt. Vernon, Missouri. Artist's rendering by Hingwah Hatch, August 1990. Watson has had repeated abductions since 1983 after she and her husband, Ron, watched small non-human beings float a black cow from a nearby pasture described in Chapter 3.*

of the chest, such as a crescent moon-shaped object (Plates 7-8); or a circle around a triangle (Plates 22-24). Other reported symbols on uniforms include a caduceus or cylindrical helix inside a pyramid or triangle (Plate 14), inverted triangles, overlapping triangles (Plates 31-32), or winged emblems (Plate 43).

The head is usually drawn as egg-shaped or light bulb-shaped with the

pointed end down. Large, black, almond-shaped eyes dominate a flat face that narrows to a pointed chin. The nose is either a slight pucker or simply small slits. The torsos are often described in two basic categories: robust or extremely thin, almost without shoulders, in relationship to the large head. The arms are described as thin and longer in proportion to human arms. The "fingers" are variously described as three or four claw-like appendages or fingers tapered to long thin points; four or five appendages that flare at the ends in something like suction pads; or three fat fingers that are often compared to "mittens," or three, long "almost tentacles."

Plate 11 -
David Huggins.
New Jersey.
Adult male.
Huggins painting in
1987, based on
physical, daytime
encounter in 1950s
at his central
Georgia farm home.
"These Little Guys
seemed to float down
out of the sky. They
seemed to be able to
appear and
disappear."

The feet are often covered in boots or have the appearance of extending straight out of the legs, hoof-like, perhaps because of an overall body suit. The round ends of the eyes either face each other flaring back toward points at the sides of the face, "like enormous wrap-around sunglasses," one abductee said. Or the points of the eyes face each other near small nose slits.

"There are no ears," is a common description, or only small openings on the sides of the head are remembered. The mouth is most often drawn as a small, straight line below nose slits.

Plate 12 -
Deborah Bain.
Flippin, Arkansas.
Adult female.
Sketched in 1993.
Memory of three-
and-a-half foot tall
being during
abduction when she
was eighteen years
old in 1972.

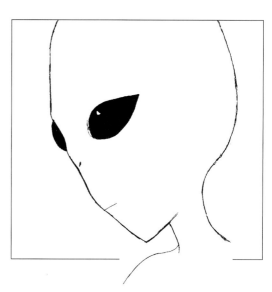

263

Plate 13 -
K.R.
Flint, Michigan.
Adult male.
Sketch February 9, 1992.
Numerous close encounter
and abduction experiences
since teenager. "Little
wands with blue light at
the tip can paralyze you."

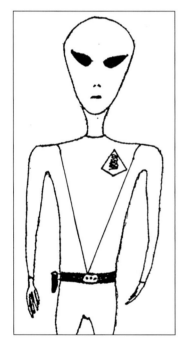

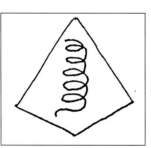

Plate 14 -
Bill Hamilton.
Reseda, California.
Adult male.
Drawn April 12, 1993.
Encountered small, grey
being in March 16, 1993,
abduction experience.
Hamilton remembered
patch with helix spiral
inside pyramid on left side
of grey-colored body suit.

Plate 15 -
G. A.
New Mexico desert.
Adult male.
Drawn in April 1991.
Based on alleged close
encounter experience in
1947. Artist rendering by
Lisa Dusenberry.

Many abductees feel that the small beings (three to four feet), in contrast to taller beings, are biological androids programmed for specific physical tasks. One man who served in the U. S. Navy had his own encounter with this type and called them "bellhops. They pick you up and take you where you're supposed to go and then they bring you back."

Whatever the beings' origin or function, some confidential sources claim to have seen autopsy photographs and reports of at least a few small, grey beings that indicated an anatomical structure more akin to insects, but containing a chlorophyll fluid found in plants. In his encounter, the Navy man said the small, grey "bellhops" smelled like a fresh vegetable market and he asked me, "Are they smart bugs or smart plants?"

Taller Grey Beings, No Hair

Others in the grey category are described as taller, (Plate 16) five to six feet, with varying shades of white-grey to darker grey skin tones, large black eyes, possibly two or three layers of eyelids, which might explain Helen Harris's comment that she could see "eye pans," but not eyes. Nose and ears are again only small holes. Long fingers. Head proportionally large for thin necks and bodies. Leotard-like body suits.

Others are drawn wearing long capes or gowns (Plates 17-22) and are sometimes accompanied by smaller beings, which some abductees believe are "programmed androids." Collars have been seen which one Colorado male abductee said, "is stupid for something from outer space," irritated at the incongruent high-necked and layered collars he and his wife saw during their abduction in November 1980.[3]

Plate 16 -
G. R.
Jacksonville,
Florida. Adult male.
Drawn Sept. 16, 1989.
"Abduction in 1963
or 1964 when three
or four years old.
(Being was) about
five feet tall. No
ears, small mouth.
Tight fitting clothes.
Color (of jump suit
was) royal blue with
magenta. Long
fingers."

[3] Detailed in *An Alien Harvest, Chapter 6, 2nd Edition* © 2014 by Linda Moulton Howe.

Plates 17-18:
D. K.
Longmont, Colorado.
Adult male.
Drawn under
hypnosis July 9, 1984,
by D. K. after
abduction with his
wife in November
1980. Being sketched
in charcoal this page
and with yellow, layered
collar next page were
picked out for this
author as being the
"extraterrestrial biologi-
cal entities, or EBEs"
mentioned in leaked
government documents
about the "alien pres-
ence" on Earth.

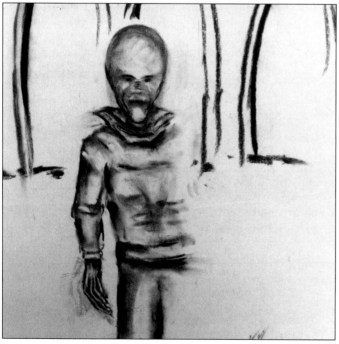

Plate 19 - *D.K. said being was more grey-skinned than he drew under hypnosis. Called being "the creep" because it examined D.K. and "took my mind out and added something. There's more to life, more to the world. There's more to everything than anybody knows. There are more than three dimensions. Every-where, it all works together. Everything co-exists. There's different dimensions we can't go into."*

Plate 20 -
*A.R.
Jenkintown,
Pennsylvania.
Adult male.
Drawn in 1992 after multiple abduction experiences.
A.R. says "I've seen a machine hooked up to me to collect sperm after I first thought a strange, blond woman was there." Being in Plate 20 he said had a "flattened nose with odd ridges and eyes like a cat's."*

Plate 21 -

L.D.

Indianapolis, Indiana.

Adult female.

*Taller being in long-sleeved gown
accompanied by three smaller grey
entities that L.D. thought were androids.
Drawn in 1987 after hypnosis about
possible 1965 abduction when L.D. was
eighteen. Has had numerous abduction
experiences since she was four years old.*

Plate 22 - *Grey being wearing high-collared cape seen repeatedly in the many abduction experiences of adult female Jeanne Robinson since she was four years old. Drawn by Jeanne Robinson in Springfield, Missouri.*

Other Talls in the five to six feet range of hairless beings are described as "the color of cardboard" or tan, perhaps the mushroom color that Cindy Tindle tried to explain. These drawings were made by a California adult female who said "cardboard-colored" beings were the "doctors" who always gave her medical and gynecological exams.

Underneath the beige triangular bib was a small, black box used in their work, but she was uncertain about its exact function. Another being wore a "steel blue leotard and a light grey sash. He was the Leader," she said, who had a circle-around-triangle patch on his blue body suit. Other abductees have also perceived "leaders," suggesting a hierarchy among the various beings.

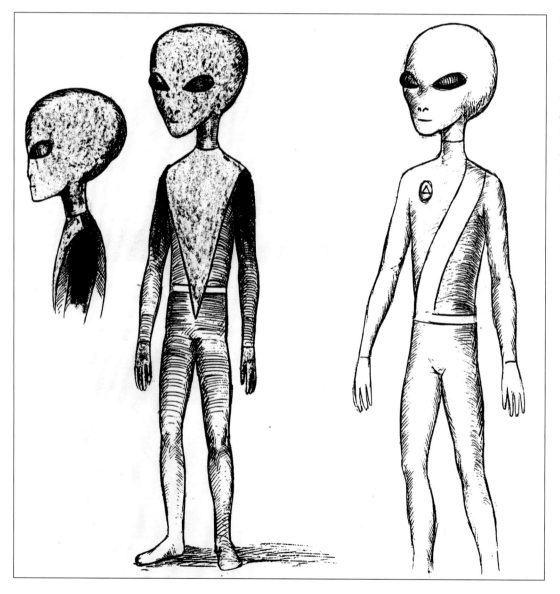

Plate 23 - L. D. Southern California. Adult female. Drawn 1990. Compare with Plate 24, circle-around-triangle patch.

Plate 24 - *Circle-around-triangle patch drawn by Missouri abductee, Jeanne Robinson. She remembered it on "left breast of uniform." L.D. on previous page drew symbol on right side in Plate 23.*

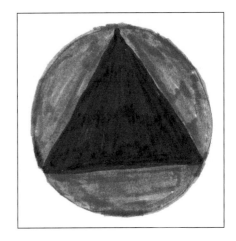

Plate 25 - *D. A. Missouri. Adult Male. Drawn August 6, 1992. Abducted with wife and 1-year-old daughter in October 1976. "I had no control over my thoughts. The being took everything from my mind, but I knew nothing about him."*

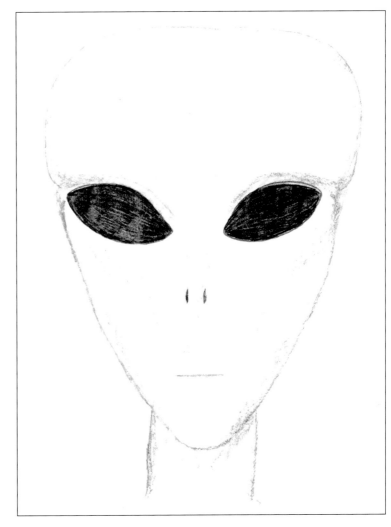

Plates 26- 27:
V. M.
New York City.
Adult male.
Painting in 1993
based on
September 1985
encounter in New Hope,
Pennsylvania. "Female
being, about five-and-a-
half feet tall, very thin,
with pure white skin, was
standing about 30 yards
away. Her body seemed to
glow in a translucent-
colored light consisting of
blues and reds. Her eyes
transfixed me and I felt
as though my mind was
being 'looked through.' I
was under the absolute
control of this entity who
was accompanied by three
little creatures in blue
coat uniforms" that had
dark, net-like pattern
over their grey faces.

Plate 28 -
N.L.C.
Sonoma, California.
Adult female.
Drawn August 12, 1990.

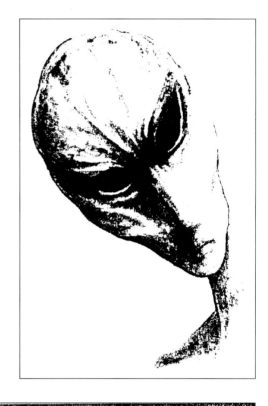

Plate 29 -
L. R.
Saratoga, California.
Adult female.
Drawn May 10, 1992.

Some abductees also feel the big, black eyes are artificial coverings as we might wear sunglasses to screen out sunlight and that underneath are "cat eyes" or "snake eyes" with vertical pupils. (Plate 30) This issue is more evident in the next category of taller beings.

Very Tall Humanoids, With or Without Hair

Other non-human beings, with or without hair, include six to eight-feet-tall humanoids, sometimes depicted with very large noses, and most often drawn with "large cat eyes." (Plate 31)

Plate 30 -
L. P.
Bakersfield,
California.
Adult female.
Drawn 1990.
Being was at least seven
feet tall, had large nose,
and vertical pupils. "He
was in charge of
everything, over everyone
else," including smaller Grey
androids, she thought.

Author's Note: *Betty Hill and her husband, Barney, were abducted from the White Mountains in New Hampshire on September 19-20, 1961. Afterward, Betty had dreams which she wrote down and were included in the Appendix of* The Interrupted Journey © 1966 by *John G. Fuller. Mrs. Hill wrote: "...their (alien)* noses were larger *than the average size although I have seen people with noses like theirs — like Jimmy Durante."* Durante was a mid-20th Century singer nicknamed The Schnozz for his large, beaked nose.

Plate 31 - *Six to seven-foot tall male and female humanoids with "pearlescent, translucent complex-ion" encountered by New Jersey adult female in 1987. She thought the male's eyes were more golden and the female's pale blue, "like a cat's without any whites showing," she said. The abductee stressed that when she first saw the tall male humanoid, his eyes were solid black. "He took something off, like shields, and there were cat eyes underneath." She said these beings wore a patch of two overlapping triangles, open at each end, which signified "the merging of two worlds." She did not know which worlds or why. Artist renderings by L. Hoffmann.*

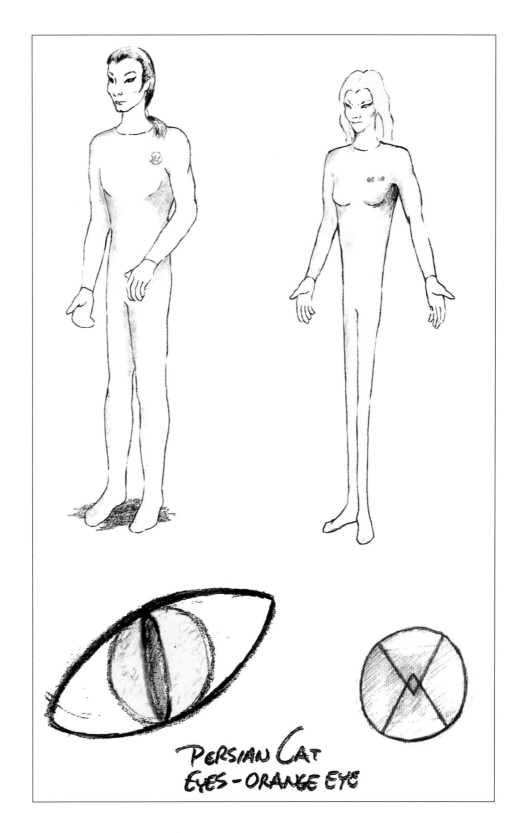

PERSIAN CAT
EYES - ORANGE EYE

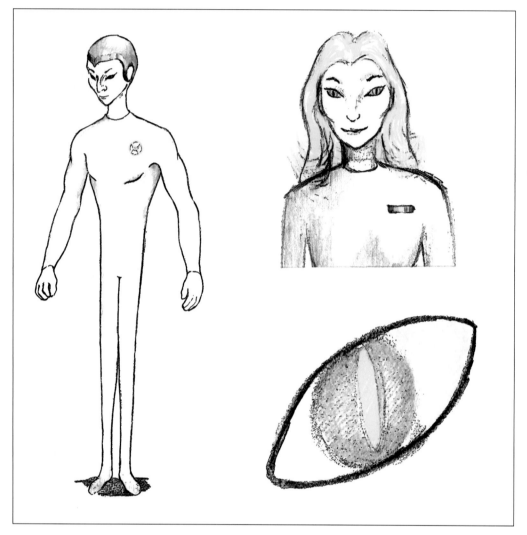

Plate 32 - *Tall, large-nosed humanoid that worked with "cat-eyed" tall blond and dark-haired beings during a New Jersey adult female's abduction experience in 1987.*

Working with the tall blond and dark-haired humanoids was another large-nosed being who wore a tight skull cap that fit around ears. (Plate 32)

Other people have also drawn a similar alien being. In the 1974 edition of the book *UFOS: Past, Present & Future* by Robert Emenegger with research by Allan Frank Sandler,[4] the Photo Section showed a black and white drawing of an alien humanoid who might have landed at Holloman AFB/White Sands in 1973 and/or April 25, 1964. Caption in Photo Section read: *"The sketches on this and the following page are an artist's conception of UFO occupants based on eyewitness descriptions."* The being was depicted with a large nose, large eyes with vertical pupils, a layered headdress which curved around large ears, and held a rod in its left hand that was wound with a helix-shaped coil. (Plate 33) Nearby was a disk-shaped craft.

[4] *UFOS: Past, Present & Future* by Robert Emenegger © 1974 by Allan Sandler Institutional Films, Inc.

Plate 33 - *Drawing of large-nosed alien being and disk-shaped craft in hypothetical landing at Holloman AFB from the Photo Section of* UFOs: Past, Present & Future *by Robert Emenegger © 1974 Allan Sandler Institutional Films, Inc. Reproduction of this drawing is strictly prohibited without the written permission of Allan F. Sandler.*

[5] *An Alien Harvest* © 1989 by Linda Moulton Howe.

Plate 34 - *January 1989 drawing by former Navy petty officer William Cooper, allegedly based on black and white photographs of extraterrestrial beings he saw in June 1972, while stationed in Hawaii.*

A former Navy petty officer named William Cooper sent me drawings in January 1989, which he said were based on black and white photographs he had seen while stationed in Hawaii in June 1972.[5] One of his drawings (Plate 34) resembled both the large-nosed being in a skull cap drawn by the New Jersey female abductee and the being in the Emenegger and Sandler book.

An alien-human meeting was also described to me on April 9, 1983, at Kirtland AFB in Albuquerque, New Mexico, when Air Force Office of Special Investigations Special Agent Richard C. Doty told me that the United States government had a project called Sigma in which communication had been made with one or more extraterrestrial groups. Doty showed me an alleged presidential briefing paper[6] that said communications with extraterrestrials had been "ongoing to date" since April 25, 1964. Doty said there had been a *pre-arranged* meeting on that date between alien beings and United States military and scientists at a specific latitude and longitude coordinate in the northeast corner of White Sands Proving Grounds, a missile-testing range north of Holloman AFB.

In March 1983, I asked Emenegger if the large-nosed being depicted in the 1974 edition of his book was a red herring to throw people off, since the small, grey, no-nose type had received the most publicity. He told me the drawing was based literally on photographs and 16mm films provided by Department of Defense officials assigned to work with him and Sandler on their independent television production in the early 1970s entitled *UFOs: Past, Present and Future.* In that film, the landing at Holloman was characterized as hypothetical. The documentary and the book originally had the same title, but later in 1979 the film was updated and the title changed to *UFOS: It Has Begun.* That version had an expanded segment about animal mutilations narrated by computer scientist, UFO investigator, and author Jacques Vallee.

During our conversation about an alleged landing at Holloman AFB by beings with the vertical pupils and large noses, Emenegger recommended that I study Assyrian history (ancient Mesopotamia) for insights about another intelligence's involvement with our planet.

In the book *The Sumerians,*[7] one of the world's foremost archaeologists, C. Leonard Woolley, wrote:

"(The Sumerians) were a dark-haired people — 'black-heads,' the texts call them — speaking an agglutinative language somewhat resembling ancient Turkish (Turanian) in its formation though not in its etymology. ... What their original home was we do not know.

"...The southern Mesopotamians at the beginning of the fourth millennium B. C. had big, long and narrow heads (with prominent noses.) They were akin to the predynastic people of Egypt, but differed from all other predynastic and dynastic Egyptians." (Plate 35)

In a footnote, Professor Woolley includes this startling fact from another archaeologist, Sir Arthur Keith in his book *Al-Ubaid*, pages 216 and 240.

"The Neolithic[8] people of <u>English long barrows</u> (Author's emphasis.) were

[6] *Chapter 7, An Alien Harvest - Further Evidence Linking Animal Mutilations and Human Abductions to Alien Life Forms* © 1989 and 2nd Edition © 2014 by Linda Moulton Howe. Available at Earthfiles.com

[7] *The Sumerians* by C. Leonard Woolley © 1965, W. W. Norton & Company.

[8] Late Stone Age beginning about 8,000 B. C.

also related to them (Sumerians) — perhaps distantly; the Sumerian type made its appearance in Europe in Paleolithic times,[9] for one of the earliest of Aurignacian skulls — that found at Combe Capelle in the Dordogne, France, is near akin to the ancient Arab type."

Woolley writes further on Page 42 of *The Sumerians*: "On the technical side alone, the (Sumerians') knowledge of metallurgy proved by the use of alloys and the skill shown in the casting of these alloys is remarkable and was assuredly *not acquired in the course of two or three generations*." (Author's emphasis.)

The Sumerians built massive, multi-level ziggurats (step pyramids). One might have been the Tower of Babel referenced in the Bible. Herodotus, the famous Greek historian of the fifth century B. C., described the shrine on top of Babylon's ziggurat built for the god Marduk and said it contained a great golden couch on which a human woman spent the night alone, suggesting perhaps a sexual liaison with the god. Ancient Near East language scholar and author Zecharia Sitchin,[10] a pioneer in the effort to understand the origins of the Sumerian culture, has concluded from his translation work that the Sumerian "gods" were an advanced extraterrestrial civilization that eons ago had used genetic manipulation in already-evolving primates to create "primitive workers" to mine and do other physical labors on this planet. Later, through subsequent genetic manipulations of primitive *Homo sapiens* by those "gods,"

[9] Old Stone Age beginning around 40,000 years ago.

[10] *Genesis Revisited* © 1990 and *The Earth Chronicles, Books I-V,* © 1976-1993 by Zecharia Sitchin, Avon Books.

Plate 35 - *Typical Sumerian features on stone wall plaque depicting Enannatum, ruler of Lagash, about 2450 B.C., from* Mesopotamia *by Julian Reade,* © 1991 *The Trustees of the British Museum, British Museum Press.*

the Sumerian culture evolved in an interactive relationship with those gods.

Archaeologist Woolley remarked about the unusual relationship between the Sumerian community and their gods. "While terrifyingly aloof, the gods were at the same time particularly close to man. The religion was anthropomorphic (human characteristics were ascribed to the gods) and the gods were but men writ large. The (ziggurat) temples were their houses in the city's midst ... (and the gods were) eating the meats of sacrifice of which their worshippers also partook.

"The fact is that throughout the religion of the Sumerians, (it) is one not of love but of fear, fear whose limits are confined to this present life, fear of Beings all-powerful, capricious, unmoral."

Another archaeologist, Harriet Crawford[11] described the Sumerians' use of statuary in their relationship to the gods. "The Sumerians regarded statuary as a means to an end, the end being to obtain favours from the gods by reminding them constantly of the devotion and virtue of their servants on earth." Perhaps the statues were more literally photographs of the day and not the mythic imagination in which they are often categorized.

Crawford reported that "A large cache of votive statues was found at Tell Asmar buried below the floor of the Square temple, apparently during extensive renovations. It seems that they were regarded as too sacred to be thrown away and so were deposited in sacred ground below the floor of the shrines. ...

"Two figures stand out from the group by reason of their size (tall) and their *enormous eyes*. (Author's emphasis.) ...These are two of the very rare representations of gods known from ancient Mesopotamia."

Perhaps one similarity to that particular body type is found in terra-cotta figurines found in Ur from about 4500 B. C. depicting beings from south Mesopotamia that are strikingly tall and slim with large eyes and high, dome-shaped heads. (Plate 36) Most of these figurines were either painted or sculpted with balls or dots around the shoulders. One is holding a child whose head is elongated, as the adult's heads are, and whose eyes are enormous, a facial feature consistently depicted on Ubaid figurines.

[11] *Sumer and the Sumerians* by Harriet Crawford of the Institute of Archaeology, University of London © 1991, Cambridge University Press.

Plate 36 - *Terra-cotta figurines from Ur in southern Mesopotamia about 4500 B. C., or earlier, depicting tall, thin beings. The one on the left clearly shows enormous eyes and a head with a prominent dome that might be an insight to what is beneath the pleated or ropy headgear so prevalent among the Sumerian gods. The figure on the right depicts an adult holding a child whose head is also elongated and the eyes are enormous and black, a characteristic of Ubaid figurines. From* Botschaft aus dem Kosmos *by Michael von Hesemann,* © *1993 Verlag, "Die Silberschnur" and* Mesopotamia *by Julian Reade* © *1991 The Trustees of the British Museum, British Museum Press.*

High-domed heads of the Sumerian gods were usually draped in a pleated or ropy headdress. One Akkadian cylinder seal shows five gods in their unique hats. (Plate 37) Another stele shows Hammurabi, king of Babylon standing in front of the Sun-god Shamash, "supreme chief justice" of the Mesopotamian world. (Plate 38) Close-ups are offered in Plate 39, probably another depiction of the Sun god Shamash at Ur about 1900 B.C; Plate 40, an Assyrian sculpture about 865 B.C. from Nimrud palace of Ashurnasirpal II; and Plate 41, an ancient unknown god found at Jabbul, near Aleppo in northern Mesopotamia.

Plate 37 - *Akkadian cylinder seal impression from about 2,300 B.C. of five Mesopotamian gods, including the Sun god Shamash in the middle with what looks like a saw, to cut trees. The dramatic headdresses are prominent.* Mesopotamia, *British Museum.*

Plate 38 - *A stone inscription of the Sun god Shamash before the Babylon King Hammurabi in southern Mesopotamia around 1792-1750 B. C. From* Ancient Iran *by Georges Roux © 1964 by George Allen & Unwin Ltd., U. K.*

Plate 39 - *Statue that clearly features the prominent, ribbed headdress of the Mesopotamian gods, this one perhaps the Sun god Shamash from Ur about 1900 B.C.* Mesopotamia, *British Museum.*

Plate 40 - *Assyrian sculpture about 865 B.C. from Nimrud palace of Ashurna-sirpal II. The head of a god on the body of a winged lion was to provide magical protection for the palace. Photograph by author at British Museum, London.*

Plate 41 - *Ancient unknown god found at Jabbul, near Aleppo in northern Mesopotamia. From* Ancient Iraq *by Georges Roux © 1964 by George Allen & Unwin Ltd., U. K.*

The gods of Sumer and those of Egypt were surprisingly similar, according to scholar and author Wallis Budge who produced the 1,356-page *An Egyptian Hieroglyphic Dictionary* in 1920.[12] Budge did not think there was any evidence that the Egyptians or Sumerians copied each other and wrote: "We are therefore driven to the conclusion that both the Sumerians and the early Egyptians derived their primeval gods from some *common but exceedingly ancient source.*" (Author's emphasis.)

Oriental Studies and Sanskrit scholar Robert K. G. Temple was also impressed by the similarities between the two cultures. He wrote in his book *The Sirius Mystery,*[13] "Archaeologists have a difficult task trying to explain the many similarities between Sumer and Egypt, indicating some still undiscovered common origin for the two cultures — an entirely forgotten civilization whose remains must exist somewhere."

After seven years of research about the Dogon tribe in Mali, Africa, Temple hypothesized that the lost civilization was an extraterrestrial one from the star Sirius. In his book, he described how Dogon priests told French anthropologists Marcel Griaule and Germaine Dieterlen that "the starting-point of creation is the star which revolves round Sirius and ... contains the germs of all things. Its movement on its own axis and around Sirius upholds all creation in space." The Dogon priests said the small second star revolved around Sirius every fifty years. The French anthropologists footnoted their research: "The question has not been solved, nor even asked, of how men with no instruments at their disposal could know the movements and certain characteristics of stars which are scarcely visible."

The astronomical facts are that Sirius, also called Alpha Canis Majoris or the Dog Star, was very visible and important to Sumeria, Egypt and other ancient cultures. Sirius is only 8.6 light-years from our solar system and is the brightest star in the night sky. It does have a small companion star known as Sirius B that revolves around it every fifty years. Sirius B was the first white dwarf star to be discovered. But that dwarf is totally invisible to the eye and was not known until 1862 when Alvan Clark, an American astronomer, first saw it with a telescope.

Temple asked, "How did the Dogon know such extraordinary things and did it mean that the Earth had been visited by extraterrestrials?" He answered his own question with an eloquent appeal for all of us to study other emerging facts of our history which might re-define our evolution. *"In considering the very origins of the elements of what we can call human civilization on this planet, we should now take fully into account the possibility that primitive Stone Age men were handed civilization on a platter by visiting extraterrestrial beings who left traces behind for us to decipher."*

[12] *An Egyptian Hieroglyphic Dictionary* © 1920 by Sir E. A. Wallis Budge, London.

[13] *The Sirius Mystery* © 1976 and 1987 by Robert K. G. Temple, Destiny Books.

Tall Humanoids With Red Hair

When I was in Peru in 1987, I also heard about other tall beings with copper red hair, crystal blue eyes, and very white skin that were seven to eight feet tall. The man who told me about them was an archaeology student whose father worked as a traveling nurse in the rural areas of Peru. Edwin Flores told me that his father had traveled in 1981 to a remote village called Pillpinto high in the mountains six hours by car from Cuzco. When he returned, he asked his son why "very tall Irish people" were living in the rugged mountains. His father explained that he had seen them at the outskirts of the village. Flores said his father had not been back since 1981, and he didn't know if the "tall Irish" were still there. I proposed that we go to Pillpinto and find out.

It was a difficult road, climbing most of the time, with hairpin turns. We were stopped twice by security police. I didn't learn until later that we were driving right toward one of the hide-outs of the Communist-inspired rebels known as the "Shining Path," who had been blowing up trains and buildings in Peru. Flores explained to the police that I was an American documentary filmmaker and writer investigating information about extraterrestrial phenomena and that we were looking for "tall Irish" living near Pillpinto. We were surprised when the police said, "Si." They knew about the red-haired people.

At the outpost closest to Pillpinto, two policemen pointed up into the sky and told about a large, round, bright object that had landed on top of one of the mountains. The police said they had climbed up there and if we did, too, we could still see the "burned oval" where the light landed. The police estimated it would take a day to reach the site. I was tempted, but time was limited, and I wanted to at least see if the tall Irish people were still living in Pillpinto. So, we continued on to the village.

When we stopped, our car was surrounded by dozens of children. When Flores explained why I was there, the children began pointing toward houses. He said the children knew about the tall, red-haired people and that they would take us to a man who also knew about them.

My heart began to beat faster as we walked toward the door of a small, adobe home, preceded by the laughter and chatter of the children who surrounded us. The sun was setting and in the twilight shadows, I asked myself what I was going to do if I actually found myself in front of an eight foot, red-haired being from another world.

Flores knocked and the door opened. In front of us stood a man about five-foot-four with clear blue eyes. There were copper patches in his dark, brown hair. I asked Flores if he could find out where the man's parents were. After a long answer in Spanish, Flores said, "His parents live in that house over there. Nothing unusual. But he knows about the 'tall Irish.' He says they used to live outside the village and have moved on. He said there is another man here who knew them."

We walked further surrounded by the children. Flores knocked on the second door. Another man answered and his eyes were clear blue, too. He also had copper patches in his dark hair. He knew about the red-haired people, but said they didn't live there anymore. He did not know where they had come from, either, or where they had gone.

In 1993, Missouri artist Lisa Dusenberry sent me a photograph (Plate 42) of a humanoid she had drawn based on the testimony of a man from southwestern Tennessee who encountered an unusual humanoid during an abduction experience that was similar to the Peruvian description.

He said, "She was eight feet tall, wore a full-length purple, hooded robe, and had long, red hair." He felt she was kind and loving and he was comfortable with her.

Plate 42 -
S. F.
Memphis,
Tennessee.
Adult male
encountered tall,
red-haired being
during an
abduction. Similar
type described by
abductees in
Nevada and
southern California.
Drawing by
Lisa Dusenberry.

Another woman in southern California saw the drawing in Plate 42 and said the female was the same as she had seen during her abduction. A woman and her teenage daughter who were abducted from a rural Nevada town also described red-haired humanoids. Also, tall, copper-haired, blue-eyed beings were involved in the Brian Scott case in southern California in the mid-1970s.

Shorter Humanoids With Blond Hair

Another humanoid type that has been repeatedly described has blond hair and stands five to six feet tall. (Plates 43–45)

In March 1982, a Springfield, Missouri woman experienced four hours of missing time and wanted to remember what had happened. In a hypnosis session with John Carpenter, she recalled that six-foot-tall blond, male humanoids (Plate 43) examined her body as if focused on a particular objective she did not understand. Artist Lisa Dusenberry, who has helped Carpenter and several abductees illustrate memories, sent me a drawing with notes about the abduction.

"The Missouri woman recalled that at the point where she was supposed to turn south in her car, she didn't. She felt as if the car was being pulled by a force faster and faster toward a light at treetop level above and ahead of her. No engine sound, smooth, no bumps, felt like car was floating.

"Then she's in a clearing in the woods with a disc-shaped craft (silver) that has three legs underneath, a light shining toward the ground, and steps that fold down. She is drawn into craft and through several rooms to a larger room with a platform like padded white-silver chrome that molds to body. 'Knows' to lay down. Sees half a dozen men about six feet one or two inches tall, good build, long blond hair, high cheekbones, blue eyes. They wore tight jumpsuits (brown) with matching shoes and belt. Pale yellow stole draped over one shoulder. Winged emblem on chest. Circle with "hawk-eagle" head in center and wings on each side.

"Men were pleasant, caring and said they were her friends. Told her they are going to do some tests, but they won't hurt. Witness feels slight stinging in breast area, some type of injection on each side in armpit area. They want to see how Earth women feed their babies and how they are shaped.

"They then helped her off table (did not talk, could read their thoughts). They said she might see them again some time.

"Witness walked to door, down steps. All of a sudden, she was back in her car. Turned and saw door closing on craft and legs going in as it took off with a whistling, whiny sound. Shot off ground and was gone."

A blond humanoid has also been involved in a Maryland woman's abduction experiences. In June 1992, M.S. suddenly awoke from sound sleep to see bright, blue light coming through the mini-blinds on her bedroom windows. Then it was morning and she discovered a dead circle of grass in her front yard. In the days to follow, helicopters of different sizes and colors periodically flew around her house. Later, in either a vivid dream or conscious memory, the woman encountered a blond humanoid and drew him in Plate 44. Her drawing resembled a Pennsylvania man's watercolor of another blond humanoid shown in Plate 45, who was also associated with a strange helicopter. These abductees do not know each other and do not know about each other's cases.

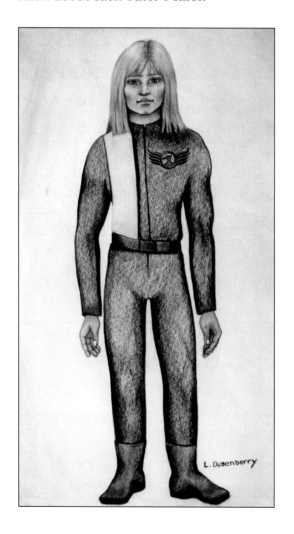

Plate 43 -
M. J.
Springfield, Missouri.
Adult female.
March 1982
abduction involved
six-foot-tall, blond-
haired, blue-eyed male
humanoids wearing a
winged symbol on the left
side of their brown jump-
suit. Drawing by Lisa
Dusenberry.

Plate 44 -
M.S.
Maryland.
Adult female.
Drawn in November
1992 after abduction
experience in which she
believed she saw this
man consciously. "Pure
blond hair, not white.
Black eyes, no pupil.
Benevolent authority,
but lethally serious with
command."

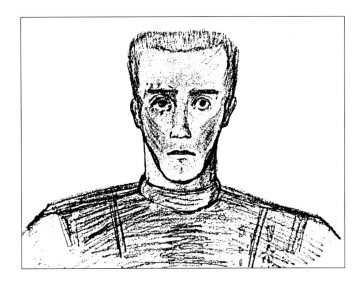

One man from Pennsylvania who has had abduction experiences for several years, painted the watercolors in Plates 45 and 46 after vivid dreams about odd helicopters. Abduction researchers associate vivid dreams with the UFO abduction syndrome. A.R. told me, "It seems that the message was: helicopters can be UFOs. In the first dream, when I looked outside my window, there was a feeling of fear. I saw this glowing object with twin rotor blades. It made a helicopter noise. I felt it was coming for me.

Plate 45 -
A.R.
Jenkintown,
Pennsylvania.
Adult male.
Water color depiction
by A.R. shortly after
November 1992 vivid
dream he associated
with his lifetime
abduction experiences.

That same week, I had another helicopter dream. I noticed it did *not* have rotor blades aft or on top. It flew very close to the house and landed right outside the window. Suddenly, a short stocky man appeared in the room. He looked mean. He had yellow hair and a light complexion. His hair was in a crew cut and he wore a Nazi-like uniform. He grabbed me and looked me in the eyes. His eyes were yellow. He told me he would return."

Plate 46 - *"Helicopter" without rotor blades outside A.R.'s window, silent and motionless prior to appearance of yellow-haired man in vivid dream, November 1992.*

Other blond beings were reported frequently in the 1950s. Several encounters in England were described in *The Humanoids*,[14] edited by Charles Bowen. One witness was a scientist and amateur astronomer named Cedric Allingham. The date was February 18, 1954. Many people were reporting round disks and glowing lights over Europe that year. Mr. Allingham said that a silver disk landed near his home on the northeastern coast of Scotland. A human-looking man about six feet tall emerged wearing a one-piece jumpsuit that also covered his feet. The most unusual feature was the humanoid's forehead which was described as being unusually large and high, nearly twice as big as a human forehead.

[14] *The Humanoids*, Edited by Charles Bowen, © 1969 by Neville Spearman Ltd., England.

In September 1954, an English woman living near Ringwood named Jennie Roestenberg was outside with her two children at 5 o'clock in the afternoon when they were astonished to see a disk-shaped object the color of aluminum hover over their house. It was close enough that she could see transparent panels or windows on the disk. At those windows were two humanoids with very white skin, long hair to their shoulders and "foreheads so high that all their features seemed to be in the lower half of the faces." They were wearing transparent, round helmets and turquoise blue clothing like tight ski suits.

Twenty years later on November 5, 1975, in Snowflake, Arizona, a treecutter named Travis Walton was hit by a beam of light from a diamond-shaped object in the air and suffered five days of missing time. After hypnosis, he remembered encountering two human-looking male beings who wore round, transparent helmets on their heads. Travis thought they were astronauts who had come to save him from smaller, grey-white beings he also encountered at the beginning of his abduction experience in the same craft. The humanoids had blond hair long enough to cover their ears. Their skin was bronze-colored, like a deep and even tan. The bodies were muscular and they wore leotard-type suits that were blue, similar to Jennie Roestenberg's report in England in 1954. Travis Walton remembered that the humanoids he saw had bright, golden-hazel eyes and there was something odd about them. Perhaps the pupils were not round.

Praying Mantis

Another type is often compared to a praying mantis insect. (Plates 47-50) Abductees say the creatures are six to eight feet tall. The skin is green and the eyes are enormous. Rust-colored irises flecked with gold surround large, black, vertical pupils. Abductees sense that these beings, although hideous to look at from a human point of view, are non-violent, extremely ancient in age, and have knowledge about "all details of human existence." One man said he thought the "insect creatures were genetically engineered by a tall humanoid species."

Plates 47 and 50 were drawn by a Central California woman who has seen the praying mantis types in abductions since she was a teenager. Plates 48-49 were painted by a man who encountered an insect-like creature during the daytime near the barn at his Georgia farm home when he was eight years old. He associated the creature with a silver disk in the sky and small, grey beings that have appeared in his life many times and which he considers to be androids programmed to do work for the praying mantis beings and tall humanoids.

Plate 47 -
L.P.
Bakersfield,
California.
Adult female.
Drawn 1990,
based on
encounters
in abduction
experiences
since
childhood.

Plates 48-49:
Creature encountered by David Huggins at Georgia farm when he was eight. He associated it with small, grey beings that he thought were androids programmed to do work for the praying mantis type and tall humanoids.

Plate 50 -
L. P.
Bakersfield,
California.
Adult female.
Drawn in 1990
based on teenage
abduction
experience with
tall "praying
mantis" being.

Lizard

A six-foot-tall, green, scaly-skinned humanoid with large, yellow irises that surround black, vertical pupils (Plates 51- 53) is similar to the "Lizard Guy" seen by Ron and Paula Watson near their Mt. Vernon, Missouri home in July 1983. Other abductees, such as Jeanne Robinson of Springfield, Missouri, have encountered this "reptile type." Jeanne described the chest as having "bones" that protruded under the scaly skin and gave the impression of body armor.

Some abductees wonder if these "lizards" are another type of android, like the "Bigfoot," created to do physical tasks for another controlling intelligence. Others insist the reptile humanoids are an independent species with its own agenda.

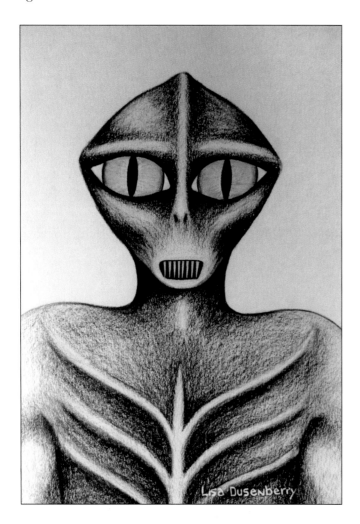

Plate 51 -
Jeanne Robinson.
Springfield,
Missouri.
Adult female.
Artist rendering in
1990 by Lisa
Dusenberry
based on Robinson's
description.

Another Missouri woman saw a "repulsive-looking" entity with thin arms and "ugly face like a giant grasshopper." Lisa Dusenberry sent a drawing with notes so I could compare the case to other "lizard" drawings I have received. (Plate 52)

> "M.J. was in bed sleeping when she began floating out of bedroom toward a light and through wall. Felt the sensation of being pulled by a force with fast movement.
>
> The being stood about 5'9" with green body, looked scaly and rough. Felt electricity going through her hands. Saw pea-green eyes with pupils like a cat (vertical slits), black and yellow. Eyes slanted down toward outer face. No hair. Small mouth. Thin arms, hands like a duck with tan or brown webbing. Three or four long fingers with nails on end.
>
> After hypnosis, she felt that "they need human beings to make them stronger. Trying to get our genes — threat of dying out. Inbreeding with us to see if what we have can make them stronger."

Like so many other experiencers of the UFO abduction syndrome, the Missouri abductee did not understand clearly what the survival problem is or why Earth life should be involved in an alien species' regeneration.

Plate 52 -
M. J.
Springfield,
Missouri.
Adult female.
1991 abduction,
encountered 5'9"
reptilian creature.
Drawing by Lisa
Dusenberry after
M.J.'s August 13,
1991, hypnosis
session with John
Carpenter.

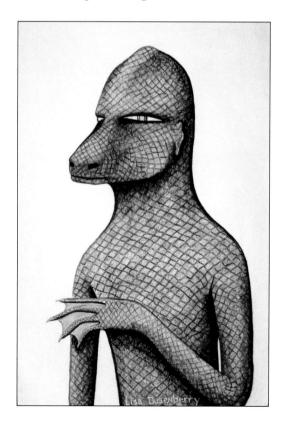

Plate 53 -
"Lizard guy"
seen through
binoculars by
Ron and
Paula
Watson,
Mt. Vernon,
Missouri,
July 1983.
Artist
rendering by
Hingwah Hatch
for author.

"Bigfoot"

Possibly working with the "lizard" types as a physical labor force for something else out there are eight-foot-tall, reddish-brown, hairy, ape-like creatures with large, round eyes and vertical pupils. (Plate 54) A Montana rancher shot at one in the 1970s and it *disappeared in a flash of light.* That case, combined with others about translucent beings, has provoked speculation that we humans are being manipulated by an intelligence that has sophisticated technology that can make us see anything it wants us to see. Some beings might even be holographic projections.

Plate 54 - *"Bigfoot" seen through binoculars by Ron and Paula Watson, Mt. Vernon, Missouri, July 1983. Artist rendering by Hingwah Hatch for author..*

Men In Black (MIBs)

An alleged military source wrote to me about the enigmatic "men in black" usually described as about five feet tall, olive-skinned or "skin like a corpse," and wearing human clothes that don't match the human time frame of the encounter, often appearing in clothes from decades earlier. The source wrote that MIBs "are the genetically engineered humanoid counterpart to the praying mantis, both created by a tall species to perform long-term tasks. They take on the appearance of humans. Some of these genetically engineered beings have greater intelligence than their creators, the tall humanoids." (Plate 55)

This source implied official knowledge about a civilization from another galaxy. But there was no explanation about why such a distant civilization would create androids to come here and harvest genetic material from humans and Earth animals.

Plate 55 -
J. C.
Lakewood,
New Jersey.
Adult male.
Sketch on
February 16, 1992.
"Man in black"
seen at foot of bed,
October 1989.

Translucent Beings, Balls of Light, Shadow Beings

Some people report translucent beings, balls of light, and shadow beings who emerge through "tears" or "holes" in the air of their bedroom or come through walls, windows and other solid objects.

This leads many people to question whether their experiences are real. Moving through solid objects seems dream-like to the human mind because there is no context in which to relate such action to solid, 3-dimensional reality as we know it. (Plate 56)

Plate 56 -
L.P.
Bakersfield,
California.
Adult female.
Drawn in 1990
based on teenage
experience.

EPILOGUE

"It may be difficult for us to avoid seriously entertaining that most disturbing and also exciting of notions: that intelligent beings from elsewhere in the galaxy have already visited Earth, already know of our existence, may possibly be monitoring us at this moment with a robot probe somewhere in our solar system, and may have the intention of returning in person some day to see how the civilization they established is really getting on."

ROBERT K. G. TEMPLE
THE SIRIUS MYSTERY, 1987

People who have reported seeing UFOs were studied by psychologists at Carlton University in Ottawa, Canada. In the November 1993 *Journal of Abnormal Psychology,*[1] investigators summarized their findings. The researchers found the eyewitnesses to be as intelligent and mentally healthy as other people and not more prone to fantasy. Of forty-nine adults who had seen unidentified flying objects, ten said they had seen a craft close-up; ten said they had seen an alien being; seven described verbal contact with alien beings; eight reported telepathic contact; seven remembered total body paralysis; eight reported missing time; and two recalled going aboard a spacecraft.

Also, in the first week of November 1993, the cover of *Time Magazine* headlined: "Cloning Humans — The first laboratory duplication of a human embryo raises the question: Where do we draw the line?"[2]

The article described the negative responses from around the world and stated: "A Brave New World of cookie-cutter humans, baked and bred to order, seemed, if not just around the corner, then just over the horizon. Ethicists called up nightmare visions of baby farming, of clones cannibalized for spare parts ... Protesters took to the streets, calling for an immediate ban on human-embryo cloning."

Perhaps eons ago an alien intelligence used DNA manipulation in a directed panspermia program to create new life forms on this planet, as Nobel Prize scientists Svante Arrhenius and Francis Crick have speculated. (Introduction) Perhaps that same intelligence, skilled in genetic sciences, had

[1] *Journal of Abnormal Psychology, 1993* November Issue, © 1993 American Psychological Association, Washington, D. C., Pages 624-632.

[2] *Time Magazine,* November 8, 1993.

no qualms about using cloning for its own evolution. The small grey entities reported so often in the abduction syndrome are nearly indistinguishable from one another. The abductees themselves were first to suggest that those might be genetically created and cloned androids for various tasks under the control of yet another higher intelligence. Perhaps DNA manipulation and endless cloning lead to sterility. Then an entire civilization would be challenged to resurrect itself. After thirty years of case studies in the human abduction syndrome and worldwide animal mutilations, one clear pattern is the alien pre-occupation with reproductive organs, sperm and ova. In an odd symbiosis, perhaps another life form needs us for its existence and wants us to survive.

Yet, humanity stands at its own crossroads about how life will continue to evolve on Earth with its global environmental deterioration? Those who conclude that an advanced intelligence is creating the worldwide crop circle patterns also sense that something is trying to wake us up to our past and present so we will have a future. That future will most likely involve more interaction with beings and intelligences other than human.

The revolution about to occur — a new consciousness that we are not alone in the universe — carries with it the unpredictable consequences of human reactions to it. Michael Lindemann, a futurist in the 1990s, tried to understand the angry denial of the complex alien phenomena by our current social, political, economic and religious systems. He concluded:

"The inescapable profundity of the alien presence has become a source of social pathology in our time. As a culture, we have not yet learned how to tell the truth about something so huge, so strange, and so unexpected. Individuals who make an honest effort to deal with it often discover that their personal stability is at risk. Consequently, the alien presence requires us all to grow, to become stronger and clearer, and to help one another to find our way in a genuinely new world."

Volume II, *High Strangeness* will include the testimonies of scientists, other civilian professionals and military personnel about their highly strange encounters with other realities.

Out of these experiences, a new cosmology is emerging that says there are many more dimensions than this one — that Earth exists in one particular dimension that has a particular atomic frequency — that other frequency forms from other dimensions can penetrate and even overlap our Space-Time, as different radio and TV signals can move together in a single space to be separated at a receiver by a frequency tuner —that there are many other universes which can be radically different from ours in appearance and physical make-up — and that intelligences other than human are *forcing* glimpses of other realities upon us.

APPENDIX I

The Geometry and Diatonic Ratios of the Crop Circles
by Gerald S. Hawkins

<u>Theorem I</u>
    Let three equal circles that share a common tangent make an equilateral triangle. If a circle is drawn through the centers of two, concentric with the third circle, then it can be proved that the ratio of areas of the concentric circles is 16:3, corresponding to the musical note F''. The two circles taken as satellites give the note C.

<u>Theorem II</u>
    For an equilateral triangle, the ratio of areas of the circumscribed and the inscribed circle gives C''. The annulus between the circles when divided by the area of the inscribed circle gives G'.
Corollary: If the triangle is isosceles, and the circles are concentric, then the ratio of areas is 4 x (side)2/(base)2 : 1, and the ratio from the annulus is one unit less.

<u>Theorem III</u>
    For a square, the ratio of the areas of circumscribed and inscribed circles gives C', and the annulus gives C. Four applications of this theorem give a reduction of 16, and the notes become C'''' and B'''.

<u>Theorem IV</u>
    For a hexagon, the ratio of areas of circumscribed and inscribed circles gives F.

<u>Theorem V</u>
    Theorems II-IV are a special set within the family of regular polygons – only the triangle, square and hexagon will give a diatonic ratio from the circumscribed and inscribed circles. V is a general theorem from which I-IV can be derived.

APPENDIX II

Other Geometry Discoveries in English Crop Formations
by Gerald S. Hawkins

Fordham Place, 1990
Two equal circles with centers one radius apart share a common chord on which can be constructed a circle of exactly $\frac{1}{6}$ radius, giving the note G″. Furthermore, two circles with centers on the midpoint of the chord can be constructed to yield a ratio of areas of 5:2, the note E′.

Ickleton, 1991
A cardioid can be constructed with a generating circle of unit diameter. With the origin at the cusp, and polar angle measured from the base, the radius vector can be derived by Euclidean geometry at 60° and 30°. The values are $\frac{3}{2}$, note G, and $1 + \frac{1}{2}\sqrt{3} = \frac{15}{8.04}$, the note B.

Barbury Castle, 1991

(i) The circumference of a circle of radius r is equal to 6 arcs with chord r, and radius of curvature r.

(ii) If a set of equally spaced concentric circles is divided into m equal sectors, the shape generates odd numbers because the circumference of the nth circle equals the sum of n arcs when $n = 2m - 1$.

(iii) If in (ii) the complete circumference of the first circle is included in the sum, then the shape generates even numbers, because $n = 2m - 2$.

(iv) If Theorem II is applied twice to an equilateral triangle, the ratios give notes C″″ and B″′.

(v) Ten equal circles in contact can make a figure where the centers of nine define an equilateral triangle. The ratio of the area of the circle containing the figure to the circumscribed circle of the triangle is $\frac{13}{12} + 1/\sqrt{3} = \frac{5}{3.01}$, note A.

APPENDIX III

A Posthumous Experiment Involving The Diatonic Scale

England's *Journal of the Society for Psychical Research* had a "Report On The Oliver Lodge Posthumous Test" in its September 1955 Volume 38, No. 685 issue. Oliver Lodge was a prominent physicist who lived in the village of Lake, two miles from Stonehenge. He investigated the electromotive force in the voltaic cell, electromagnetic waves and wireless telegraphy, and the application of electricity to disperse fog and smoke. He also studied lightning and electricity and was a leader in psychic research. After his young son Raymond's death in World War I, Lodge focused much of his research on life after death and produced *The Survival of Man* (1909), *Raymond, or Life and Death* (1916) and *Past Years* (1931). Before Oliver Lodge died in 1940, he served twice as President of the London Society for Psychical Research.

The *Encyclopedia of Occultism and Parapsychology* said Lodge "missed no opportunity to affirm his belief in public that death is not the end, that there are higher beings in the scale of existence, and that intercommunication between this world and the next is possible."

On June 20, 1930, Oliver Lodge placed a sealed packet with the London Society for Psychical Research that contained a message he hoped to transmit through a medium after his death to prove that his consciousness survived his body. He died on August 21, 1940, and the Society waited until 1946 to investigate Oliver Lodge's "posthumous test." A committee was appointed to work with mediums and when the sealed envelope was opened, the group discovered seven more envelopes, one inside the other. The message that Oliver Lodge wanted to communicate from the after life was inside the innermost envelope. The rest contained instructions regarding the procedure Lodge wanted the mediums to follow.

The September 1955 *Journal* report stated: "The final message chosen by Sir Oliver as evidence of his identity and survival, dated 10 June 1930, consisted, in his own words, of the following:

> 'An elementary exercise (on the white keys of the piano only) which has more or less been an obsession. I have never written it out before, but I have strummed it on tables and chairs thousands and possibly a million times.'"

Oliver Lodge's five-finger exercise included the diatonic notes C E G E D F E D C E G E D E C and his detailed instructions about how he fingered the sequence of white keys.

Several mediums came close to communicating the musical content, but the Society deemed the experiment a failure because it was decided there were too many envelopes with too many clues leading up to the final description of Lodge's musical exercise. Once Lodge's final envelope had been opened, the test was at an end.

In 1955, after considering Lodge's posthumous challenge, Robert Thouless wrote in Vol. 38, Issue No. 686 of the Society's *Journal* that the best posthumous test would be one in which "the target is the key to a message in cipher. The main requisite, I think, is that a satisfactory test must be one which allows for an indefinite number of checks without spoiling the test."

A few who remembered Oliver Lodge's posthumous experiment have joked that perhaps the physicist persisted with his test in the diatonic geometries set down in cereal crops around the world.

It's interesting to note that the diatonic ratios equivalent to C" and G' have been reported in the 1993 Guildford Hog's Back formation (Plate 88, Chapter 1); the 1992 Oliver's Castle formation (Plates 21; 38-40; 54 in Chapter 1); and the 1991 Barbury Castle "geometry lesson" (Plates 1-2, Chapter 1). On the piano keyboard, Page 57, Chapter 1, C" equals the alphabet letter O and G' equals the letter L.

Did Oliver Lodge "sign" his work after death from another dimension?

APPENDIX IV

Pathology report by John Altshuler, M. D., concerning Sylvania, Alabama, mutilated cow, February 24, 1993. Pages 143-146, Chapter 2.

JOHN H. ALTSHULER, M.D.

HEMATOLOGY
(Specializing in Coagulation Disorders)

Greenwood Executive Park-Bldg. 10
7485 East Peakview Ave.
Englewood, CO 80111
740-7771

March 9, 1993

Ms. Linda Moulton Howe
P.O. Box 538
Huntingdon Valley
PA 19006-0538

Re: Two tissue samples from udder excision
Mutilated Cow found Feb. 24, 1993
at the Kenneth Hiland farm in
Sylvania, Alabama. Exumed Thurs.,
Feb. 25, 1993 by Linda Moulton Howe.

REPORT REGARDING MUTILATION OF COW FOUND FEBRUARY 25, 1993

Two bottles were received, one labeled "Both mutilator's cut
& known cut at scene", the second was cow hide with
mutilator's cuts as described to me by Ms. Linda M. Howe. The
enclosed drawings both show outlines of tissues received in
each bottle as well as sections taken for microscopic study.
All tissue was fixed in 50% alcohol and subsequently fixed in
10% buffered formalin prior to sectioning for microscopic
review.

GROSS EXAMINATION OF TISSUES

Both tissues (one from each bottle) were of cow hide and were
covered with white tan hair. All borders of both tissues
revealed sharp, smooth edges without any jagged edges or
tearing surfaces. There were no teeth marks on the tissues
and fragments of tissue were not identified as would be seen
if the edges were to represent chewing or tearing of hide by
predator attack. The borders of the tissue were pliable and
non-charred. There was no "plastisizing" change in the
tissues, i.e., firm to hard rolled edges often seen on tissue
that is exposed to high temperature cutting. Neither cautery
burn effects nor laser type burned surfaces were seen in any
of the tissues.

MICROSCOPIC EXAMINATION OF TISSUE

All sections examined revealed normal epidermis, papillary
and reticular dermis structures and normal hypodermic fat.
Hair follicles are normal as well as adnexal skin structures.

CONCLUSIONS

1. The tissue submitted show borders that are consistent with
   sharp dissection.

2. There is no evidence of heat or cautery artefact either by
   gross or microscopic examination.

3. There is no evidence to support the thesis that the edges
   of the tissues submitted are consistent with tearing or
   chewing as would be seen by predator attack.

Sincerely,

John H. Altshuler, M.D., Pathologist

APPENDIX V

Pathology report by
John Altshuler,
M. D., concerning
Crossville,
Alabama,
mutilated calf,
February 27,
1993, Pages
147-148,
Chapter 2.

JOHN H. ALTSHULER, M.D.

HEMATOLOGY
(Specializing in Coagulation Disorders)

Greenwood Executive Park-Bldg. 10
7485 East Peakview Ave.
Englewood, CO 80111
740-7771

MICROSCOPIC REPORT ON CALF FOUND MUTILATED 2/27/93

MICROSCOPIC EXAMINATION
Multiple sections taken from each specimen reveals the same findings through out. Because the hide specimens have thick white tan hair on their surfaces, microtome sectioning of the tissue was very difficult. Tissue was shaved as cleanly as possible and resubmitted for microscopic slide preparations. The following are the findings:

Hide epithelium is squamous in type and shows hyperkeratosis as well as a plethora of hair shafts and hair follicles. There are many infundibular structures identified in the reticular dermis and hair shafts are seen passing through the papillary dermis to the superficial layers of squamous epithelium.. At borders of mutilator cuts there is a tinctorial change of the reticular dermal collagen (Hematoxylin and Eosin stain) from the normal eosinophilia to a basophilic color. There is also a smudging of collagen bundles with loss of architecture of collagen bundles. Disruption of much of the tissue has occurred because of difficulty in cutting the tissue with the microtome knife. None-the-less there is dermal vacuolization present in some of the deeper collagen tissue. Nuclear degeneration is seen in the areas of bluish collagen change, however no nuclear pallisading (string bean effect) is seen in any of the sections. The nuclear pallisade effect is typical of cautery artefact created by high heat application to tissue.

SUMMARY OF FINDINGS AND CONCLUSIONS
The presence of collagen basophilia and collagen destruction with nuclear damage are abnormal. These findings are limited to cut edges of the tissues. Normal tissue lies adjacent to these abnormal areas. Although one cannot conclude as to the type of instrument used to apply heat to these tissue edges, the findings are consistent with tissue exposure to high temperature such as a red hot wire or instrument blade. As the abnormal tissue findings are in microscopic foci next to normal tissue, one may rule out the possibility of generalized hide changes of heat such as prolonged exposure to ultraviolet light, a physical agent well known to cause similar changes in skin tissues.

John H. Altshuler
John H. Altshuler, M.D.

APPENDIX VI

Multiple Witness Abductions:
The Judy Doraty and Cindy Tindle Case (Chapters 3 and 4)
by
John Carpenter, M.S.W.
Psychiatric Hypnotherapist © 1993

The shared abduction experience of Judy Doraty and her daughter, Cindy Tindle, is significant. When an alleged UFO abduction contains multiple participants, the information is not confined to one individual's mind. Details can be cross-checked between the different perspectives. Confabulation and fantasy are unlikely if specific details from different hypnosis sessions match. If one were to ask each member of a small group of people to create an abduction tale, each might produce some general similarities, but not exactly similar details of events, and certainly not observations of each other. Further, if details reported by two or more people not only match each other, but match details in *unpublished* research, the correlations are highly unlikely to be coincidental.

Innocently fabricated "false memories" or psychological representations of repressed sexual trauma do not explain independently reported experiences which match even in *different perspectives* of the same event. Matching, but different perspectives of the same event, are found in the two hypnosis sessions of Judy Doraty and Cindy Tindle ten years apart, one in 1980 and the other in 1990. If repressed sexual traumas were the source for an individual's claims, then the resulting creation would be an intricate and symbolic tapestry of that individual's personality, history, psycho-dynamics, life experiences and perspective — not an account matching in great detail with another person's independent recollections.

There has been no satisfactory medical or psychological explanation for the mutual and simultaneous onset of periods of amnesia among participants in the UFO abduction syndrome. Not only do they seem to enter periods of amnesia at the same moment, but abductees usually return to conscious awareness at the same time in the same sequence of events. No injuries or other physical causes have been identified that would explain these simultaneous periods of missing time. If these reports were hoaxes, one would expect the incidents to be recalled with identical detail. However, people recalling simultaneous UFO abductions tend to report a set of experiences that contain an overlapping and correlating subset of events. In real life, no two people are able to share a reality in *exactly* the same manner due to differences in physical location, attention, perception, interpretation, concentration and personal predisposition due to historical and emotional influences. Judy Doraty and her daughter, Cindy, report matching memories with different perspectives based upon what each experienced together or apart, but nothing that is contradictory.

Skeptics have expressed concern over the influence of both the hypnotic trance state and the beliefs of the particular hypnotist in suggesting to the subject that these experiences actually occurred. The case of Judy and her daughter Cindy clearly demonstrates that when these two women were hypnotized by two different therapists with different techniques ten years apart, specific matching details still emerged from their recall.

One of my own approaches during hypnotic regressions is to deliberately lead a subject toward logical sensible responses, which are actually contrary to the abduction data. This approach tests the person's suggestibility. To resist carefully-worded suggestions and respond with unusual or unexpected details that actually match another individual's account is remarkable. I find further reinforcement when each person's spontaneous memories in independently-retrieved testimonies correlate with *unpublished* research data.

Judy Doraty, Cindy Tindle and other UFO abductees describe events that each experiences as <u>real</u> and each person tells his or her story from their perspective which includes language and emotions consistent in a genuine and unsettling encounter with something quite beyond normal realities. The psychological responses of abductees include great stress and emotional upset that would be expected in encounters of bizarre non-human beings and alien surroundings.

It might be assumed that during the ten years between their hypnosis sessions that Judy Doraty could have inadvertently or deliberately given details of her experience to family members, including Cindy. Despite Cindy's claim that she did not recall that May 1973 night well, any offhand remarks by Judy could have encouraged the creation of some common knowledge. However, there is absolutely no evidence to support such assumptions. Judy said she fully understood the importance of remaining silent about details recalled while under hypnosis. She insisted that she deliberately did not reveal any details to Cindy or any other family member because she had hoped that one day Cindy might agree to a hypnotic regression of her own that could possibly validate Judy's disturbing recollections. It is a fact that she and Cindy had not lived near each other for any length of time nor had they maintained regular communication. Cindy clearly stated that her mother never shared any details. Cindy said she had only a vague implication that "more happened than just the sighting." Cindy also said that as a teenager she had little interest in what happened in Houston and was frightened by the suggestion of hypnosis in her early twenties when Linda Moulton Howe asked Judy in 1980 if her daughter would also undergo regression. Cindy even admits that she made fun of her mother's avid interest in UFOs despite Cindy's own memories of close-up sightings, "one as huge as a football field," hovering very low over her and at least seven other witnesses.

Skeptics can also easily claim that Cindy simply viewed the 1980 Emmy Award-winning documentary *A Strange Harvest* by Linda Moulton Howe which contained portions of her mother's hypnosis session with Dr. Leo Sprinkle. There are three major problems with those claims: 1) Cindy had never heard of the documentary because her mother did not tell her about it. 2) The documentary was broadcast in Colorado where it was produced, not on national television. 3) Cindy's first hypnosis session lasted for three hours and included many details that were not included in the edited ten minutes of Judy's hypnosis session in *A Strange Harvest*. Doubters can also claim that Cindy simply read a copy of Linda Moulton Howe's 1989 book *An Alien Harvest - Further Evidence Linking Animal Mutilations and Human Abductions to Alien Life Forms*. That large book contains a complete transcript of Judy Doraty's hypnosis session. However, Cindy had never heard of Howe's book and by her own admission has not had time to read because her life was dominated by raising three children and other domestic matters.

If Judy and Cindy were trying to hoax a story, it is highly unlikely either would have anything to gain by undergoing independent hypnosis sessions ten years apart in two different states with two different therapists.

Personally, I was impressed with Cindy's straightforward, humble and genuine personality. She is an intelligent, hard-working, "earthy" young woman, raising three children and trying to survive financially while desiring more education. Her curiosity had grown over the years about what, if anything, had happened in May 1973. That curiosity lead to her first hypnosis session with me for Linda Moulton Howe's documentary *Earth Mysteries: Alien Life Forms* on August 6, 1990.

That night before the session, Cindy said: "I know I saw it (the light) ... Maybe all we did was just see something. Maybe there is more to it. Hell, I don't know. I <u>want</u> to know. I can't remember much of anything after (the light). I just want to see if I'm nuts! That's why I was curious to see if anything really did happen, you know?"

Cindy would have been quite satisfied to have remembered nothing more about that night in 1973. Instead, she was absolutely astounded at what was revealed vividly and emotionally as the curtain of amnesia was finally lifted. She witnessed and described peculiar events and odd entities in a scenario totally unfamiliar to her own life, but not at all unfamiliar to researchers studying abduction data. Her own shock and immediate disbelief merely added more credibility to the correlating information she provided.

It was a memorable moment at the end of the three-hour hypnosis session when Cindy innocently asked, "Did I say anything like my mother did?" She did not realize then how much had emerged and how closely it paralleled her mother's story.

Judy Doraty was tearful and relieved when I called to tell her that, after ten long years of waiting and wondering, she should know her daughter did have a hypnotic regression that produced important correlations with her own perplexing recollections.

Correlations Between Hypnosis Sessions
For Judy Doraty (March 13, 1980) and
Her Daughter Cindy D. Tindle (August 6, 1990)

Description of Light Beam:

<u>Judy Doraty</u>

<u>Cindy D. Tindle</u>

*"It's like a spotlight shining
down on the back of my car."*

*"It's like a spotlight up in the sky.
I'm looking out the back window.
It was out my left-hand side. It
hurts my eyes. It's going the same
direction as our car."*

*"It's a pale yellow light. It's
like a search light, but it wasn't
bright. I notice that it's not just
a light. But it has substance. It was
like you could put your hand in and
feel it. It is like dust particles, like if
you see through sunlight – there was
a swirling motion to it."*

*"It's almost like I'm getting dew
sprayed on me. It's in the light –
yellow light. It feels moist as I'm
glaring into this light. This had
like particles in it – like static on a
TV screen – snowy, like dust
swirling in sunlight."*

    Although the more commonly-reported color of a UFO beam of light is white or blue, Judy and Cindy described the same pale yellow color of the beam lifting the calf. I have heard a similar description in other abduction cases of "snowy" or "TV static" within a beam of light. Although not commonly publicized, the "swirling" effect on soil, dust and leaves has been noted in other cases as well. It is also interesting to note that both Judy and Cindy reported a <u>tactile</u> sensation near the light.

Description of Animal in Beam of Light:

Judy Doraty

Cindy D. Tindle

"I can see an animal being taken up in this light. I can see it squirming and trying to get free. A baby calf – brown and white. And it's like it's being sucked up."

"Oh, my land! They're pulling up a cow! No, it's a baby calf (later said "brown and white"). It's moving around, but I don't hear anything. It acts like it's bawling, but I can't hear it. Oh, this can't be right! They can't be doing this. This just don't happen! It's just pulling the calf up – the light is. It's about half way up in the air in this light, and it's moving around – it's trying to get away. It's scared. Its feet are kicking. It gets up so high and then it just disappears."

"The tongue is cut, but it's not cut lengthwise, but up and down."

"It looks like a tongue. Like she's (alien being) scraping the hide off of a tongue. Looks big – no, oh, Lordy! I hope it ain't the calf – 'cause it's not big like a big cow's tongue. It's bigger than ours – it's real long. It's almost like a perfect – like it's even come out of the throat area."

Description of Physical Environment:

Judy Doraty

"There's basins. They look like basins. They're scooped-out areas. I don't know if it's a drain. But they're some sort of basins."

"Instruments of some kind ... like a knife, but more like a razor – like a straight razor type. And there's long tubes that take samples. I can see stuff running through the tubes, but I don't remember where it goes."

"There's light in the room, but I don't know (where it comes from). It's just there."

"The room is kind of rounded, and it's just all together. There's no seams or nothing. Everything seems built-in ... light grey."

"They have the large swivel chairs, the chairs that turn."

Cindy D. Tindle

"It looks like it's almost got a basin in there. A big basin ... looks like it funnels down like this into the floor."

"Jesus Christ, she's (alien entity) got a scalpel – like a straight razor. There's little test tubes which fits, slips into the walls."

"They've got lights somewhere, but I don't know where the lights are. Everything's lit up in there."

"Everything's rounded, kinda. I don't know what kind of a room this is. I've never seen anything like it ... steel grey, cold."

"Like a swivel chair – like a high back leather chair that can be swung back and forth."

Both women reported "basins," "drains," "straight razors," "tubes," and a removed "tongue." Cindy's detailed recall of the type of cut on the tongue matches with chilling accuracy the manner in which mutilated animals have been discovered with their tongues neatly removed "from deep within the throat." Cindy also reported witnessing a cleanly cut "dog's snout," as if sliced vertically off a dog's head leaving the severed end as "smooth as glass." This matches other reports of surgically-precise excisions of organs and tissues in the worldwide animal mutilation phenomenon.

Descriptions of Non-Human Beings:

Judy Doraty

Cindy D. Tindle

"Had very, very large eyes. They were piercing and frightening. The eyes do not blink. If they had a nose, it was very small. I did not see a mouth ... a small chin, rather pointed ... they have a body suit on ... grey, I guess."

"Oh, God! Oh, these characters are scary-looking. How in the hell did they ever get me out there? He looks buggy – like a bug – oh, Lord! It's got big eyes – black – no pupils. They've got slits for a mouth. They're skinny. He's got a head like a bug – real rounded with a pointed chin – like an ant – no hair. I don't think they have ears ... wearing a grey jumpsuit."

"They have very large eyes. They're very hypnotic ... just like a cat. It's almost like, I guess – a snake?"

"They've all got big eyes – almond-shaped – bigger in the front and slanting towards the side of the head. Oh, wait a minute, they look like a snake! The pupils – are really like a cat's, I guess. They got the long pupil, yeah, they look just like a snake – or like a lizard or something."

"They pivot. They are very quick with their work. But they appear to pivot – kind of like on their heel."

"He turns too quick. Quick and jerky."

The description of cat or snake-like eyes with vertical pupils has been reported numerous times to researchers, but not publicized as often. It is not clear whether this is a different entity altogether, or some form of physical alteration or change in the same more commonly-reported "big black eyes with no pupils."

Description of Alien Communications:

Judy Doraty

"They talk, but not with their mouth. They talk like someone talking through their nose, holding their nose and talking in a high pitch – it has a funny sound – a nasal quality – kind of a Chinese sound – kind of a sing-song."

Cindy D. Tindle

"It's almost like an Oriental type-sing-song. Ying, yang, yong – sing-songy – ying, yang, yong – like that. But I don't know if it's coming from his throat or what." (Cindy also described hearing clicking sounds which she thought were made among the aliens themselves.)

The majority of abductees say there is telepathic communication which often includes the description of "sing-song sounds like a radio inside my head playing Mickey Mouse talking real fast."

Other abductees have also reported hearing "chirping" or "clicking" sounds.

Recognition of Each Other Inside Abduction Experience:

<u>Judy Doraty</u>

"I know I have a feeling of fear. I'm just afraid they're going to do to her what they did to the animal! I'm so afraid they're going to cut her or something."

"I just visualize her on a table. They put her to sleep I guess. They don't care. They just go about their work as if it's nothing. They don't seem to have any emotions. They take some samples from her, just scrapings like, ... they go inside her mouth."

<u>Cindy D. Tindle</u>

"I see my mother in a window. It looks like she's screaming, 'That's my daughter!' I feel hurt for her because she's so scared. And I know I'm okay."

"I'm on a table – looks like steel. They pushed me down. It feels like they've got me strapped down! I tried kicking one of them. I'm scared! I don't know what they're doing to me. They're grabbing at my hands. I'm screaming NO! at them. They don't care. He's going for my face. They're pushing my mouth up against my braces and it hurts the inside of my cheeks. They want to look at my teeth. They touch me with a probe on the forehead, and it feels like I go out or relax – almost like a sedative-type thing. I started gagging; they put this thing in my mouth. They're scratching on the inside of my throat."

Probably the most significant type of correlating detail in abduction encounters with multiple participants is when each witness sees the other(s) and can accurately describe what each is doing at the same moment in time during the sequence of activities. Judy had been watching Cindy during this part of the exam. Cindy recalled seeing her mother at that same point in the exam process. Judy became extremely upset recalling that moment. Cindy noted the intense emotions on her mother's face, in her scream, and feels saddened by her mother's fears. Judy and Cindy are looking at each other through some kind of opening or window and each described a different perspective on the same scene and moment.

▲

It's important to stress that in the Springfield hypnosis session, I never asked Cindy to look around to see where her mother was. That detail emerged spontaneously in the natural recall of her memory as it surfaced out of amnesia. Cindy did not fully comprehend why her mother was so upset. Cindy did not know that her mother had just observed the tissue sampling of the calf's organs in a nearby room and was afraid that her daughter would be next. Cindy never saw the calf physically worked on by the beings, so it's reasonable to assume that while Judy watched, Cindy was in another room being examined as she described and later saw the animal parts after the excisions had been done.

These sets of correlations provided much detail not known previously by Judy and Cindy, but are quite familiar to abduction researchers: the physical nature of the beings, the shape and feel of the craft interior, and the table examination with a sedating procedure. Judy was never sure what they were doing inside her daughter's mouth, but Cindy's session ten years later provided the surprising insight that the creatures might be studying her braces.

After the Abduction:

Judy Doraty

Cindy D. Tindle

"Then it (UFO) just shot straight up and sat right up next to the moon like a star. It went from very, very big to very, very little in a matter of seconds."

"This is going to sound crazy, but I feel like we're flying up in this huge object. It's taking us up next to the moon, but I know physically I can't be doing that ... just 'cause we couldn't get up there and back that suddenly."

These quotes came from a confusing moment for both mother and daughter. The scene had switched to later in the May 1973 evening after what appeared to have been the first phase of the abduction in which both mother and daughter were in the same alien craft. Afterward, they are at an aunt's home where as many as seven or more family members were gathered to watch the strange "football field-sized object" that approached a nearby field and slowly descended. But for Cindy, cricket sounds vanished in the night air and "time seemed to stop" as if she were abducted a second time for unknown reasons. Cindy recalled a strange sensation of looking at the windows in the craft and then suddenly being with her cousin Sharon in an upstairs bedroom, watching part of the scene from that window. Cindy told her cousin, "If they're real Martians, they'd be able to read our minds and they could take their ship up and sit next to the moon." Cindy thought she was talking about this in an upstairs bedroom and even her mother, Judy, recalled seeing Cindy in an "upstairs window." But the aunt's home did not have any upstairs or second level and the cousin's bedroom did not have any windows.

Under hypnosis, Cindy learned that she had been abducted that night a second time with her cousin Sharon while underneath the huge craft in the field just after the cricket sounds had vanished. One assumes that Cindy watched from the craft's window and saw her mother on the ground below, and that Judy actually saw Cindy in the window of the craft, but thought it was the house. Both women shared a "screen memory" or distortion of reality apparently placed in their respective minds deliberately by the alien intelligence.

The reinforcing details of independently-retrieved accounts must cause us to pause and consider who? or what? is abducting humans and killing and mutilating thousands of animals on this planet — and why?

BIBLIOGRAPHY

ADAMS, Tom. *The Choppers ... And The Choppers*: Mystery helicopters and animal mutilations, Revised Edition, © 1992. Published by Project Stigma, P. O. Box 1094, Paris, Texas 75460.

ANATI, Emmanuel. *Camonica Valley* © 1964, Lund Humphries, U.K.

ANDREWS, Colin and DELGADO, Pat. *Circular Evidence* © 1989, Bloomsbury Press, U.K.

ANDREWS, Colin and DELGADO, Pat. *Crop Circles, The Latest Evidence* © 1990, Bloomsbury Press, U.K.

ANDREWS, George C. *Extra-Terrestrial Friends and Foes* © 1993, Illuminet Press.

ANDREWS, George C. *Extra-Terrestrials Among Us* © 1986, Llewellyn Publications.

BARTHOLOMEW, Alick, Editor. *Crop Circles - Harbingers of World Change* © 1991, Gateway Books, U.K.

BOWEN, Charles. *The Humanoids* © 1969, Neville Spearman Ltd., U.K.

BLAVATSKY, H. P. *The Secret Doctrine: The Synthesis of Science, Religion, and Philosophy, Volumes I and II* © 1888, Theosophical Publishing Co., Ltd., London.

BRITISH MUSEUM. *Mesopotamia* with Julian Reade © 1991, British Museum Publications Ltd., U.K.

BRITISH MUSEUM. *Ancient Persia* with John Curtis © 1989, British Museum Publications Ltd., U.K.

BRITISH MUSEUM. *Assyrian Sculpture* with Julian Reade © 1983, British Museum Publications Ltd., U.K.

CRAWFORD, Harriet. *Sumer and the Sumerians* © 1991, Cambridge University Press, U.K.

CRICK, Francis and ORGEL, L. E. "Directed Panspermia," *Icarus, International Journal of Solar System Studies*, Vol. 19, No. 3, © 1973, Academic Press, Inc.

EMENEGGER, Robert. *UFOs: Past, Present & Future* © 1974, Allan Sandler Institutional Films, Inc.

FOWLER, Raymond E. and ANDREASSON, Betty. *The Andreasson Affair* © 1979, Prentice-Hall, Inc.

FOWLER, Raymond E. and ANDREASSON, Betty. *The Andreasson Affair, Phase Two* © 1982, Prentice-Hall, Inc.

FOWLER, Raymond E. and LUCA, Betty Ann. *The Watchers* © 1990, Bantam Books.

FULLER, John. *The Interrupted Journey* © 1966, Berkeley Publishing.

GIMBUTAS, Marija. *The Civilization of the Goddess: The World of Old Europe* © 1991, HarperCollins Publishers.

GIMBUTAS, Marija. *The Language of the Goddess* © 1989, Harper & Row Publishers, Inc.

GLEICK, James. *Chaos, Making A New Science* © 1987, Penguin Books.

HALL, Manly P. *The Secret Teachings of All Ages*, 19th Edition, © 1973, Philosophical Research Society, Los Angeles, Calif.

HARTMAN, H., LAWLESS, J.G.; MORRISON, P., *Search for the Universal Ancestors* © 1985, NASA SP-477.

HAWKINS, Gerald S. and WHITE, John B. *Stonehenge Decoded* © 1965, William Collins Sons.

HAWKINS, Gerald S. *Mindsteps To The Cosmos* © 1983, Harper & Row.

HESEMANN, Michael. *Botschaft aus dem Kosmos* © 1993 Verlag "Die Silberschnur."

HOPKINS, Budd. *Intruders, The Incredible Visitations At Copley Woods* © 1987, Random House.

HOWE, Linda Moulton. *An Alien Harvest - Further Evidence Linking Animal Mutilations and Human Abductions to Alien Life Forms* © 1989; 2nd Edition © December 2014 by LMH Productions.

HOWE, Linda Moulton. *A Strange Harvest:* A documentary film © 1980 and 1988, McGraw-Hill and LMH Productions.

HOWE, Linda Moulton. *Earth Mysteries: Alien Life Forms*, A documentary film © 1990, LMH Productions.

JACOBS, David M. *Secret Life: Firsthand Accounts of UFO Abductions* © 1992, Simon & Schuster.

KRAMER, Samuel Noah. *The Sumerians: Their History, Culture, and Character* © 1963, University of Chicago Press.

LUCKENBILL, Daniel David. *Ancient Records of Assyria and Babylonia, Parts 1 and 2* © 1989, Histories & Mysteries of Man Ltd., U.K.

MOONEY, James. *Myths of the Cherokee and Sacred Formulas of the Cherokees* © 1992, Charles and Randy Elder-Booksellers, Nashville, Tennessee.

NOYES, Ralph, Editor. *Crop Circle Enigma* © 1990, Gateway Books, U.K.

ROPER Organization. *Unusual Personal Experiences - An Analysis of the Data from Three National Surveys* © 1992, Bigelow Holding Corp.

ROUX, Georges. *Ancient Iraq* © 1964, 1980, 1992, George Allen & Unwin Ltd., U.K.

SCHAAFSMA, Polly. *Indian Rock Art of the Southwest* © 1980, School of American Research.

SITCHIN, Zecharia. *The Earth Chronicles, Books I-V*
    Book I: The 12th Planet © 1976, Avon Books.
    Book II: The Stairway To Heaven © 1980, Avon Books.
    Book III: The Wars of Gods and Men © 1985, Avon Books.
    Book IV: The Lost Realms © 1990, Avon Books.
    Book V: When Time Began © 1993, Avon Books.

SITCHIN, Zecharia. *Genesis Revisited* © 1990, Avon Books.

SPACE STUDIES BOARD. *The Search for Life's Origins, Progress and Future Directions in Planetary Biology and Chemical Evolution* © 1990, National Academy Press.

TALBOT, Michael. *The Holographic Universe* © 1991, HarperCollins Publishers.

TAYLOR, Busty. *Crop Circles of 1991* © 1991, Beckhampton Books.

TEMPLE, Robert K.G. *The Sirius Mystery* © 1976 and 1987, Destiny Books.

THOMPSON, Keith. *Angels and Aliens: UFOs and the Mythic Imagination* © 1991, Addison-Wesley Publishing Co., Inc.

THOMPSON, Richard L. *Alien Identities, Ancient Insights into Modern UFO Phenomena* © 1993, Govardhan Hill Inc.

VALLEE, Jacques. *Passport To Magonia: From folklore to flying saucers* © 1969 and 1983,
        Contemporary Books, Inc.

VALLEE, Jacques. *Dimensions: A casebook of alien contact* © 1988, Contemporary Books.

VALLEE, Jacques. *Confrontations, A Scientist's Search for Alien Contact* © 1990,
Ballantine Books.

WALKER, C. B. F. *Cuneiform, Reading the Past* © 1987, British Museum Publications Ltd.

WALTON, Travis. *The Walton Experience* © 1978, Berkley Medallion Books.

WALTON, Travis. *Fire in the Sky* © 1997, Marlowe & Co.

WOLF, Fred Alan. *Parallel Universes, The Search for Other Worlds* © 1988, Simon & Schuster.

WOOLLEY, C. Leonard. *The Sumerians* © 1965, W. W. Norton & Co.

WOOLLEY, C. Leonard. *UR 'of the Chaldees'* © 1982, Herbert Press Ltd., U.K.

INDEX

A

A Strange Harvest 99, 100, 102, 104, 188, 194, 200, 227

Aberdeen, South Dakota 96

Active Noise Control (ANC) 156

Adamiak, Shari 10, 17, 23

Adam's Grave, Wiltshire, England 11

Adams, Roger D.V.M. 128

Adams, Tom 127, 149-156

Adriatic Sea xxi

Aerial Phenomenon Research Organization (APRO) 200

AFB, Bergstrom, Austin, Texas 150

AFB, Kirtland, Albuquerque, New Mexico xii, 96, 99, 194, 278

Air Force Office of Special Investigations (AFOSI) xii, 96, 99, 194, 278

Africa, Canary Islands 95, 127

Aircraft and helicopters 27, 95, 102, 109, 112, 114, 123, 148-156, 227, 288-290

Akkadian cylinder seal 282

Al-Ubaid 278

Alabama 115-116, 123, 128, 143, 147, 151, 165, 169

Alabama, 1993 animal mutilations 126-148, 157-158

Alabama State Troopers 135

Alan Sandler Institutional Films, Inc. 276-277

Alberta, Canada, Animal mutilations 150

Albertville, Alabama 123, 126

Albertville, Alabama Police Dept. 112, 114, 127, 135-136

Albertville, Saskatchewan, Canada 70-72

Albuquerque, New Mexico xii, 96, 99, 102, 194, 278

Alchemical sigil 40

Alexander, Steve 11

Alien ancestors 242

Alien hierarchy 270

Alien intelligence/s 11, 156, 245

Alien life forms 99, 199, 235

    Alien actions during human abductions:

        "Bellhops" 265

        Calf raised and lowered in beam of light 199-212, 313

        Calf tissue excised 222-223, 313

        Calf carried by alien beings 234

        Clicking sounds from alien beings 234, 316

Cold stare and glares 215, 218, 220, 223, 241

"Doctors" that do medical exams 198-199, 270

Emotional indifference to human 215, 220-221

Examinations, Of human belly button 217

      Human female breasts 287

      Human teeth 215-216, 317

      Human throat 220

Gynecological exams 234-235, 237, 270

"Leader" in charge 270, 274

Move through solid walls and windows 295, 299

"Nice" to human 220, 223

Peeled cow tongue "like carrot" 223, 313

Physical movements, rapid or jerky 208, 219, 223, 229

Psychological tests 238

Robotic, mechanical 208

Removed human ova, sperm, fluid and tissue 197, 199, 235, 247, 267

Removed tissue from calf 222-223, 244, 313-314

Removed tissue from human mouth 221, 317

Screen memories, deceptions 205-206, 225, 237, 243, 247, 255, 260, 318-319

Sedated human 217, 317

Worked very quickly 221-222, 315

Alien Actions, Other Associations

    Animal disappearances 95, 196

    Floated cow from pasture 196, 229

    Missing time 155, 197-198, 200, 202, 234, 290, 300

    Mutilated animals 95, 201-229, 237, 243-246, 313-314

    Paralyzed cow 229

    Partial visibility of alien arm and hand 252

    Sudden disappearance and reappearance 227, 251

    Touched human "like electric shock" 252

Alien anatomy 210-211, 255, 265, 294, 315

Alien base on earth 222

Alien clothes 196, 208, 218, 229, 231, 260, 265, 270, 287, 290-291, 298

    Collared cloaks 243, 265, 286

    Headgear 227-228, 276, 290

    Symbols on 260-261, 270-271, 275, 287

Alien communications xiv, 250, 316

    About environmental contamination 235

    Face-to-face encounters 237, 241, 253

    Mental telepathy 24, 225, 237, 240, 242-245, 250-251, 316

    Pre-arranged meeting 278, 300

    Verbal 300, 316

    Vivid dreams 245-246, 250, 288-290

Alien craft xv, 39-40, 198, 183, 194, 196-197, 199, 227, 300, 314

    Inside craft

        Air, "sweet and smelly" 210

        Animals and animal parts 222-224, 313-314

        "Basins" and "floor funnels" 223, 314

        Colors, Grey and white 210, 237, 314

        Laboratory-like 210, 224, 256, 258

        Round rooms 210, 222, 258, 314

        "Shadowy light" 210

Different alien being descriptions xii, 201, 225, 250-299, 315

    Ancient 242

    Androids, Genetically engineered 240, 242-243, 247, 255, 265, 268, 291, 297-298, 300

    "Bigfoot" 196, 229-230, 232-233, 294, 297

    "Greys" 205, 239, 242-243, 246, 260-273, 300-301, 315

    Humanoids 234-235, 255, 274, 276, 286-287, 292

        Blond 240, 242-243, 276, 288, 291

        Surrounded by light 249

    Insect-like and "stick" figures 206, 211-220, 240-243, 257, 315

    Interdimensional entities xi, 255, 260, 301

    "Lizard" 229, 231-232, 240-241, 255, 294-297

    "Military" 155

    "Oriental" 153, 256, 258-260

    "Praying Mantis" 207, 240, 242, 291, 298

    "Reptile" 242, 260, 294

    Shadow-like 299

    Snake-eyed or cat-eyed 201, 208, 214-215, 218, 220, 232, 235, 241, 257-259, 267, 274-277, 293-295, 297, 315

    Tall, dark-haired humanoids 276

    Tall, hairless humanoids 234

    Translucent 297, 299

Photographs and 16mm film of alien beings 277-278

Physical features

    Arms 262, 295

    Chin 211, 218, 256, 262

    Ears 214, 265

    Eyes 154, 207-208, 214, 218-219, 223, 234-235, 237-239, 241, 249, 251, 255-257, 261, 265, 274-276, 285, 290-291, 294-295, 297

        Eyelids and Blinking 217, 265

        Vertical pupils 229, 256, 274

    Face, Flat 261, 267

    Feet 249, 263

    Fingers 252, 262, 265, 295

Forehead, High 290

Hair 206, 208, 212, 251, 255, 270, 285-287, 290-291, 295

Hands 211, 213, 219, 224-225, 252, 262, 295

Head shape 218, 256, 261-262, 265

Height 206, 214, 222, 224, 228-229, 231, 234, 238-239, 260, 265, 270, 274,
        286-287, 290-291, 294, 297-298

Lips 256

Mouth 207, 241, 263, 295

Nose 262, 274, 276

Skin, Color and texture 212, 217-218, 224, 227-228, 232, 234, 236, 238-
        239, 241, 251-253, 255-256, 260, 265, 270, 275, 290-291, 294-298

Odor 265

Torso 207, 211-212, 223-224, 235, 257, 262, 265

Alien presence, Reasons for 194, 235, 237

Animal mutilations and human abductions 222, 241, 243-244

Cross-breeding 295

Extraction of genetic material 236, 298

Hybrid creation 235

Regeneration 295

Sustenance, Biochemical absorption 243

Testing earth soil, water, vegetation 222

Issue of competing species 247

Alien technology 194, 200, 216-217, 219, 222

Artificial eye coverings 274-275

Balls of light 299

Beams of light that lift 247

Black box 270

Burning tissue 246

Excisions by light 244, 246

Holographic projections 297

"Little wands of blue light" 264

TV-like machine 211, 222-223

Robotic machine 246

Rod wound with coil 276

Transparent headgear 227-228, 276, 290

Alien treaties 242

Allingham, Cedric 290

Almeria caves, Spain 26

Alpha Canis Majoris (Sirius) 284

Alphanumeric code 57

Alton Barnes, Wiltshire, England 9, 11, 13, 16-17, 20-23, 25-26, 33, 36, 39, 51, 78, 82, 189

Altshuler, John M.D. 98, 108, 134, 139-141, 145-146, 148, 165, 167, 174, 177, 180, 184-188,
    306-307

Alvey Labs, Illinois 49

Amber-orange unidentified lights 11, 23, 33, 35, 39, 95

American Psychological Association 300

Amnesia 155, 197-198, 200, 202, 234, 290, 300, 311

An Alien Harvest xii, 98, 124, 194, 201, 234, 265, 277-278, 310

An Egyptian Hieroglyphic Dictionary 284

ANC (Active Noise Control) 156

Anderson, Don 98

Andes Mountains, Peru xvii-xx, 259, 285-286

Andrews, Colin 9-11, 23-25, 27, 40-41, 54, 78, 84-86

Andrews, George C. 167

Androids 240, 242-243, 247, 255, 265, 268, 291, 297-298, 300

Angelic beings xiv, xvii

Animal disappearances 149, 168, 196, 200, 227, 229-230, 255

Animals, Frightened 75, 135, 157, 188-190, 192

Animal mutilations xiii, xv, 92, 94-96, 98-99, 101, 108, 116, 132, 143, 149, 153, 169, 181, 184, 194, 197-198, 200, 227, 234-235, 243, 245

    Aircraft and helicopters 27, 95, 102, 109, 112, 114, 123, 148-156, 227, 288-290

    Alabama (1993) 112-148, 157-158

    Alien Motives for 194, 222, 235, 237, 243-244

    Animals found with excisions:

        Alive 160

        Birds 170

        Bulls 151, 158

        Calves 104-105, 138, 140, 142, 147-148, 159, 161, 178, 184, 190-193, 222, 234

        Cats 167

        Cows, heifers 96-97, 100-104, 106-108, 126, 128-129, 131-123, 134-137, 140, 142, 146, 150, 157-158, 165, 169-173, 176, 179-180, 185-186, 188, 191, 194, 200

        Deer 96, 167

        Dogs 158, 163, 167, 170, 179, 224

        Elk 167

        Goats 126-127

        Horses 96, 98, 109, 162, 164, 188, 227

            "Slashings" 162, 166, 190, 193

        Mule 126

        Newborn 181-182, 188, 227

        Rabbits 167, 174

        Sheep 167, 170, 189

        Squirrels 126

        Steers 97, 127-128, 158, 175, 183, 246

        Unborn 134-135, 165

    Associated with circles in grass 96

Associated with silver disks 126

Barbed wire, Pulled down 107

Bloat 158-159

Buried and exhumed cow 143-146

Cause of death 128, 162-163, 165, 180

Excisions, Types of 94, 139, 197

    Accessory sex gland 178

    Back and rib hide 136

    Belly 108, 127, 134, 144, 146-147, 160, 172, 180, 185

    "Biopsy plugs" 163, 170, 193

    Bladder 100, 104

    Blood, Lack of 94-100, 105-108, 126-128, 134, 138-139, 158-163, 167-169,
           174, 178, 181, 184-188, 191

           Internal pooling 127-128

           Presence of 136, 139, 150, 158, 162, 185

           Removal of 245

    "Burned," darkened tissue 108, 140, 158, 161, 188

    Circular and oval 94, 97, 100, 126, 140, 159-160, 169, 179, 183, 186

    Ear 96, 100, 160-161, 165, 181, 191, 193

    Eye, Circle of tissue around 100, 124, 162, 172, 174

           Eyeball 96, 100, 134, 159-164, 174, 181, 185-186, 201, 146

    Esophagus 137, 172, 186

    Head removed 158, 174, 179, 188

    Head and neck, Stripped of flesh 96, 98

    Heart 100, 102, 150, 158, 201, 222, 245

           Desiccated 109

    High heat, hemoglobin cooked 94-95, 97-98, 108-109, 138, 140-141, 148,
           163, 167, 174, 177, 180, 184, 186, 188

    Hide-deep 100, 106, 126, 169, 171-172, 185-186

    Hole in left side 137, 140, 185

    Hooves and legs 147, 160, 162, 185, 188

    Internal organs 95, 98, 100, 147-148, 168, 181, 234

    Jaw flesh 97, 100-101, 128-129, 132, 135-136, 157, 161, 165, 169, 171,
           179-180, 183-184, 188, 224, 246

    Lips 96, 160, 165, 169

    Nose 169

    Optic nerve 181

    Paws 158, 168, 179

    Ribs taken from backbone 234

    Rectum 100-101, 104-106, 128, 132, 140, 142, 147, 157, 159-160, 165, 169,
           171-172, 178, 181, 184, 188, 191, 246

    Scalloped 106, 188

    Serrated 148, 175-177

Sexual organs 96, 100-101, 105-106, 126, 128, 132, 140, 142, 147, 150,
        158, 160, 165-166, 169-172, 178, 181, 184, 191, 193, 201
    "Shocked with electricity" 166
    Sharp instrument, Cut with 96, 136, 143, 146, 158, 160, 164-166, 178,
        186, 191, 193, 227
    Skull, Cone-shaped plug 181
    "Slashings" 162, 166, 190, 193
    Surgical 96, 98, 100, 162, 167-169, 186, 193, 227
    Tail 100, 104-105, 191
    Teats 100, 107, 132, 150, 157, 169, 186, 188
    Teeth 97, 100-101, 171, 188, 246
    Throat 172, 186, 188
    Tongue 96, 100-101, 128-129, 159-160, 165, 169, 171, 179-180, 185-186, 188, 201
    Torso, Cut in half 168
    Trachea 136, 172
    Udder 100-101, 106-107, 126, 134-135, 140, 143, 145, 158-159, 179, 185-186
"Eyewitnesses," Hypnosis and vivid dreams 201-246
    Calf raised and lowered in yellow beam of light 200-201, 209-212
Map, North America 110
Map, Worldwide 109
Other cows, Reactions to mutilations 135, 157, 161, 188, 190, 192
Pathology
    Altshuler, John M.D. 98, 108, 134, 139-141, 145-146, 148, 165, 167, 174,
        177, 180, 184-188, 306-307
    Evidence of high heat at excisions lines 94-95, 97-98, 108-109, 138-141,
        146, 148, 163, 167, 174, 177, 180, 184, 186, 188
    Predator issue 96, 102, 104, 136-138, 140, 143-148, 163, 165-166, 192-193
        Coyotes 143, 157-158, 170, 188-190
    Sharp instrument excisions 96, 136, 143, 146, 158, 160, 164-166, 178,
        186, 191, 193, 227
    Tissue samples 144-146, 148, 184, 186, 188
Physical traces and anomalies
    Animal lifted and lowered in beam of light 199-212, 313
    Broken and burned bushes 99
    Burned oval on mountain in Peru 285
    Dead circles in grass or pastures 97, 229
    Ear tags removed from calves 191-193
    Holes, Circle near mutilated animal 99
    Lack of decay 187-188
    Lack of tracks 95-96, 99, 109, 127, 158, 161, 163, 169, 174, 183, 186, 188, 200
    Lack of struggle marks 161, 178, 186
    Mutilated calf hide turned inside out 234
    Polished hooves 181

Putty-like substance/ powders on or near mutilated animals 128-132, 181

Predators, Lack of at mutilation sites 159, 161, 172

Statistics 109-110

Worldwide 96, 149, 156, 197, 225

Years, 1989-1993

(1993) 112-168

(1992) 183-188

(1990-1991) 174-182

(1989) 169-173

England (1992-1993) 189-193

Anniston, Alabama 126

Anomalous trauma victim 194, 197, 199

Anthers 49

Appaloosa mare, Lady 95-100-101

Apical dominance 67

Apollo, U.S. astronauts 7

APRO 200

Apu gods xvii

Arab 279

Arab, Alabama 134

Archaeology, Depictions of beings other than human 249

Peru 285

Sumerian 278, 280, 284

Egyptian 284

United States 248

ARD, Germany 27

Argus 43

Armstrong, Neil 7

Armstrong, Randall 157-158

Arnold, Karl 227-229, 250

Arrhenius, Svante August xi, 300

Arthur Koestler Foundation 25

Ashdown, Arkansas 135

Ashtabula, Ohio 65

Assyrian 278, 282-283

Astral travel 259

Athay, Gregg Police Officer, Nounan, Idaho 169

Atlanta, Georgia 174, 202

Atlas of Topographical Anatomy of the Domestic Animals 101

Atomic frequency 301

Aurignacian skulls 279

Austinberg, Ohio 62, 64-65

Australia xiii, 3-4, 27, 43-44, 87, 95, 249

Automatic writing 237

Autopsies 128, 265

Avebury, Wiltshire, England 4, 9, 11, 13, 18-19, 76, 78

Avon, England 76

Aztec, New Mexico 153

B

Babylon 279

Bacterial infection 180

Bailey, Larry, Chief of Police, West Hennepin, Minn. 163

Bain, Deborah 263

Baker, Carey and Teri ix, 115, 143

Bakersfield, California 274, 293, 299

Barbury Castle 2, 4-5, 11, 27, 58, 60, 76

Barnehurst, Kent, England 152

Bartels, Ron 172-173

"Batman" emblem 122

BBC-TV, England 27

Beam of light, Lifting calf 200, 209-212

Bear Lake County, Idaho 104, 107, 169

Beard, Pat and James 123-125

Bears 189

Beauchesne, Ed 70

Beckhampton, Wiltshire, England 8, 76

Bedell, Duane 186

Beings, Non-human 196-299

    Tall 8, 248-249, 265, 270, 280, 285, 291, 298

    Also see: Alien life forms, Animal mutilations, Human abduction syndrome

Belial xvii

Bell Jet Ranger 153

Bellina, Joseph M.D. 98

Bennewitz, Paul 234

Benton County, Arkansas 102-103

Bentonville, Arkansas 102-103

Bergstrom Air Force Base 150

Berkshire, England 76

Berry Pomeroy, England 11, 59-61

Berryville, Arkansas 180

Bhutan 259

Bible 249, 279

    Ezekiel 249

    "Fire enfolding itself" 249

    Garden of Eden 249

Genesis 249

Giants in the earth 249

Orange ball of light 249

Physical features of "creatures" 249

Sons of God 249

Unidentified "creatures" 249

Bigelow Holding Corporation 199

Biological entities xiv

Biological transceivers 242

Blaine County, Oklahoma 158, 179

Blessinger, Tom 109

Blond humanoids 240, 242-243, 276, 288

Boaz, Alabama 136, 138

Boaz Drug Laboratory, Alabama 136

Boelter, Todd 163

Boreham Wood, Wiltshire, England 13, 15-16

Bosque County, Texas 150

Boston University 53, 58

Bostrom, Pete 47

Botschaft aus dem Kosmos 281

Bouldin, Joe 186

Bovine anatomy, Skull and teeth 100-101

Bowen, Charles 290

Bower, Doug 25, 27

Bowman County, North Dakota 159

Box, Mike, Police Detective, Plano, Texas 167

Bract plant tissue 3, 45, 51, 83, 91-92

Brave New World 300

Brazil, Indiana 74

Brein, Michael 10

British Army 27

British Isles 259

British Museum 279, 281

Brown County, South Dakota 96

Brown, Sally 162

Buckinghamshire, England 76

Budge, Sir Wallace E. A. 284

Buffalo, South Dakota 159

Buffalo Springs, North Dakota 159

Bunn, Brent, Sheriff, Bear Lake County, Idaho 169

Buried and exhumed cow 143-146

Butler, Kentucky 75

Buttram, Waymon 135-136, 158

C

Cairo, Egypt 259

Cajuers, France, Military base 167

Caldwell, Kansas 94, 97, 183-184

Calf, Taken up in beam of light 199-212, 313

Calgary, British Columbia, Canada 100

California 153, 259, 287

Cat mutilations 167-168

Calumet, Oklahoma 184

Cambridge, England 6

Camcorder focus problem 122

Camenzind, David D.V.M. 178

Camouflage, UFO 196

Canada xiii, 3-4, 27, 43, 67-71, 78, 87, 95, 101, 132, 139, 149, 154, 167

Canadian County, Oklahoma 158

Canary Islands, near Africa 95, 127

Canter, David Prof. 166

Capillaries 128

Carbon 75

Carlton University, Ottawa, Canada 300

Carney, Ellen 170

Carpenter, John M.S.W. 202-206, 224, 226, 234, 238, 245, 287, 295, 308-319

Carson, Tim and Polly 9-10, 23

Cascade County, Montana 176

Cash, Betty 154

Cash-Landrum, UFO/helicopters 153

Castor, Delbert 165

CAT scan 245

Cattle, Mutilated 94-195, 201-246

Cattlemen's associations 95

Cause of death, mutilations, 128, 162-163, 165, 180

CBC-TV, Canada 11, 27

CBI, Colorado Bureau of Investigation 166

CBS, Denver, Colorado 152

Cedar Bluff, Alabama 114, 123-125

Cell changes, plants See: Crop circle formations

Celtic cross 23, 40, 54

"Celtic Wheel" or "Charm Bracelet," Avebury, Wiltshire, England 13, 22, 59

Cement, Oklahoma 183

Center for the Study of Extraterrestrial Intelligence (CSETI) 9-11, 23-24, 33, 39-41

Center for UFO Studies (CUFOS) 238

Central America 95

Central Intelligence Agency (CIA) 82

Centre for Crop Circle Studies (CCCS) 52, 76-77, 91

Channel 9-TV, Australia 27

Chaos, Making A New Science 6

Chaos theory 6

"Charm bracelet" or "Celtic Wheel," 13, 22, 59

Chattanooga, Tennessee 143

Cheesefoot Head 76, 83, 85-86

Cherhill, Wiltshire, England 76-83, 87

Cherhill Down 78-79

Cherhill White Horse 79

Cherokee Indians 115

Cherrett, Carol and Brian 190-193

Chlorophyll 255

Chorley, David 25, 27

Chorost, Michael 43-44

Christ, Jesus xix, xxi, 116

Chromosomes 244

Cimarron, New Mexico 234

Ceramic-hard circles 227, 229

Circles, Geometry 53-59

Circlevision 25-26

Circular Evidence 54

Clairmont, Danny 67

Clark, Alvan, Astronomer 284

Clark, Mrs., Barnehurst, England 152

Clark, South Dakota 62

Cloning 300-301

Clostridium bacteria 180

CNN-TV 202

Coagulation necrosis 177

Coker, Gary 120-122

Cole, Tommy, Chief of Detectives, Albertville, Alabama Police 112, 114, 127-128, 135-136

Collagen, Bovine, normal and cooked 108

Collegeville, Pennsylvania 50

Collinsville, Alabama 128

Colorado 149-150, 165-166, 188-189

Colorado Bureau of Investigation (CBI) 166

Colorado River, Utah 248

Colorado Springs, Colorado 188

Colorado State University, Colo. 165

Columbia Center, New York 76, 87-88

Combe Capelle, France 279

Compass, Rotation of, England, 39

Conroy, Ed 155

Control System, Alien xiv, 294

Cooper, William 277

"Copter Fires On Man In Field" 151

Corhampton, England 58

Cormia, Jim 87

Corn rectangle 63-65

Corn ear and tassel anomalies 63-65

Cosmology xx, 301

Cosmos Journal 57

Cowger, Bill 185

Cows, Reactions to mutilations 135, 157, 161, 188, 190, 192

Coyne, George and Shirley 155

Coyotes 143, 158, 170, 188

Craft See: Alien life forms, Animal mutilations, Crop circle formations, Human abduction
    syndrome, and Lights

Cranfils Gap, Texas 150

Crawford, Harriet 280

Creek-Forest, Texas 167

Creel, Mike D.V.M. 127-128, 138-139

Creevy, Vincent 15, 77

Crestone, Colorado 151

Crete xxi

Crick, Francis xi-xii, 300

Cro-Magnon 279

Cromwell, Oliver 24-25, 57

Cropcircle Communique, documentary 11

Crop circle formations 2-93
    England 1991
        Wheat geometry, Barbury Castle, Marlborough 2, 4-5, 11, 27, 58, 60, 76, 305
        Wheat, Mandelbrot Set, Ickleton 6
    Canada 1992
        Wheat and oat circles, Albertville, Saskatchewan 70-72
        Wheat circle, dead porcupine, Estevan, Saskatchewan 74-75
        Wheat circle, flattened porcupine, Milestone, Saskatchewan 67-69
        Wheat circles, Nipawin, Saskatchewan 73
    England 1992
        Wheat, ringed circle, Alton Priors 43
        Barley dumbbell, Berry Pomeroy, Totnes 59-61
        Wheat circles, Boreham Wood, Alton Barnes 13, 15-16
        Wheat pictogram, "Celtic wheel," or "Charm bracelet," Avebury,
           England 13, 15, 22, 59
        Wheat pictogram, East Meon, Circlevision hoax, 13, 15, 25-27, 76, 83

Wheat pictogram, Milk Hill, Alton Barnes 11, 13, 15, 17, 27-30, 60

Wheat pictogram, Ogbourne Maizey 13, 15, 20

Wheat geometry, Oliver's Castle 13, 15, 21, 25, 39-42, 45, 55-57, 305

Wheat pictogram, Silbury Hill, Avebury 13, 15, 18-19

Wheat pictogram, "Snail," Alton Barnes 13, 15-17

Barley pictogram, Stonehenge 12-13, 15

United States 1992

Corn rectangle, Austinburg, Ohio 62-67

Potato circle, Clark, South Dakota 62

Wheat anomalies, Limerick and Linfield, Pennsylvania 30-32

Sweet flag grass circle, Troy, Illinois 47-49

England 1993

Wheat pictogram, Cheesefoot Head 76-77, 85

Wheat pictogram, Cheesefoot Head 76-77, 86

Wheat pictogram, Cherhill 76-83

Wheat dumbbell, Devises 76-77, 84

Wheat pictogram, East Kennett, 76-77, 86

Wheat geometry, Etchilhampton 59,76-78, 83-84

Wheat geometry, Guildford Hog's Back, 76-77, 86, 305

Wheat pictogram, Windmill Hill 76-77, 85

United States 1993

Rye pictogram, Columbia Center, New York 87-88

Wheat pictogram, Kennewick, Washington 89-92

Diatonic ratios and scales 3, 54, 57, 59, 83, 304-305

Geometry 53-59, 302-303

Maps, 1992 14-15; 1993 77

Porcupine deaths, black residue 67-68, 74-75

Plant analysis 43-51, 62-92

Accelerated growth 65, 71-72

Cell pit changes 44-46, 62

Rapid heating 47-49, 68-69

Changes in seed growth 49-50, 60-61

Bent, swollen and cracked growth nodes 30, 50-51, 61, 91-92

Ion transport in bract tissue 51, 83, 91-92

Scientific investigations 43-92

Deetken, Chad, Crop circle investigator 71-72

Hawkins, Gerald S., Astronomer and mathematician 53-59

Levengood, W. C., Biophysicist 4, 27, 29-30, 40, 42–51,59, 62, 65- 69, 71-72, 75, 83, 87, 91-92

Yarkosky, Sherry, Chemist and plant physiologist, 49

Sounds, Crackling like static electricity 60

Stalks, Flattened and unbroken 40, 42, 58, 62, 65, 82, 83, 90-91

Unidentified moving lights; structured craft 4-5, 11, 33-40, 60-61

Cross-breeding 279

Crossfire: The Plot That Killed Kennedy 102

Crossville, Alabama 127, 136-138, 140, 147, 188, 307

Crowley, Aleister 258-259

Crystals, Cherokee 115

CSETI (Center for the Study of Extraterrestrial Intelligence) 9-11, 23-24, 33, 39, 41

CSU Diagnostic Laboratory (Colorado State University) 165-166

Cuzco, Peru xvii, 285

D

Dallas, Texas 167

Dawson, Alabama 128-129, 131

Dead Sea Scrolls xvii

Dean, Travis 184

Deception, "screen memories" 205-206, 225, 235, 237, 243

Deetken, Chad 67-68, 70-72, 74, 77-78, 82-83

Dehydration 47

DeKalb County, Alabama Sheriff's Dept. 113, 120, 135-136, 140, 143, 147, 150, 157

Delgado, Pat 54

Denver, Colorado 102, 139, 177, 194

Department of Defense, U.S. 278

Devises, Wiltshire, England 76-77, 83-84

Diatonic ratios and scales 3, 54, 57, 59, 83, 302-305

Dieterlen, Germaine, French anthropologist 284

Different alien descriptions 242-244, 260-299

    Also See: Alien life forms, Animal mutilations and Human abduction syndrome

Dimensions xiv, 260, 267, 301

Dinosaurs 242

Directed panspermia xi-xii, 300

Disks 11, 35, 290

    Aluminum-colored 290

    Holloman AFB 276

    "Not from this earth" 194

    Orange, 300-foot-long 200

    Silver-colored 227, 229, 250, 287, 290-291

Disease, cattle 140, 192-193

Dispatch, St. Paul, Minnesota 96

"Divine wisdom" 258

DNA xi-xii, 244, 279, 300-301

    Catalogued from eye 246

Dog Star, Sirius 40, 284

Dogon tribe, Mali, Africa 284

Doroty, Judy 199, 201-202, 221-222, 225-226, 235, 255, 257-258, 308-319

Doty, Richard C. 96, 99, 278

Dowell, Colette 77-78

Dowsers 7

Dreams, Vivid 245-246, 250, 288-290

Druffel, Ann 152

Dudley, Marshall 43

Dusenberry, Lisa 228, 264, 286-288, 295

E

Earth Mysteries: Alien Life Forms 174, 230, 233, 310

"Earth's plight" 235

East Field, Wiltshire, England 34

East Kennett, Wiltshire, England 76-77, 83, 86

East Meon 13, 15, 25-27, 76, 83

EG&G, Las Vegas, Nevada (Edgerton, Germeshausen & Grier) 194

Egypt 40, 278

Eisenman, Robert xvii

El Reno, Oklahoma 184

Elbert County, Colorado 109

Electrical probe 163

Electro-cautery 139-140

Electro-surgical 177

Electron microscope 131

Emenegger, Robert 276-278

Enannatum, of Lagash, Mesopotamia 279

Encyclopedia of Occultism and Parapsychology 304

Energy dispersive spectroscopy 130

English long barrows 8, 12, 278

Environmental chain reaction 222

Environmental pollutants 244

Esau, Katherine 44

Estevan, Saskatchewan, Canada 74

Etchilhampton, Wiltshire, England 59, 76, 83-84

Euclid 3, 56, 58

Evolution, Planned 242

Excisions, See: Animal mutilations

Experimental aircraft 154

Exton, England 13

Extraterrestrial xii, xiv, 250, 260, 277-279, 284

Extraterrestrial biological entities xi, 255

Extra-Terrestrial Friends and Foes 167

Extra-Terrestrials Among Us 167

Eyes, Sumerian gods 280

Eyewitnesses 11, 37-38, 93, 196, 198, 225, 288
    Of, Alien beings 227, 250, 300
    Of, Alien beings and disk-shaped craft 227, 229, 300
    Of, Alien being with animals 196-197, 229-235
    Physical encounters 292, 300
    With binoculars, 35-36, 229-232, 296–297

F
Fazio, Richard 175
Feather, Carl 62, 64-65
Federal Aviation Administration (FAA) 112, 150
Federal Bureau of Investigation (FBI) 102
Finck, Alton, Darlene and Tim 159-161
Flint, Michigan 264
Flippin, Arkansas 263
"Floating," In association with alien beings 196
Flores, Edwin 285-286
Flusser, David xvii
Fogley, Doug, former Arkansas State Police Sgt. 102
FOIA (Freedom of Information Act) 150
Motcombe, Dorset, England 193
Fort Collins, Colorado 165
Fort Hood, Texas 150, 153
Fort Payne Times Journal, Alabama 136
Fortean Times 193
Fowler, Raymond E. 155
FOX-TV 174, 194, 226
Fractal geometry 6
France, Sheep mutilations 167
Franklin County, Nebraska 172
Frequencies, Monitored 148
Froxfield, England 13, 15
Frozen music (geometry) 4, 53
Fort Payne, Alabama 114, 117-119, 122, 143
Fuller, John 198
Fyffe, Alabama Police Dept. 112, 115, 147
Fyffe Fire and Rescue 148

G
Gadsden Times, Alabama 120, 122
Galileo xiv, 59
Gene splicing 244
Genes, Human and bovine 244

Genesis Revisited 279

Genetic code xi-xii

Genetic hybridization and manipulation 242, 279

Geometry 2-4, 6, 27, 53-59, 302-303

Georgia 115, 123, 197, 291-292

Geraldine, Alabama 114, 116-117, 135-136, 157

Germany 27; Horse "slashings" 193

Germination 66, 71-72

Giants, Cherokee 115

Gillingham, Dorset, England 192

Gimbutas, Marija 82

Glasgow University 4, 52

Glastonbury, Pete 11, 59-61

Glastonbury Tor 33

Gleick, James 6

Glenn, Calvin D.V.M. 96

Gloucester, England 76

Gobi desert 259

God 258

Gods of Egypt and Gods of Sumer 284

Good Morning, America (ABC-TV) 27

Government knowledge 112, 154, 194-195, 278, 298
    Policy of silence 195

Grandfield, Bruce 73

Grant, Kenneth 258-259

"Grapeshot," Crop circles 78, 81

Graves, Tex, former Sheriff, Logan County, Colo. 102, 105-106, 132, 137

Great Falls, Montana 176

Greece xxi

Greek historian, Herodotus 279

Greeley Tribune, Colorado 164

Green Forest, Arkansas 179-180, 192

Green River, Utah 248

Greencastle, Indiana 75

Greenup County, Kentucky 182

Greer, Steven M.D. 9-11, 23-25, 34-35, 38-41

Griaule, Marcel, French anthropologist 284

Grove Oak, Alabama 101, 105, 107, 140, 142

"Guardian," Canada 154

Guildford Hog's Back, England 76-77, 83, 86, 305

Guntersville, Alabama 150

Guthrie, Carl D.V.M. 172-173

H

Haith, David 190

Hall, Manly P. 40

Halogen lamps 24, 39

Hamilton, Bill 155, 264

Hamilton, William D. xi

Hammurabi, King of Babylon 282

Hampshire, England 58, 76, 166

    Horse "slashings" 190

Hampson, Janet 168

Hampton, Hampshire, England 166

Hansen, Myrna 234-235

Harbingers of World Change 4

Harding County, South Dakota 159-161

Harley, Roger 189

Harris, Helen 250-255, 265

Hart Canyon, New Mexico 153

Harvard Medical School 198

Harvard University xiv, 199

Hatch, Hingwah 230-233, 247, 261, 296-297

Hawaii 277

Hawkins, Gerald S. 53-59, 83, 86, 302-303

HBO (Home Box Office) 99

Heads of Sumerian gods, Dome-shaped 8, 280-283

Hebrew 40

Helicopters and aircraft 27, 95, 102, 109, 112, 114, 123, 148-156, 227, 288-290

Hemoglobin, Cooked in excisions of mutilated animals 94-95, 97-98, 108-109, 138, 140-141, 148, 163, 167, 174, 177, 180, 184, 186, 188

Hemorrhage 128

Herboldsheimer, Hubert 132

Herkimer County, New York 76, 87-88

Hermetic (alchemical) Order of the Golden Dawn 258

Herodotus 279

Hesemann, Michael von 281

Hicks-Raburn King County, Washington Police Dept. 170

Hidden Masters 259

Hieroglyphs, For star Sirius 40

Hiland, Kenneth 143-146, 158

Hill, Betty and Barney 153, 198, 225

Himalayan region 259

Hitler, Adolph 258

Hiwasse, Arkansas 185

Hoax contest 44

Hoaxed formations 46,
    East Meon, Circlevision hoax, 13, 15, 25-27, 76, 83
Hoaxers 13, 25, 27, 47, 59, 79, 82-83
Hoffmann, L. 275
Holes, Circle of 99
Holloman AFB, New Mexico 276
    UFO landing 277-278
Holograms xiv, 255, 297
Homo sapiens xii, 225, 279
Honnicutt, Alan M.D. 180
Hope, Arkansas 108, 134-135
Hopi Indian xxi
Hopkins, Budd xiv, 235, 238
Horseshoe (Barrier) Canyon, Utah 248
Houston, Texas 199, 210, 255, 258
    UFO/Helicopters 153
Howard, Ted Deputy, Greenup County, Kentucky Sheriff's Dept. 181
Howe, Linda Moulton 10, 152, 200, 226, 310
Hoyle, Fred xii
HUFON Report, 1992 (Houston UFO Network) 155
Huggins, David 262-263, 292
Human abduction syndrome
    Also see: Alien life forms and Animal mutilations
    Drawings, By abductees, re: alien encounters:
        A. A., New Jersey, Tall, dark-haired male humanoid with vertical pupils
                and tall, blond female humanoid with light blue "cat
        eyes" 275
                Tall, large-nosed being with tight-fitting skull cap and close-up
                of blond, cat-eyed female humanoid 276
        A. R., Pennsylvania, Orange, flat-nosed, snaked-eyed being 267
                Blond humanoid male 289
                "Helicopter" without rotor blades 290
        Bain, Deborah, Arkansas, Small Grey 263
        California female, Older "hybrid" child 236
        D. K., Colorado, Taller humanoid in collared cape 266
                Smaller Grey in collared "leotard" 266
                Close-up smaller Grey 267
        Doraty, Judy, Texas, Snake-eyed Grey that excised tissue from calf 201, 257
        G. A., New Mexico, Small Grey 264
        G. R., Florida, Taller Grey 265
        Hamilton, Bill, California, Small Grey with spiral symbol on uniform 264
        Huggins, David, New Jersey, Two small Greys 262
                Small Greys floating from air on Georgia farm 263

"Praying mantis" at Georgia farm 292

"Praying mantis" types with small Grey 292

J. C., New Jersey, "Man in black" 298

K. R., Michigan, Small Greys with "blue light wands" 264

K. S., Michigan, Small Grey 262

L. D., Indiana, Taller Grey in robe with three smaller "androids" 268

L. D., California, Taller "cardboard-colored" beings; symbol of

triangle-inside-circle on body suit 270

L. R., California, Grey with bright eyes 273

L. P., California, Very tall being with enormous eyes, vertical pupils 274

"Insect" being 291

Very tall "Praying mantis" being with abductee 293

"Shadow beings" with small Grey entering bedroom 299

M. J., Missouri, Tall, blond-haired humanoid 288

Tall reptilian being 295

M. S., Maryland, Blond humanoid 289

N. L. C., California, Taller Grey being 273

Robinson, Jeanne, Missouri, Jagged crescent symbol on uniform 260

Grey "baby thing" 236

"Praying mantis in charge" 240

"Lizard Guy" with snake eyes and "scary mouth" 241

Grey "handler" and smaller "android" 243

Close-up Grey "handler" in collared cloak 269

Close-up triangle-inside-circle symbol on alien uniforms 271

"Reptilian" humanoid with bony chest plate 294

S. F., Tennessee, Tall, red-haired, blue-eyed being 286

Tindle, Cindy, Texas, "Bald old man" with "Oriental eyes" 258

"Soft-eyed" Grey, Snake-eyed Grey, and "Stick" figure 257

Grey "stick" figure 257

Dog's snout in alien "laboratory" 224

UFO with yellow beam lifting up calf 210

"Stick" figure "like a bug" 211

3-fingered alien hand, "like mitten" 213

Snake-eyed Grey that "glared" 215

"Soft-eyed" Grey that was nice 219

V. M., New York, Taller, hairless female being with large, black eyes 272

Three Greys in "blue coat uniforms" 272

Watson, Ron and Paula, Missouri,

Greys, "Lizard Guy" and "Bigfoot" with cow 196, 230-233

Paula Watson examined by Greys and "Lizard Guy" 247

Small Grey, triangle symbol surrounding "jagged crescent" 261

"Lizard Guy" and cone-shaped craft 296

"Bigfoot" 297

Hypnosis to penetrate amnesia
Doraty, Judy 200-202, 221-222, 225, 308-319
Hansen, Myrna 234-235
Robinson, Jeanne 237-240
Tindle, Cindy 201-226, 308-319
Watson, Paula 234
Percentage of unusual experiences, U. S. population 199
Symptoms, Abduction syndrome
Headaches 200
Missing time 155, 197-198, 200, 202, 234, 290, 300
Physical body marks 198
Repeated nightmares 198
Sensation of strong force pulling through wall 245, 299
Vivid dreams 245-246, 250, 288-290
Human, As another intelligence's work force 279
Huntsville, Alabama 126
Hybrid 235-236, 240, 242

I
IBM 6, 9
Ickleton, England 6, 27
Idaho 169-170, 189
ilyes 89-91
Incas, Peru xvii-xx
"Indalo" 26
Independence, Minnesota 162
India 259
Indian Rock Art of the Southwest 248
Indiana, Dark rings in grass 74, 76
Indianapolis, Indiana 268
Institute of Archaeology, University of London 280
Intelligences, Alien See: Alien life forms
Interdimensional entities xi, 255, 260, 301
Intruders, The Incredible Visitations at Copley Woods 235
Ion conductivity tests See: Crop circle formations, Plant analysis
Ireland xxi
Irving, Robert 27, 82-83
ITN-TV, England 27

J
Jabbul, near Aleppo, Mesopotamia 282-283
Jacksonville, Florida 265
Jacobs, Robert 184

Japan 3-4, 95
Jarvis, Jared 126
Jenkintown, Pennsylvania 289
Jernigan, E. Wesley 248
Johnson, Elroy Sheriff, Brown County, South Dakota, 1970s 96
Johnson, Mona and Wayne 161
Johnson, Sue 117-118, 120
Journal of Abnormal Psychology 300
Journal of the Society for Psychical Research 304-305
Jupiter 59

K
Kansas 183
Keith, Sir Arthur 8, 278
Kelner, Mark 159
Kennedy, Andrew D.V.M. 166
Kennewick, Washington 76, 80, 90-92
Kent, England 76
Kentucky 76, 181
King Charles I 25
King of Evil xvii
King of Righteousness xvii
Kingston, Isabelle 7-8
Kirtland AFB, Albuquerque, New Mexico xii, 96, 99, 194, 278
Kitson, Roy, Sheriff, Madison County, Montana, 1970s 153
KMGH-TV (CBS) Denver, Colorado 200
Knott, Duff Deputy, Weld County, Colorado Sheriff's Dept. 165
Koestler, Arthur 25
Koyllur Riti xvii-xx
Kronig, Jurgen 18, 20-21

L
Labenek, Diane 154
Labyrinths, Soul journey xxi
Lackford, Simon 78
Lady, Appaloosa mare 95, 100-101
Lagash, Mesopotamia 279
Lakewood, New Jersey 298
"Lam, an extraterrestrial" 259
Lamb, Barbara 9, 20
Lancing, West Sussex, England 76-77
Languages, Unknown speech 153
Las Vegas, Nevada 194

Laser 98, 102, 108, 139-140, 177, 186

Late Stone Age 278

Lawrence County, Tennessee 151

Lazar, Robert 194

Leduc, Alberta, Canada 188

Leicester Mercury, Leicester, England 193

Lerner, Richard 99

Levengood, W. C. Ph.D. 4, 27, 29-30, 40, 42–51,59, 62, 65- 69, 71-72, 75, 83, 87, 91-92

Lewis, Berle 99

Liberty, Mississippi 188

Lights, Unidentified 114-115, 186, 197, 234, 250,

    As disinfectant 245

    Amber-orange 11, 23, 33, 35, 39, 95

    Associated with animal mutilations 227

    Atsil-dihye gi, Cherokee 115

    Balls of 60-61

    Beam from diamond-shaped UFO 290

    Beams of 95, 149, 204-210, 227, 310-313

    Blue cylinder-shaped 103

    Blue shining into bedroom 288

    "Brighter than moonlight" 112, 118

    Change shape 35-38

    Disappear or reappear suddenly 123-125, 18

    "Fire-carrier," Cherokee 115

    Follow cars 184

    Large circle of 194

    Like "tornado funnel" 237

    Moist 208, 312

    Moving 33, 61, 98, 112, 120, 122-123, 198-199, 204-205

    Multi-colored and flashing 39, 184

    Oval-shaped 75

    Like searchlights 207, 227, 312

    Red cluster of 35-36

    Red-orange, pulsing 146

    Square-shaped 33

    Strobing 154-155, 245

    Triangle of 35

    Wheel of 34

    Yellow beam lifting and lowering calf 200-201, 209-212, 312-313

Limerick, Pennsylvania 30, 32, 50-51

Lindemann, Michael ix, 301

Linfield, Pennsylvania 30, 32, 50-51

"Little men" 201

"Little People," Cherokee 115

Little River News 135

Liver, Desiccated 109

Livestock disappearances 149

"Lizard Guy" 229, 231-232, 240-241, 255, 294-297

Lockeridge White Horse, Wiltshire, England 13, 17, 27-28

Lodge, Oliver 304-305

Logan County, Colorado 100-102, 105, 137

London, England 76

Long barrows, England 8, 12

 Neolithic relation to Sumerians 278

Long Island, New York 152, 174

Longmont, Colorado 266

Look Magazine 198

Lopp, David 151

Lorenzen, Jim 200

Los Alamos Laboratory, New Mexico 194

"Lu," Old European script 82

Luca, Betty Andreasson and Bob 155

Lucretius v

Lungs, Desiccated 109

Lynchburg, Virginia 179

Lyneham, England 5

M

Maccabee, Bruce Ph.D. 154

Mack, John E., M.D. xiv, 198-199

MacNish, John 25-26

Madison County, Montana 153

Madison, Nebraska 178

Madsen, Al 97

Magic ritual, Hebrew symbols for 40; Devices 258

Magnetic lines of force 7

Mallan, Lloyd 152

Mandelbrot, Benoit 6

Mandelbrot Set 6-7, 27

Mansell, Chris 26-27, 34-40

Maps, Alabama, 113

 England 14

 Wiltshire crop circles, 1992 15

 Wiltshire crop circles, 1993 77

Maple Valley, Washington 169-171

Marduk, Sumerian god 279

Marian apparitions xv, 93

Marlborough, England 2, 5, 13, 20, 26, 33-34

Marrs, Jim 102, 244

Marshall County, Alabama 113, 126, 140, 150

Marshall County Animal Welfare Society 134, 157-158

Martineau, John 15

Maryland 288-289

McArthur, Mary 68

McCall, Idaho 109

McClendon, David 147-148

McKinney, Clinton 74

McPherson, Fred 159

Mead, Colorado 165

Meade County, South Dakota 159

Medford, Oregon 183

Meeker County, Minnesota 96-97

Memory block 155

Men In Black (MIBs) 298

Mental health professionals 197, 199

Mental telepathy 225, 237, 240, 243-245

Meon Valley, England 166

Merlin Hotel, Marlborough, England 34

Mesopotamia 8, 278-282

Mesopotamia, British Museum 282-283

Mexico 95

Meyers, Arlen M.D. 102

MIBs 298

Michael, Prince of Light xvii

Michigan 30, 40

Microwave energy 45, 47

Middle East 249

Milam County, Texas 95, 234, 236, 250, 255

Milestone, Saskatchewan, Canada 67-68

Military and intelligence sources, 112, 155-156, 255

Milk Hill, Wiltshire, England 11, 13, 15, 17, 27-30, 34, 60

Mind control 205, 225, 235, 247, 271

Missing time 155, 197-198, 200, 202, 234, 290, 300, 308-319

Missouri 183, 197, 202, 227-229, 250, 286, 295

Mitchell, Terrance 97

Montana 176, 297

Moon 7, 26, 53, 59; Alchemical sigil 40

Mooney, James 115

Moore, Oklahoma 158

Motcombe, Dorset, England 190-192

Motives for animal mutilations and human abductions 194, 222, 235, 237, 241, 243-244

Mt. Vernon, Missouri 196, 229-230, 247, 261, 294, 296-297

MUFON (Mutual UFO Network) 67, 87, 91, 159, 183, 186

Mystery School 258

Myths of the Cherokee and Sacred Formulas of the Cherokee 115

N

NASA xii, 126

     SETI (Search for Extraterrestrial Intelligence) Program 250

Nation's Center News, Buffalo, South Dakota 159

Navy, U. S. 265, 277

NBC-TV 154

Neanderthals 279

Necropsies 102, 104, 109, 159-160, 163, 173, 186, 188

Nellis AFB, Nevada 194

Nelson, Edwin B. 16

Neolithic 8, 17, 27, 278

Nepal 259

Nevada 194, 287

Nevejan, Annick 34-35, 38-39

New England 153, 240

New Hampshire 150

New Harmony, Alabama 157-158

New Jersey 152, 277, 298

New Mexico 149-150, 197, 264

New Raymer, Colorado 164

News-Leader, Springfield, Missouri 187

Newsweek xii

Nile River 40

Nimrud palace of Ashurnasirpal II, Mesopotamia 282-283

Nipawin, Saskatchewan, Canada 73

Nippon-TV, Japan 27

Nobel Prize xi-xii, 300

Noise cancellation 156

Non-earthly technology 156

Non-human beings See: Alien life forms

Norris, Montana 153

Northview, Missouri 186

Nounan, Idaho 107, 169

Nuclear testing, space and undersea 222

O

Oakley, Idaho 104

O'Brien, Christopher 151

Occult 258-259

Octave frequencies 54

Office of Naval Intelligence (ONI) 194

Ogbourne Maizey, England 13, 15, 20

Ogbourne St. Andrew, England 7, 13, 15

Ogletree, Ron, Post Commander, Alabama State Troopers 135-136

O'Kane, Mark 99

Okemah, Oklahoma 137, 140, 185

Oklahoma City, Oklahoma 158

Solar system 300

Old European script 82

Old Stone Age 279

Oldbury Castle, Cherhill 78-79

Oliphant, Ted former Officer, Fyffe, Alabama Police Dept. 101, 105, 107, 112, 114, 116, 123, 128-129, 135-137, 140, 142, 147-148

Oliver's Castle, Wiltshire, England 13,15, 21, 25, 39-42, 45, 55-57

    Diatonic ratios of 55-57

Operation Blackbird, England 27

Orange lights, See: Lights

Oregon State University, Corvallis, Oregon 177

Orgel, Leslie xii

"Oriental" type non-humans, See: Alien life forms

Orr, Dale Asst. Chief Deputy, DeKalb County, Alabama Sheriff's Dept. 136, 147

Oscillation amplitudes, Bract tissue 51, 59, 83, 91

Other beings 196-299

Other dimensional beings xi, 255, 260, 301

Out There: Remote Viewing of High Strangeness Material 225

Ova and sperm 197, 301

Oxford Polytech College 52

P

P.M. Magazine, Germany 25

Paleolithic 279

Panspermia xi-xii, 300

Papoose Mountains, Nevada 194

Paris, Texas 149, 153

Parker, David 6

Past Years 304

Patches, Alien symbols 260-261, 270-271, 275, 287

Pathology, Animal mutilations 160, 165

Altshuler, John M.D. 98, 108, 134, 139-141, 145-146, 148, 165, 167, 174, 177, 180, 184-188

    Sharp instrument excisions 96, 136, 143, 146, 158, 160, 164-166, 178, 186, 191, 193, 227

    Evidence of high heat at excisions lines 94-95, 97-98, 108-109, 138-141, 146, 148, 163, 167, 174, 177, 180, 184, 186, 188

    Predator issue 136-138, 143-148

    Tissue samples 144-146, 148, 184, 186, 188

Patterson, Eva 109

Pennsylvania 288-289

Pericardium 102

Perkins County, South Dakota 160

Peru xvii-xx, 249, 285-286

Peters, Mike 164

"Phantom" helicopters 149, 151, 155-156

Phelps, Jerry 90-91

Philosophical Research Society 40

Photographs and 16mm film of alien beings 277-278

Photographs, UFOs Time lapse 120-122

Photomicrographs, Bovine collagen 174

    Plant cell pits 46

Photon energy, Beam of 244

Physical traces and anomalies

    Broken and burned bushes 99

    Burned oval on mountain in Peru 285

    Dead circle of grass 288

    Ear tags removed from calves 191-193

    Holes, Circle of near animal mutilation 99

    Lack of decay in animal mutilations 187-188

    Lack of tracks in animal mutilations 95-96, 99, 109, 127, 158, 161, 163, 169, 174, 183, 186, 188, 200

    Lack of struggle marks in mutilations 161, 178, 186

    Mutilated calf hide turned inside out 234

    Polished hooves 181

    Putty-like substance, powders on or near animal mutilations 128-132, 181

Piano keyboard, Alphanumeric code 57

Pictograms, Crop formations 13, 15-20, 22, 25-30, 59-60, 76- 83, 85-92

Pillpinto, Peru, Tall "Irish" 285-286

Pine, Chuck 94, 97, 183-184

Pinelandia Biophysical Laboratory 43

Plano, Texas 167-168

Plants, See: Crop circle formations

Pleiades xvii, 243

Poole, Dorset, England 190

Popesko, Peter D.V.M. 101

Porcupines, Associated with crop circle formations 67-68, 74-75

Port Angeles, Washington 91

Portland, Oregon 175

Portsmouth, New Hampshire 198

Posthumous experiment of Oliver Lodge 304-305

Potato plants, Circle of dead 62

"Praying mantis" alien being 207, 240, 242, 291, 298

Predator issue 96, 102, 104, 136-138, 140, 143-148, 163, 165-166, 192-193

    Coyotes 143, 157-158, 170, 188-190

    Lack of, animal mutilation sites 159, 161, 172

Presidential briefing paper about extraterrestrials, Alleged 278

Prince of Darkness xvii

Prince of Light xvii

Project Sigma 278

Protein-nucleic acid xii

Psychic research 304-305

Putnam County, Indiana 74

Q

Questa, New Mexico 158

Questers, Central New York 87

Quincunx 54

R

Radar and electronic surveillance 148

Radioactivity 130, 154, 194, 244

Radio signals from space, Anomalous 250

Rae, Madelaine A., D.V.M. 177

Rael, Eloiso 158

RAF (Royal Air Force), England 5

Ragsdale, Edwina 187

Rainsville, Alabama 115, 143, 145-146, 157

Raymond, or Life and Death 304

Rappahannock, Virginia 53

Rapture, To heaven 116

Ratios, Diatonic 56

RCMP (Royal Canadian Mounted Police) 75, 100

Reade, Julian 279, 281

Recent waves of animal mutilations 169

Red Cloud, Nebraska 137, 172-173, 188

Red Mountain, Montana 153

Reeder (Adams County), North Dakota 159

Rees, David 152

Regeneration, Alien 243-244, 301

Rennick, Joe

Report On Communion 155

Reproductive systems, Use of, See: Alien life forms, Animal Mutilations and Human abduction syndrome

"Reptile" alien being 242, 260, 294

Reseda, California 264

Retrieval of crashed alien disks xii, 194

Reynolds, Gary, Commander, Lynchburg, Virginia Police Dept. 179

"Rib," Crop circle formations 29

Richards, Harold, Sheriff, DeKalb County, Alabama 135-136

Richardson, Ron, Deputy, Weld County, Colorado Sheriff's Dept. 165

Rideout, Bruce Prof. 30, 32, 50-51

Ridicule, Fear of 104

Riggs, Charlie 193

Rings, In grass and hay 75-76

Ringwood, England 190, 290

Robertson, Julia 32

Robinson, Jeanne 236-246, 269, 294

Roestenberg, Jennie 290-291

Roper Survey-1992, *Unusual Personal Experiences* 197-199

Rorschach psychological test 238

Rose Medical Center, Denver, Colorado 102

Roswell, New Mexico 234

Rousey, Archie, Deputy, Carroll County, Arkansas Sheriff's Dept. 179-180

Roux, Georges 282-283

Rowell, Keith E. 175

Roy, Archie 4, 52

Royal Cemetery at UR, Mesopotamia 249

Russell, Ron 10, 17, 23, 25-26, 33, 84-86

Russia 3

Rystrom, Don, former Deputy, Benton County, Arkansas Sheriff's Dept. 102

Ryszka, Davina 158

S

Sacred centers, Seven 259

Sacrifices, Food for Sumerian gods 280

Saguache County, Colorado 151

Salem, Oregon 250-255

Salisbury Plain, England 23

San Antonio, Texas 155

San Luis Valley, Colorado 95, 98, 151

Sandler, Alan Frank 276

Sangre de Christo Mountains, Colorado 98, 151

Saratoga, California 273

Sarsen sandstone 7, 9, 53

Satanic cults 101, 140, 158, 163, 166-167, 179, 183, 187

Saylor, Donna 140

Scalpels 140, 193

Scanning electron microscope 130

Schlueter, Roger and Kathy 75

Schmitt, Harrison, former U.S. Senator, New Mexico 102

Schnabel, Jim 59, 82

School of American Research, Santa Fe, New Mexico 248

Schuessler, John 154

Science News 58

Scotland 290

Scott, Brian 287

Scranton, South Dakota 161

Scraping tongue 223, 313

Screen memories 205-206, 225, 237, 243, 247, 255, 260, 318-319

Search for the Universal Ancestors xii

Seattle, Washington 169

Seeds, See: Crop circle formations

SETI (Search for Extraterrestrial Intelligence, NASA) 250

Sexual liaisons, Sumerian gods and humans 279

Shaftesbury, England 104, 190

Shamballah 259

"Shared dreams" 198

Sharpton, Rick D.V.M. 136

Shock, Lack of blood 127

Siefried, Richard 183

Sigils 40

Silbury Hill, Wiltshire, England 7, 9, 11, 13, 15, 18-19, 22, 59, 76, 83

Silent helicopters 227

Silver, Alchemical sigil 40

Simon, Benjamin M.D. 198

Sirius 40, 284

Sirius B, Companion star 284

Sistek, Connie 65

Sitchin, Zecharia 279

Skirum, Alabama 120-121

Slant-eyed giants, Cherokee 115

"Slashings," Horses 166, 193

Smith, Stephen 143, 145, 157

"Snail" 13-17

Snake, The 82

"Snake-eyed" or cat-eyed beings 201, 208, 214-215, 218, 220, 232, 235, 241, 257-
        259, 267, 274-277, 293-295, 297, 315 Also See: Alien life forms

Snippy 98

Snow, Chet Ph.D. 40-41

Snowflake, Arizona 290

Sompting, West Sussex, England 76-77

Somsen, Steve 170

Sonoma, California 273

Sophia (wisdom) 258

Sorensen, Peter 81

Soul xvii, xxi, 26

Sound Beach, Long Island, New York 174

Sounds in crop formations, Crackling like static electricity 60

South America 95

South Dakota 159-161, 191

South Yorkshire, England 76

Southern Cross xviii

Space-Time 301

Spain 26, 115; "Indalo" symbol 26

Sperm and ova 197, 301

Spider, The 82

Spiral symbol, Soul journey xxi

Sposito, Carlo 175

Springfield, Missouri 95, 186-187, 202-203, 226, 233, 236-237, 269, 287-288, 294-295

Sprinkle, Leo Ph.D. 200-202, 221, 234-235

St. Catharines near Toronto, Canada 168

St. Paul, Minnesota 96, 163

Stalks, See: Crop circle formations

Star Beacon, Ashtabula, Ohio 63-64

Star Wars 123

Steinman, William 153

Sterling, Colorado 100, 102, 105-106, 132, 137

Stiefel, Steven 119

Stoll, Bob D.V.M. 109

Stone Age 284

Stonehenge 12-13, 25, 33, 304
      As computer 53

Strainic, Michael 67

Stratford, South Dakota 96

Strawn, John 126

▲

Strieber, Whitley 155

Stripling, Juanita 135

Structured craft 35-38

Sturgis, South Dakota 159

Subconscious mind 245

Sumerians, Mesopotamia

    Babylonian god, Marduk 279

    Divinity 8, 279-282

    God-human relationships 249, 280-283

        Enormous eyes of gods 280-281

        High dome-shaped heads of gods 280-283

        Pleated or ropy headgear of gods 282-283

        Sexual liaisons, gods and humans 279

    Physical description 249, 279

    Religion 280

    Royal Cemetery of Ur, Skeletons 249

    Sumer 259

    Sumer and the Sumerians 280

    Sun-god Shamash 282-283

    Technology 279

    Ubaid figurines 280-281

    Ziggurats 279

Surrey University, England 166

Sweden, "Horse slashings" 193

Sylvania, Alabama 114, 143-146, 306

Symbiosis, 301

Symbols, For Sirius 40

    For Yod or Yodh 40

    Unidentified 248

Syracuse Herald-Journal, Syracuse, New York 88

T

Tall beings 8, 234, 248-249, 265, 270, 276, 280, 285, 298

    Also see: Alien life forms

Tall "gods" 8, 279-283

Tawsmeade copse, England 33

Taylor, Busty 22, 34

Taylor, Ron 87-88

Technology, Alien, See: Alien life forms

Teeth, See: Animal mutilations and Human abduction syndrome

Tehachapi Mountains, California 155

Telepathy, Mental 24, 225, 237, 240, 242-245, 250-251

Tell Asmar, Mesopotamia 280

Temple, Robert K. G. 284, 300

Tennessee 43, 115, 123, 286

Tennessee Valley Authority (TVA) 150

Testament of Amram, Dead Sea Scrolls xvii

Texas 149-150, 202-203, 259

    Cat mutilations 167-168

The Advertiser, Poole, England 190

The Andreasson Affair 155

The Andreasson Affair, Phase Two 155

The Choppers – And The Choppers 153

The Civilization of the Goddess, The World of Old Europe 82

The Columbus Dispatch, Columbus, Ohio 166

The Humanoids 290

The Interrupted Journey 198

The Magical Revival 259

The New York Times 168

The Secret Teachings of All Ages 40

The Sirius Mystery 284, 300

The Star Progress, Berryville, Arkansas 180

The Sumerians 8, 278

The Survival of Man 304

The Tennessean, Nashville, Tennessee 151

The Watchers 155

The Weekly Post, Rainsville, Alabama 143, 145-146, 157

Theorems, Geometry by Gerald S. Hawkins 58-59, 86, 302-303

Theos (God) 258

Theosophical Society 258

Theosophy 258

Third dimension 299

Thompson, R. E., former U. S. Attorney, New Mexico 102

Thomson, Shelley 225

Thorne, James 179-180

Thouless, Robert 305

Thrash, Luanne 157

Tibet 259

Time Magazine 250, 300

Tindle, Cindy 199-236, 255, 257-260, 270, 308-319

Tissue preservative 145, 148

Titanium 130-131

Totnes, England 59-60

Tower of Babel 279

Tracks, See: Animal mutilations

Tramlines 30

▲

Translucent beings 297, 299
Triangles 4-5, 13, 21, 24, 35, 39-40, 56-58, 74, 76, 83, 302-303
    Also, See: Alien life forms, Symbols
Troy, Illinois 47-49, 75
Tsunil kalu, Cherokee "Slant-eyed" giants 115
Turkish (Turanian) language 278
Tustin, California 168
Twilley, Hubert and family 118-120
Two Spirit Theology xvii
Tyson's Hog Farms, Hiwasse, Arkansas 185

U
United States xiii, 3, 62, 87, 95, 99, 132, 139, 149, 154, 156
Uffington, England 27
UFOs 4-5, 11, 39, 98, 150-151, 198, 200, 250, 278, 290, 312-319
    Videotapes 60, 114, 122-125, 143, 154-155
    Also see: Alien life forms, Animal mutilations, Crop circle formations, Human
    abduction syndrome, and Lights
University of California, Berkeley 250
University of Minnesota School of Veterinary Medicine 163
University of Wyoming, Laramie 200-201
Unsolved Mysteries (NBC-TV) 154-155
Unusual animal deaths, See: Animal mutilations
Unusual aircraft, Flying below radar 153
Unusual Personal Experiences, 1992 Roper Survey 199
Ur, Mesopotamia 280-282
Ursinus College, Pennsylvania 30, 50
Utica, New York 76, 87-88

V
Vallee, Jacques 278
Van Patten, Charles D.V.M. 162
Vancouver, British Columbia, Canada 167
Vandervoort Farm, Guntersville, Alabama 150
Varner, Danny, Deputy, Benton County, Arkansas Sheriff's Dept. 185-186
Veenhuizen, William 169-171
Verchomin, Dorthea and Roman 188
Very tall humanoids, 274-276
    Also, See: Alien life forms and Tall beings
Veterinary Diagnostic Laboratory, Oregon State University 177
Videotapes, Unidentified moving lights 60, 114, 122-125, 143, 154-155
Vigay, Paul and Mavis 77
Vincel, Carla 203

Virginia 115
Vitatoe, Scott 138
Voltaire 59
Von Durckheim, Constantin & Mucki 11

W
Waco, Texas 153, 197
Waggon and Horses Pub, Beckhampton, England 8, 25
Wakefield, Cash and Michael 89
Waller, Jean 183
Walton, Travis 290-291
Wanaque Reservoir, New Jersey 152
Ward, Maria 23-24, 39-40, 57
Warren, Vic, Supervisor, Animal Control, Vancouver, B. C., Canada 167
Warwickshire, England 258
Washington, D. C. 96, 194
Watchers xvii
Watkins, Roger Rev. 116-117
WATL-TV, Atlanta, Georgia 202
Watson, James xi
Watson, Paula 233, 247, 261, 196
    Ron and Paula 196, 229-234, 250, 255, 294, 296-297
Webster County, Missouri 186
Weld, County, Colorado 164
Wesolowski, Steve, Detective, Greenup County, Kentucky Sheriff's Dept. 181
West Carleton, Ontario, Canada 154-155
West Hennepin County, Minnesota 162-163, 170
West Overton, Wiltshire, England 76-77, 83, 86
West, Ron 147
West Stowell, England 13, 15, 77
West Wycombe, England 45-46
Wheat formations, See: Crop circle formations
Wheeler, Donald A. 62-65
White dwarf star, Sirius B 284
White Horse at Cherhill Down 76, 78
White, John B. 53
White Mountains, New Hampshire 198
White Sands Proving Grounds, New Mexico 276, 278
Wilde, Jayne 25
Wilkens, Maurice xi
Williams, Doris 164-165
Williams, Larry 148
Wiltshire, England, See: Maps 13, 15, 77

Wind damage, Crops 30-31

Windmill Hill, Wiltshire, England 76, 83, 85

Wing, Gordon 193

Wingfield, George 2, 4-5, 9-10, 19, 23, 25, 27, 82, 190

Wolf, Fred Alan xiv, 93

Wolverton, Keith, former Deputy, Cascade County, Montana Sheriff's Dept. 176

Wolves 189

Wood, Gervis 126

Woodborough Hill, Wiltshire, England 10, 13, 17, 23-25, 33-41

Wookey, Lyman 62

Woolley, C. Leonard 8, 278, 280

World War II 258

Worlds in the Making xi

Worldwide animal mutilations, Map 111

    Also, See: Animal mutilations

Worldwide crop circle formations 247

Wyoming 150, 181

Y

Yarkosky, Sherry 49

Yarnell, George, Sheriff, Elbert County, Colorado 165

Yearick, Archie, Sheriff, Grant County, Oklahoma 183

Yod or Yodh 40

Yunwi Tsunsdi "Little People," Cherokee 115

Z

Zeta Reticulii 260

Ziggurat step pyramids 8, 279-280

ABOUT THE AUTHOR

Linda Moulton Howe is a graduate of Stanford University with a Masters Degree in Communication. She has devoted her documentary film, television and radio career to productions concerning science, medicine and the environment. Ms. Howe has received local, national and international awards, including three regional Emmys and a national Emmy nomination. Those films have included *Poison in the Wind* and *A Sun Kissed Poison*, which compared smog pollution in Los Angeles and Denver; *Fire In The Water* about hydrogen as an alternative energy source to fossil fuels; *A Radioactive Water* about uranium contamination of public drinking water in a Denver suburb; *A Prairie Dawn* about astronaut training in Denver; and *A Strange Harvest* that explored the worldwide animal mutilation mystery that has haunted the United States and other countries since the 1960s and continues to date.

Linda was an honored medical producer in Boston's WCVB Station Excellence Peabody Award; received the Aviation & Space Writers Association Award for Writing Excellence in Television; the Sigma Delta Chi Excellence in Journalism Award; a Chicago Film Festival Golden Plaque for *A Radioactive Water;* a Denver International Film Festival First Place Award for *Borrowed Faces*; an Outstanding Film Award from the Association for Educational Communications and Technology for *Information's Electronic Future*; Colorado's Florence Sabin Award for "outstanding contribution to public health;" and several Colorado Broadcasters Association Best Documentary awards. She has traveled in Turkey, Laos, Brazil, Africa, Australia, Peru, Egypt, Europe, Mexico, Venezuela, Canada, the Yucatan, and Puerto Rico for research and productions.

Other television programs have included *The World of Chemistry* for PBS; produced and hosted a two-hour special *Earth Mysteries: Alien Life Forms* with WATL-Fox, Atlanta; produced three documentaries for UNICEF about international child survival efforts; produced the documentary *STRANGE HARVESTS 1993*. Linda was Director of International Programming for *Earthbeat*, an environmental series on Turner's WTBS Superstation, Atlanta, Georgia. She also contracted with Paramount Studios as Supervising Producer and Original Concept creator for an hour special based on her program, *Earth Mysteries*. That hour, *UFO Report: Sightings*, was first broadcast in October

Linda has written four books: *An Alien Harvest* that investigates the worldwide animal mutilation phenomenon and government policies of denial and cover-up; *Glimpses of Other Realities, Volumes I and II*, which concern U.S. military, intelligence and civilian testimonies about non-humans interacting with Earth life. Her fourth book, *Mysterious Lights and Crop Circles* detailed her investigations of the complex crop formation phenomenon in England, the United States and Canada in 1999 to 2002.

She also produces, writes, edits and reports for television, the world wide web and *Coast to Coast AM* broadcast by iHeart Media Premiere Networks throughout North America. She is Reporter and Editor of Earthfiles.com which features news about science, medicine, environmental issues and real X-Files.

Linda speaks at national and international conferences and symposiums, including NASA's Goddard Space Flight Center. She has been interviewed for television productions such as History Channel's *Ancient Aliens*; NBC's *Mysterious Origins of Man*; a *Larry King Live* special about Nellis AFB's Area 51 "Dreamland" in Nevada; and The Learning Channel TV special *Evidence On Earth*.

Linda Moulton Howe,
Emmy Award-winning
documentary filmmaker
and investigative journalist,
prior to speaking at the
Contact in the Desert
conference in Joshua Tree,
California, May 30, 2015.
Image by Sid Goldberg.

The text was created
with 11-point New
Baskerville type,
highlighted with
17-point Charlemagne,
in 14-point leading.

The author welcomes readers' comments, questions and reports about unusual sightings and experiences.

Linda Moulton Howe
Reporter and Editor
Earthfiles.com
P. O. Box 21843
Albuquerque, New Mexico 87154
email: earthfiles@earthfiles.com